INTRODUCTION TO PROBABILITY THEORY

INTRODUCTION TO

Probability Theory

James R. McCord, III DEPARTMENT OF CHEMICAL

ENGINEERING, MASSACHUSETTS INSTITUTE OF TECHNOLOGY

Richard M. Moroney, Jr. CONSULTING MATHEMATICIAN

THE MACMILLAN COMPANY, NEW YORK

COLLIER-MACMILLAN LIMITED, LONDON

LIBRARY OF CONGRESS CATALOG CARD NUMBER: 64-10970

THE MACMILLAN COMPANY, NEW YORK
COLLIER-MACMILLAN CANADA, LTD., TORONTO, ONTARIO

DESIGNED BY JACK MESEROLE

PRINTED IN THE UNITED STATES OF AMERICA

A SERIES OF MATHEMATICS TEXTS UNDER

THE EDITORSHIP OF CARL B. ALLENDOERFER

TO OUR TEACHERS

PREFACE

THIS BOOK CONTAINS A BRIEF INTRODUCTION TO THE MATHEMATICAL theory of probability, as based on the systematic development first presented by A. N. Kolmogorov. It requires as prerequisite a good course in calculus.

We had several objectives in writing this book. First, we wished to present the axiomatic approach in an elementary manner. By doing this, we hoped to develop the basic concepts of probability theory, to maintain a clear distinction between the intuitive and logical aspects, and to indicate briefly where and why advanced mathematical methods are essential for a satisfactory theory.

Another objective was to provide a relatively short route to a sound discussion of the law of large numbers and the central limit theorem. We feel that every student leaving an introductory course should have an understanding of these results, which contain the very essence of the concept of probability.

We aimed also at developing those elementary parts of the theory of probability which are fundamental to the studies of statistics, stochastic processes, operations research, game theory, chemical reaction engineering, etc.

A final objective was brevity. We have restricted our discussions and illustrations, sometimes drastically, in order to give a truly brief introduction. Some results are stated without proof and others with only heuristic justification, but we have endeavored to ensure that all statements are technically correct and to indicate the nature of the reasoning used in most cases.

In order to help the reader acquire that experience which we consider indispensable for a good understanding of the theory and for an ability to apply it, we have supplied about 300 exercises at the ends of the chapters. Answers to almost all of these are given at the end of the book.

These exercises range from pure mathematics to pure applications. Most of the more difficult or unusual ones are indicated by an asterisk. A few involve mathematical or physical concepts—e.g., differential equations and chemical reactions—that obviously are to be ignored by those readers not prepared to solve them.

A series of 33 exercises included at the very ends of Chapters 5 through 12 are concerned with the analysis of certain continuous-flow engineering processes and provide an opportunity for interested readers to consider extensively an important application of the basic concepts.

We feel that this book contains enough material for a solid one-semester undergraduate course. A shorter course, or one requiring less maturity, might cover Sections 1.1–1.5, 2.1–2.4, 3.1–3.3, 4.1–4.3, 5.1–5.5, 6.2, 6.4, 6.5, 7.1–7.4, 8.1–8.3, 9.1–9.3, 9.5–9.6, 10.1, 10.4, 10.5, 11.1–11.3, and 12.1–12.2. With some help from an instructor, an even shorter course might also omit Sections 2.2–2.3, 7.4, 8.3, 9.1–9.3, and 9.5–9.6.

We hope that, in addition to serving as a text, our book will be found useful by a variety of readers—engineers and scientists wishing to develop rapidly an ability to comprehend the innumerable modern applications, students seeking a bridge between the rudimentary texts and the advanced treatises, and those interested in pursuing any of the numerous subjects based on probability theory. With these readers in mind, we have dwelt longer than necessary on a few subjects which do not normally arise in calculus, but which we feel should be part of the background of every technical person nowadays. Thus, for example, our discussions of set theory and countable sets are somewhat longer than our later needs would seem to justify.

At the Massachusetts Institute of Technology, for the past several years, about one-half semester of the standard sophomore mathematics course has been devoted to probability. This book is the outgrowth of some notes written by us and used as the text for that course in the spring semester of 1962. We wish to thank the many members of the Department of Mathematics from whom we received valuable suggestions and other assistance.

We are particularly grateful to Professors J. L. Doob and J. W. Pratt, who reviewed the original notes, and to Professor G. E. Baxter, who reviewed the final manuscript. These gentlemen made many valuable suggestions, but we hasten to assert that the responsibility for all defects is ours.

The authors of every textbook owe much to the existing literature.

We acknowledge our indebtedness especially to the authors of those books listed in our bibliography.

Since July, 1962, the first author has been an Assistant Professor of Chemical Engineering and a Postdoctoral Engineering Fellow; under the latter appointment, he wishes to acknowledge support derived from a Ford Foundation grant to the Massachusetts Institute of Technology.

JAMES R. MCCORD, III
RICHARD M. MORONEY, JR.

Cambridge, Mass.

CONTENTS

INTRODUCTION TO PROBABILITY THEORY

CHAPTER 1 INTRODUCTION

IN THIS CHAPTER WE EXAMINE A NUMBER OF PHYSICAL PHENOMENA that "depend on chance." Our objective is to collect and organize certain "facts" about these phenomena that we believe to be true because of our experience, instinct, or intuition.

1.1 Preliminary Orientation

The theory of probability is a branch of mathematics, as are algebra and geometry, and like these it has applications in the study of natural phenomena. The purpose of this text is to give the reader a knowledge of some of the elementary results of the theory of probability, together with a feeling for when these may be applied. Because of this latter objective, some readers will on occasion find themselves being harangued on subjects whose relevance is not immediately apparent. Here, for instance, we pause to examine carefully just what a "branch of mathematics" is.

Every branch of mathematics (or mathematical discipline) consists of a collection of conditional assertions, that is, statements that *if* "something" is true *then* "something else" is true. Some of these assertions, called *axioms*, are *assumed*—to "get the branch started," as it were. All the other assertions are called *theorems* and have been shown to be logical consequences of the axioms (or, briefly, have been *proved*).

The different mathematical disciplines have different axioms. In most disciplines these axioms have been chosen so as to "model" some physical phenomenon in the sense that they are assertions validated by experience.

Example 1.1.   One of the axioms of algebra is $A + B = B + A$. This formalizes the observation that when two bricks are stacked, the

1

height of the resulting pile is independent of the order in which the bricks are placed.

Of course, if the axioms are badly chosen—for example, based on faulty observation—the resulting mathematical theory can lead to results that contradict nature. This does not mean that the mathematical discipline is "wrong" in any sense. All we can say is that the mathematical theory "doesn't apply" in the given situation because its axioms "don't fit the problem." The responsibility for deciding whether some theory "applies" to a given physical problem rests with the engineer, or physicist, or whoever applies that theory.

Example 1.2.   Referring to the previous example, suppose one of the bricks is gold and the other foam rubber, so that the height of the pile depends essentially on the order in which the bricks are placed. This does not mean that algebra is "wrong"; it simply means that for this problem the mathematical discipline of algebra does not provide a "good model."

It is now possible to explain the objectives of the remainder of this chapter. We wish to examine a class of physical phenomena, the so-called *random phenomena*, with an eye to developing a set of axioms that can form the basis of a mathematical theory of these phenomena. Stated otherwise, we wish to examine the "intuitive basis" of the theory of probability.

From a purely mathematical point of view our discussion is irrelevant, since the axioms to be introduced in the next chapter do not *have* to be based on anything. We are taking the reader on this long journey, however, because it is important that he develop a "feel" for when the axioms of probability apply to a problem. Surely the reader, should he encounter the gold and rubber bricks of Example 1.2, would instinctively reject the use of algebra for computing the pile height. Unfortunately, it appears that our "instinct" can be fallible when dealing with random phenomena and hence needs a certain amount of "cultivation."

1.2   Random Phenomena

Imagine the following physical experiment:

Experiment 1.1.   An icosahedron is constructed from some uniform material, and its faces distinguished in some way, say by numbering them from one to twenty. This icosahedron is thrown down a flight of stairs, and when it comes to rest the number on the upper horizontal face is recorded.

Our years of life on this planet give us certain "notions" about this experiment. We feel that the outcome depends on chance in that *no amount of initial measurement would permit a practical determination of the outcome*, even though we also feel here that "in theory" the outcome is predetermined by the pitch of the stairs, air density, launch velocity, etc.

Phenomena that "depend on chance" in the above sense will be called *random*. Many more examples of these will appear in what follows, but the reader may wish to pause here and try to describe an experiment whose outcome is not predetermined even "in theory."

There are many conceivable outcomes of Experiment 1.1, for instance "the face numbered 3 showing," "an odd-numbered face showing," "a face less than 10 showing." We wish to examine certain of these outcomes, but first it is necessary to distinguish between two types of statement that we shall be using.

Let us call any assertion that we are prepared to "prove" a *mathematical statement* and any statement that we "feel to be true" (on the basis of experience, instinct, etc.) an *intuitive* statement. Let us further agree that any statement of the latter type will be qualified by some phrase such as "intuitively speaking." (The reason for distinguishing these two types of statements will be clear later on.)

In Experiment 1.1 let E_n denote the outcome "the face numbered n showing." The collection of outcomes $E_1, E_2, \ldots, E_{20}$ has (intuitively speaking) the following properties:

1. The collection is *exhaustive* in that in any trial some one of the outcomes E_i occurs.
2. The collection is *mutually exclusive* in that no two of the outcomes E_i can occur in the same trial.
3. The collection is *basic* in that every outcome can be described as some collection of the outcomes E_i. [The outcome "an odd-numbered face showing" in Experiment 1.1, for instance, can be described by the statement "E_1 or E_3 or $\ldots$ or E_{19} occurred," i.e., is equivalent to the collection $(E_1, E_3, \ldots, E_{19})$.]

A collection of outcomes having the foregoing properties will be called a *collection of elementary outcomes;* the individual members of such a collection will be called *elementary outcomes*. Outcomes that are not elementary will be called *compound outcomes*.

Given some experiment, our basic idea is to associate with each of certain of its outcomes a real number, called the *likelihood* of that outcome, which describes "how likely" that outcome is: a large number for a "likely" outcome and a small number for an "unlikely" one. In Sections 1.3 and 1.4 we investigate how this may be done in two special situations.

1.3   The Classical Theory

We have seen that in Experiment 1.1 the set of outcomes E_i ($i = 1, 2, \ldots, 20$) is a collection of elementary outcomes. The outcomes in this set have another property (intuitively), namely that they are "equally likely" in that no one of them seems more or less likely to occur than any other. If we are going to assign numbers (likelihoods) to outcomes, it seems that we should assign the *same* number to each of the E_i. We choose the number $\frac{1}{20}$—i.e., one over the total number of outcomes E_i. Any number would do but, as will be seen, the present choice causes all of our numbers to lie between zero and one, in agreement with another idea to be introduced in Section 1.4.

Since *every* outcome in Experiment 1.1 can be described as some collection of E_i's, we define the likelihood of any outcome as the sum of the likelihoods of the E_i it contains or, otherwise stated, as $\frac{1}{20}$ times the number of E_i it contains. The outcome "an odd-numbered face showing," for instance, contains the ten E_i ($E_1, E_3, \ldots, E_{19}$), hence is assigned a likelihood of $(\frac{1}{20})(10) = \frac{1}{2}$. The intuitive reasoning behind this definition is clear: an outcome containing k of the E_i has the likelihood of occurrence which is the sum of the likelihoods of the k E_i, or k times the likelihood of any one of them.

We may generalize the above scheme for defining likelihoods as follows: *Whenever a finite collection of equally likely elementary outcomes exists, assign to each of the elementary outcomes a likelihood of one over the number of elementary outcomes. Assign to a compound outcome the sum of the likelihoods of the elementary outcomes it contains.*

Experiment 1.2.   A red die and a green die are thrown, and the result is recorded.

Example 1.3. Outcomes of this experiment are, for instance, "red die came up six, green die came up four" and "sum of the faces was eleven." Let E_{ij} be the outcome "red die came up i, green die came up j." The set of all E_{ij} ($i = 1, 2, \ldots, 6$; $j = 1, 2, \ldots, 6$) is a collection of elementary outcomes each of which is equally likely (intuition again). There are six i's, and for each of these any one of six j's can be picked, giving a total of 36 E_{ij}'s. Thus we assign to each E_{ij} the likelihood $\frac{1}{36}$ or, to coin a notation, $L(E_{ij}) = \frac{1}{36}$. The outcome "sum of the faces was eleven" consists of E_{56} and E_{65}, hence is assigned a likelihood of $\frac{1}{36} + \frac{1}{36} = \frac{1}{18}$. Other compound outcomes are treated in the same way.

Let us formalize the computation we made in the above example:

The mn Rule. *If A is a collection of m objects and B a collection of n objects, there are m times n distinct ordered pairs (x, y) with x an object from A and y an object from B.*

The method of assigning likelihoods we have just discussed might be called the "equally likely scheme." A closely related method is that of *geometric likelihood*, which we shall now investigate. Consider the following experiment:

Experiment 1.3. A circular target of radius $1/\sqrt{\pi}$ feet (hence of area 1 square foot) is used to block one end of a 50-foot section of $2/\sqrt{\pi}$-foot inside-diameter pipe. A blindfolded marksman fires a shot into the open end of the pipe. The point of impact is recorded, say in polar coordinates. (The purpose of the pipe is to insure that the shot does hit the target somewhere, possibly after a number of ricochets.)

An outcome of this experiment is, for instance, "shot hit at $r = 0.1$ foot, $\theta = 0.816$ radian." Let E_{xy} be the outcome "shot hit at $r = x$ feet, $\theta = y$ radians." It is clear intuitively that the collection of all E_{xy} with $0 \leq x \leq 1/\sqrt{\pi}$, $0 \leq y < 2\pi$ is a collection of elementary outcomes. Furthermore, it seems plausible intuitively that because of the blindfold the E_{xy} are equally likely. Thus, we have found a collection of equally likely elementary outcomes. Our previous scheme for assigning likelihoods, however, fails here: since there are infinitely many E_{xy} we would put $L(E_{xy}) = 0$ (i.e., $1/\infty$), and then for a compound outcome containing infinitely many E_{xy} (e.g., the outcome "$r < 1$ inch") we would be led to the indeterminate form zero times infinity.

We can resolve our difficulty by noting that every outcome E

consists of a set of points in the disk $(0 \leq r \leq 1/\sqrt{\pi},\ 0 \leq \theta < 2\pi)$ and by *agreeing to consider outcomes of equal area equally likely* (intuitively). Since the area of the whole target is 1 square foot, an outcome E with area $A(E)$ can be assigned a likelihood:

$$L(E) = \frac{\text{area of } E}{\text{area of all outcomes}} = \frac{A(E)}{1} = A(E).$$

The intuitive reasoning here might be elaborated this way: "The larger the area of some region of the disk, the more likely the bullet is to land in that region; in fact the likelihood of a hit is proportional to the exposed area." (Dividing by the area of the disk assures once more that all of our likelihoods be between zero and one.)

Under this scheme we assign to the outcome "$r < 1$ inch," for example, a likelihood equal to the area of a circle of radius 1 inch divided by the area of a circle of radius $1/\sqrt{\pi}$ foot, i.e., $\pi/144$. Of course for some outcomes, that is, subsets of the disk, we may not be able to agree on an area. We shall simply not consider these; that is, for this experiment we are defining likelihoods only for *some* outcomes.

Notice that we have assigned a likelihood of zero to a large number of outcomes—for instance, the outcomes "$r = x$ inches." A moment's thought shows that this assumption is quite reasonable: in each trial of the experiment r turns out to be *some* number, but the likelihood of its being any *particular* number is negligible. Notice too that some of the outcomes to which we have assigned a likelihood of one (e.g., "$r > 0$") are not absolutely certain to occur (but are "almost certain") whereas others, (e.g., "$r \geq 0$") *are* certain.

As before, we summarize our scheme: *If outcomes can be viewed as plane regions, and equal areas are equally likely, assign to each outcome the ratio of its area to the area of the set of all outcomes.*

A little thought will convince the reader that if outcomes can be viewed as points on a line, or in space, the foregoing scheme can be used if one replaces "area" by "length" or "volume."

Experiment 1.4.   The experiment described is sometimes referred to as Buffon's needle problem. A stick of length L is thrown onto a flat table ruled with parallel lines of spacing $2L$. It is noted whether or not the stick intersects one of the ruled lines.

Example 1.4.   Let r be the distance of the center of the stick from the nearest ruled line, and let θ be the (smaller) angle the axis of the stick makes with the ruled lines (see Fig. 1.1). Every outcome of this experiment corresponds to a point in the region of the (r, θ) plane of Fig. 1.2 bounded by the lines $r = 0$, $r = L$, $\theta = 0$, $\theta = \pi$. On intuitive grounds we claim that equal areas in this region are equally likely (if the stick thrower is not "aiming," etc.). The outcome "stick intersects

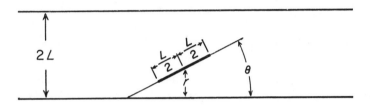

Figure 1.1

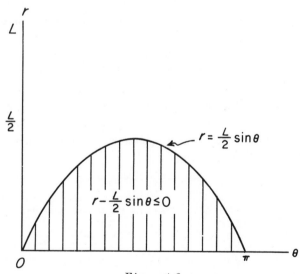

Figure 1.2

a ruled line" corresponds to the region $r - (L/2) \sin \theta \le 0$, with area

$$A = \int_0^\pi \frac{L}{2} \sin \theta \, d\theta = L.$$

Since the area of all outcomes is πL, we assign to this outcome the likelihood $L/\pi L = 1/\pi$.

1.4   The Relative-Frequency Theory

In this section we describe another way to assign numbers to outcomes of an experiment, a way which does not depend on our being able to find a collection of equally likely elementary outcomes. To begin, we assume that there is an outcome E, of some experiment, in which we are interested. We start repeating this experiment over and over, keeping track of the cumulative number of times the outcome E has occurred. Let $N_n(E)$ be the number of occurrences of E in the first n trials of the experiment, and let $R_n(E) = N_n(E)/n$. We call $R_n(E)$ the "relative frequency of E in n trials." By computing this number after each trial, we find that as our number of trials increases we get a longer and longer string of numbers; at the end of the kth trial we have the sequence of k numbers $R_1(E), R_2(E), \ldots, R_k(E)$.

Let us call on our intuition for some properties of this string of numbers. In the first place, we feel that two different people, each repeating the experiment and computing relative frequencies, could easily get different values for, say, $R_5(E)$. On the other hand, we also feel that each experimenter would find his sequence "stabilizing" at some value, eventually, and that the "stable value" for each experimenter would be the same. In other words, although we would expect some early "scatter," we would expect the sequence of relative frequencies to stabilize, eventually, at some fixed value that would be the same for all experimenters.

The foregoing intuitive discussion leads us to the following scheme for assigning likelihoods: *Given some experiment, repeat the experiment a "large" number of times (say N) and assign to each outcome E the likelihood $L(E) = R_N(E)$. To check whether N is "large enough," check whether the sequences $R_n(E)$ have "stabilized" for all outcomes of interest.*

Naturally there is some risk in this procedure, since the $R_n(E)$ may have "stabilized temporarily" at values other than their "final stable values," and there is no way we can check "for certain" that this has not happened.

Example 1.5. A weighted die is tossed and the number on the upper horizontal face recorded. Here a collection of elementary outcomes is, intuitively, the set "face i came up," $i = 1, 2, \ldots, 6$. Presumably these outcomes are *not* equally likely, since the die is weighted, so our previous schemes are inapplicable. Instead, we roll the die a million times and assign to each of the elementary outcomes a likelihood equal to the number of times it occurred times 10^{-6}. Suppose the result is 999,999 appearances of the "six" face and one appearance of the "two" face. We then assign to the outcome "six" a likelihood of 0.999999; to "two," 0.000001; and to "one," "three," "four," and "five," zero. We have to "keep our fingers crossed," however, because *an unweighted die could have given the same results* (although only if we were fantastically "unlucky").

In repeating an experiment to determine likelihoods by the relative-frequency method it is not necessary to record the number of occurrences of every outcome, because of certain very handy properties of relative frequencies. Let us observe first that

$$0 \leq R_n(E) \leq 1. \tag{1.1}$$

(This is why we normalized our likelihoods in Section 1.3.) Also note that, if E^c is the outcome "E did not occur," then $N_n(E^c) = n - N_n(E)$ and hence

$$R_n(E) + R_n(E^c) = \frac{N_n(E) + n - N_n(E)}{n} = 1. \tag{1.2}$$

Next, let A and B be two outcomes and let $A \cap B$ (read "A cap B") denote the outcome "both A and B occurred," $A \cup B$ (read "A cup B") the outcome "at least one of the outcomes A, B occurred." We have

$$N_n(A \cup B) = N_n(A) + N_n(B) - N_n(A \cap B),$$

the last term being necessary because $N_n(A) + N_n(B)$ counts twice those occasions on which both A and B occurred; hence

$$R_n(A \cup B) = R_n(A) + R_n(B) - R_n(A \cap B). \tag{1.3}$$

1.5   Summary and Discussion

In this chapter we have seen how we can use our intuition to associate numbers with outcomes of an experiment that depends on chance. The mathematical theory *starts* from this point, that is, to obtain mathematical results one must first, in some way, reduce his problem to a real or conceptual "experiment" in which certain outcomes have attached numbers. The analogous situation with respect to use of the mathematical theory of differential equations is that one must first, by "nonmathematics," decide just what differential equation he wishes to solve. Solving the "wrong" differential equation will give erroneous results, and similarly assigning the "wrong" numbers to outcomes will give poor results.

In the next chapter we shall discuss the precise demands that the mathematical theory makes of the user in order to "take over," for instance we shall see "how many" outcomes must be tagged with numbers. (Recall that in Experiment 1.3 we were not able to assign likelihoods to all outcomes. We shall see, however, that we assigned likelihoods to "enough" of them.)

The reader may well ask what the mathematical theory will do for him, since apparently by the time he has used enough intuition to get the theory started he will have solved his problem "intuitively"! In the case of a single experiment this is essentially true. What the mathematical theory supplies is statements about what happens "in the long run," i.e., when an experiment is repeated many times. As an example, in a later chapter we shall prove a mathematical result—the strong law of large numbers—that assures that *in any experiment to which the mathematical theory applies* the "stabilization of relative frequencies" discussed in Section 1.4 is almost certain to occur. (The italicized section of this statement is indispensable, since we can never prove that our mathematical theory applies to *anything;* the phrase "almost certain to occur" will be given a precise meaning.)

1.6   Exercises

1.1   Describe a collection of elementary outcomes for each of the following experiments: (a) A balanced coin is tossed once. (b) A die is thrown once. (c) A man selects a key, from a chain containing seven similar keys, in the dark. (d) The dial of a combination lock, which has numbers from 1 to 20, is spun.

1.2   Give likelihoods for the elementary outcomes of Exercise 1.1, stating carefully all assumptions made.

1.3   Give likelihoods for the following outcomes of Experiment 1.2: (a) Sum of the faces was j, for $j = 2, 3, \ldots, 12$. (b) Faces were different.

1.4   Four cards, numbered 1, 2, 3, 4 are shuffled. What is the likelihood that after the shuffle there are precisely 0, 1, 2, 3, or 4 cards in the normal place (e.g., card numbered 3 is in its normal place if it is the third card)? *Hint:* The shuffle can be regarded as an experiment with outcomes of the form (2, 1, 3, 4), for "after the shuffle the card numbered 2 was in the first position, the card numbered 1 was in the second position, etc."

1.5   (a) An experiment consists of tossing a balanced coin three times. Find a collection of equally likely elementary outcomes. *Hint:* (H, T, T). (b) What are the likelihoods of the outcomes "first two tosses came out heads" and "first two tosses came out heads and third toss came out heads"? (c) If the first two tosses came out heads, is not a tail more likely on the third toss by the "law of averages"?

1.6   Discuss the following argument: A has just worked Exercise 1.3, and tells B that the outcome "sum of the faces was eleven" is twice as likely as the outcome "sum of the faces was twelve." B disagrees, reasoning as follows: In order to get *either* an eleven *or* a twelve, one face must come up six, so there is nothing to choose between the outcomes as far as this factor is concerned. The other die is equally likely to be a five or a six, so the outcomes "sum eleven" and "sum twelve" are equally likely.

1.7   Three dice are thrown. What is the likelihood that all faces are the same? That the sum of the faces is eleven?

1.8   A point P, with coordinates (A, B), is selected in the square $\{-1 \le x \le 1, -1 \le y \le 1\}$ in such a way that equal areas are equally likely. (a) What is the likelihood that the equation

$$r^2 + 2Ar + B = 0$$

will have complex roots? (b) What is the likelihood that the roots will be identical?

1.9   With A and B as in Exercise 1.8, and $X = X(t)$, what is the likelihood that every solution of the differential equation

$$X'' + 2AX' + BX = 0 \qquad \left(\text{where } ' = \frac{d}{dt}\right)$$

shall tend to zero as $t \to +\infty$?

1.10   A stick of length L is broken in such a way that the likelihood of the break occurring in any segment of length ℓ is proportional to ℓ. What is the likelihood that one of the resulting pieces is more than twice as long as the other?

1.11   A point P is selected as in Exercise 1.8, and the stick of Exercise 1.10 is broken at points distant A^2L and B^2L from one end. What is the likelihood that the resulting three pieces can be formed into a triangle?

1.12   An integer is selected from the set of all integers from 1 to 3,000,000 inclusive, all choices being equally likely. What is the likelihood that the first (leftmost) digit of the selected integer is a 1?

1.13   A color-blind man owns three suits of three different colors. Every morning he selects a jacket and a pair of pants to wear. About how many days per year does he wear a matching suit?

1.14   The man of Exercise 1.13 was observed during one year to be wearing something brown on 200 days, something gray on 120 days, and something brown or something gray on 270 days. On how many days was he wearing something gray and something brown?

1.15   During 100 trips, an irate commuter found on arrival at a certain traffic light that it was green, yellow, and red respectively 30, 20, and 50 times. (a) What are the observed relative frequencies for green, yellow, and red? (b) If A and B denote the outcomes "green or yellow" and "yellow or red," verify Eqs. 1.1 to 1.3.

THEORETICAL EXERCISES

1.16   If A and B are outcomes of an experiment, let $A \ominus B$ denote the outcome "A occurred but B did not." Show that

$$R_n(A \ominus B) + R_n(B \ominus A) + R_n(A \cap B) = R_n(A \cup B).$$

1.17   Let $C_1, C_2, \ldots, C_n$ be n collections of objects, with N_i the number of objects in C_i ($i = 1, 2, \ldots, n$). Generalize the mn rule to this case by showing that there are precisely

$$N_1 \times N_2 \times \cdots \times N_n = \prod_{i=1}^{n} N_i$$

distinct n-tuples $(x_1, x_2, \ldots, x_n)$ with x_1 an object in C_1, x_2 an object in $C_2, \ldots, x_n$ an object in C_n.

CHAPTER 2 AXIOMATIC PROBABILITY

IN THIS CHAPTER WE SHALL DEVELOP A MATHEMATICAL MODEL OF random phenomena, using as a guide the intuitive ideas of Chapter 1. It turns out that this mathematical model is best described in terms of set theory, a branch of mathematics which is also of use in other contexts; so in Section 2.2 we give a nonaxiomatic treatment of set theory. The material in Sections 2.2 and 2.3 is outlined in intuitive form in Section 2.1.

2.1 Introduction

As an introduction to this chapter, we propose to outline the basic ideas behind the mathematical theory of probability. The first idea is to associate with each elementary outcome of an experiment a tangible object—for instance, a white marble on which is painted the description of that elementary outcome. The collection of all of these objects is denoted by Ω and is called the *sample space;* an unspecified object in Ω is denoted by ω.

Now, every member of (object in) Ω corresponds to some elementary outcome, and conversely. Hence there is an obvious correspondence between subcollections (subsets) of Ω and collections of elementary outcomes. The latter, however, are compound outcomes, so we see that subsets of Ω correspond to compound outcomes. Thus the next idea of the theory is to introduce a *collection of subsets* of Ω, denoted by $\mathsection$. Members of $\mathsection$ are called *events*. Now, each event is a subset of Ω, but not every subset of Ω is necessarily an event, because we do not always (often cannot) require that $\mathection$ consist of *every* subset of Ω. In other words, we do not always require that there be an event corresponding to every outcome.

13

The third idea of the mathematical theory is to assign to each event a real number, called the *probability* of that event. If E denotes an event, $P(E)$ is used to denote its associated probability. So far, then, we see that the mathematical theory is going to involve a triple $(\Omega, \S, P)$ where Ω is a set, $\S$ a collection of subsets of Ω, and P a rule for assigning numbers to the members of $\S$.

Given two outcomes A and B, it is possible to conceive of other related outcomes. We define $A \cup B$, the *union* of the outcomes A and B, to be the outcome "one or the other (possibly both) of A and B occurred." $A \cap B$, the *intersection* of the outcomes A and B, we define as the outcome "both A and B occurred." $B \ominus A$, the *complement* of A in B, is defined as the outcome "B occurred but A did not."

All of these outcomes correspond to subsets of Ω. We denote the subset of Ω corresponding to A by A, that corresponding to $A \cup B$ by $A \cup B$, etc. It will be seen that this duplicate notation does not cause confusion.

Suppose now that the subsets A and B of Ω are in $\S$; i.e., are events. The next idea of the theory is to require that in this case the subsets $A \cup B$, $A \cap B$, $A \ominus B$ also be in $\S$. In words, we require that if there are events corresponding to the outcomes A and B, then there must be events corresponding to the outcomes $A \cup B$, $A \ominus B$, and $A \cap B$; i.e., that $\S$ be "full" or "well-rounded" in a certain sense.

One outcome of every experiment is that "some elementary outcome occurred." Clearly the corresponding subset of Ω is Ω itself. Another conceivable outcome is "no elementary outcome occurred." We denote this outcome by $\varnothing$. For this outcome the corresponding subset of Ω is the collection of no objects at all, or, in other words, the "empty" collection. In line with our policy of keeping $\S$ "well-rounded" we require that Ω be in $\S$. Notice that this assures that $\varnothing$ is in $\S$, since $\varnothing$ is $\Omega \ominus \Omega$. Moreover, if we denote by A^c the outcome "A did not occur," we see that the corresponding subset of Ω is $\Omega \ominus A$ and will be in $\S$ if A is.

One more condition is laid on $\S$, namely that if $A_1, A_2, \ldots$ are in $\S$ then $A_1 \cup A_2 \cup \cdots$ must be in $\S$. Again, this just says that if it is reasonable to talk about the outcomes $A_1, A_2, \ldots$ then it is reasonable to talk about the outcome "at least one of the outcomes $A_1, A_2, \ldots$ occurred."

In addition to the foregoing restrictions on $\S$, we put conditions on P. The underlying idea is to have $P(E)$ equal to the likelihood of the outcome corresponding to E, hence we require first of all that $P(E) \geq 0$. Next, if two outcomes A and B are mutually exclusive, and have corresponding events A and B, we require that

$$P(A \cup B) = P(A) + P(B).$$

Moreover, we require that $P(\Omega) = 1$; i.e., that some elementary outcome is almost certain to happen. Finally, if every pair of the events A_1, A_2, . . . are disjoint (i.e., mutually exclusive), we require that

$$P(A_1 \cup A_2 \cup \cdot \cdot \cdot) = P(A_1) + P(A_2) + \cdot \cdot \cdot .$$

A triple $(\Omega, \mathcal{S}, P)$, where Ω, $\mathcal{S}$, and P satisfy all of the above conditions will be called a *probability space*.

Now that the reader has had a bird's eye view of what lies ahead, we can proceed to the construction of our mathematical model (in a form which will permit a careful distinction between "mathematics" and "real life," a distinction which was unavoidably vague in the preceding paragraphs).

2.2   Set Theory

DEFINITIONS

1. A *set* is a collection of objects.*

2. If A is a set, and b is an object in the collection of objects which is A, we say b is a member of A and write $b \, \varepsilon \, A$.

3. If A and B are sets and every member of B is a member of A, we say that B is a *subset* of A and write $B \subset A$ or $A \supset B$. The contrary statement (that there are members of B which are not members of A) is abbreviated $B \not\subset A$ or $A \not\supset B$.

4. $\{x: \text{(some statement about } x)\}$ is shorthand for "the set that consists of all those objects x for which (some statement about x) is true." For example, $\{b: b$ is a real number and $0 < b < 1\}$ stands for "the set consisting of all real numbers between zero and one."

5. If A and B are sets, we define a new set, called the *union* of A and B and written $A \cup B$, by $A \cup B$ is $\{a: a \, \varepsilon \, A$ or $a \, \varepsilon \, B\}$; i.e.,

---

* What is a "collection"? What is an "object"? Why not define these before defining a "set"?

$A \cup B$ is the collection of all objects which are members of at least one of the sets A, B.

6. $A \cap B$ is $\{b: b \, \varepsilon \, A \text{ and } b \, \varepsilon \, B\}$.

7. $x \notin A$ means x is not a member of A.

8. $A \ominus B$ is $\{a: a \, \varepsilon \, A \text{ and } a \notin B\}$.

9. $A = B$ means $A \subset B$ and $B \subset A$; i.e., every member of A is a member of B, and every member of B is a member of A. As an example, $\{x: x \text{ real and } 0 < x < 1\} = \{x: x \text{ real}, x > 0, 0 < x^2 < 1\}$.

10. One frequently encounters sets with *no members whatsoever*. Examples are $\{a: a \text{ real and } a^2 = -1\}$ and $A \ominus A$ (for any set A). It is a consequence of a pernickety point in the definition of equality between sets that any two sets A and B, each with no members, are equal. Here is why: every $a \, \varepsilon \, A$ also belongs to B because there are no such a, and every $b \, \varepsilon \, B$ also belongs to A because there are no such b. Because of this equality, it makes sense to talk about *the* empty set. We call it $\varnothing$.

11. Let $A_1, A_2, \ldots, A_n$ be given sets. We define

$$\bigcup_{i=1}^{n} A_i = A_1 \cup A_2 \cup \cdots \cup A_n$$

by

$$\bigcup_{i=1}^{n} A_i = \{x: x \, \varepsilon \, A_i \text{ for some } i, 1 \le i \le n\}.$$

If we are given sets $A_1, A_2, \ldots$ (one for every positive integer), we define

$$\bigcup_{i=1}^{\infty} A_i$$

by

$$\bigcup_{i=1}^{\infty} A_i = \{x: x \, \varepsilon \, A_i \text{ for some } i\}.$$

Similarly,

$$\bigcap_{i=1}^{\infty} A_i = \{x: x \, \varepsilon \, A_i \text{ for every } i\}.$$

THE VENN DIAGRAM

Let A be the set of all points inside and on the boundary of the rectangle in Fig. 2.1. Let B and C be the sets of points inside and on the boundaries of the two disks labeled B and C. The set $B \cap C$ is the shaded part of the figure. The reader will easily find regions corresponding to the other compound sets defined above. Fig. 2.1 is called a *Venn diagram* and is useful for visualizing relationships among sets, even when the members are not points in the plane.

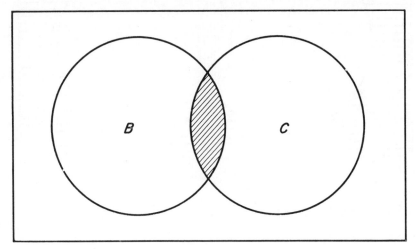

Figure 2.1

Example 2.1.   In an office of 100 girls, 65 can type, 60 can take shorthand, and 30 can do both. How many can do neither?

To solve this problem, define sets A, B, C by

$A = \{g: g$ is a girl in the office$\}$,
$B = \{g: g \, \varepsilon \, A$ and g can type$\}$,
$C = \{g: g \, \varepsilon \, A$ and g can take shorthand$\}$.

We have

$B \cup C = \{g: g \, \varepsilon \, A$ and can type or take shorthand$\}$,
$B \cap C = \{g: g \, \varepsilon \, A$ and can do both$\}$,
$A \ominus (B \cup C) = \{g: g \, \varepsilon \, A$ and can do neither$\}$.

In a Venn diagram (Fig. 2.2), we see that $A \ominus (B \cup C)$ is the horizontally shaded set. To count (the members of) this set, it is enough to count the set which is *not* horizontally shaded and subtract the answer from 100. Clearly, if we count the number of girls in B and the number of girls in C, we have counted the vertically shaded set *twice*. Since this is just $B \cap C$, we correct by subtracting that number.

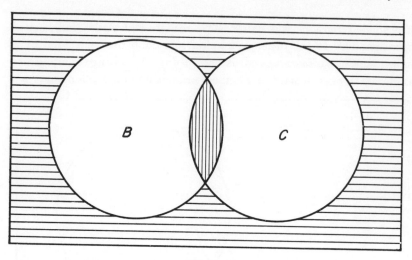

Figure 2.2

Thus letting $N(E)$ stand for "the number of members of E,"

$$N[A \ominus (B \cup C)] = N(A) - N(B \cup C)$$
$$= N(A) - [N(B) + N(C) - N(B \cap C)]$$
$$= 100 - [65 + 60 - 30]$$
$$= 5.$$

Thus, five girls can do neither.

ASSOCIATING NUMBERS WITH SETS

In solving the foregoing problem, we associated numbers with the sets that arose by assigning to each set a number equal to the totality of its members. This can always be done when all sets which arise have finitely many members (or, briefly, are finite), and the number provides a convenient description of the "size" or "mass" of each set. There are ways to associate numbers with infinite sets, too. Sets of points in the plane, for example, may be assigned numbers equal to their areas. Again in this case, we feel that the number associated with a set is a description of the "mass" of the set.

A rule for assigning a real number $f(E)$ to a set E is called a *set function*. We have seen that the set functions $N(E)$, for finite sets, and $A(E)$, which denotes the area of the plane set E, have the property that evaluating one of these functions at a set E—i.e., forming $f(E)$—

gives a feel for the "mass" of the set E. We now ask ourselves just what properties *any* set function f should have in order to be considered as an indicator of the "mass" of sets. A little reflection will convince the reader that the following properties are crucial:

1. $f(E) \geq 0$ for every E.
2. If $A \cap B = \varnothing$, $f(A \cup B) = f(A) + f(B)$.

The second property formalizes the statement that "the mass of part of it plus the mass of the rest of it is the mass of all of it." A set function having this property is said to be *additive*. To see the reason for the name "additive," consider n sets $A_1, A_2, \ldots, A_n$ such that $A_i \cap A_j = \varnothing$ whenever $i \neq j$. (A collection of sets with this property is said to be *disjoint*.) We have

$$f\left(\bigcup_{i=1}^{n} A_i\right) = \sum_{i=1}^{n} f(A_i)$$

because one need only apply the additive property repeatedly to A_1 and A_2, $A_1 \cup A_2$ and A_3, etc. A set function enjoying the first of the two properties is said to be *nonnegative*.

SETS WHOSE MEMBERS ARE THEMSELVES SETS

For each real number α, let A_α be the set $\{a : a \text{ is real and } a < \alpha\}$. Let $B = \{x : x = A_\alpha \text{ for some } \alpha \leq 1\}$. Here an object is a member of B if and only if it is a set of real numbers, in fact an A_α for some $\alpha \leq 1$. Thus B is a set whose members are themselves sets.

We have paused to say a word about sets of this type because we shall encounter them shortly, and they give rise to notational quirks which can be confusing. It is hoped that careful study of the following three statements will both point out the traps and show how they are avoided:

1. $B \not\subset \{x : x \text{ is a real number}\}$, because *no* member of B is a real number (the members of B are all *collections* of real numbers), hence no member of B is a member of $\{x : x \text{ is a real number}\}$. Indeed $B \cap \{x : x \text{ is a real number}\} = \varnothing$.
2. $\frac{1}{2} \notin B$, because $\frac{1}{2}$ is a real number and B contains no real numbers.
3. $A_\alpha \not\subset B$ for any α. In fact, every member of A_α is a real number, hence no member of A_α is in B. What *is* true is that $A_\alpha \in B$ if $\alpha \leq 1$.

2.3   Probability Spaces

We are now going to describe an abstract object, called a probability space, which can be used as a mathematical model of random
phenomena. The correspondence between phenomenon and model
will be as follows:

REAL WORLD	MATHEMATICS
Experiment	Probability space
The collection of all elementary outcomes	Sample space
Elementary outcome	Member of sample space
Compound outcome	Subset of sample space
Likelihood of an outcome	Set function on subsets of the sample space

AXIOMS

A *probability space* consists of three things:

1. A set, Ω, called the *sample space;*

2. A set, $\S$, of subsets of Ω;

3. A set function, P, defined for each set in $\S$; for which the following statements hold:

A1. $\Omega \in \S$, and $P(\Omega) = 1$;

A2. $P(E) \geq 0$ for every $E \in \S$;

A3. If $A \in \S$ and $B \in \S$, then $A \cup B, A \cap B, A \ominus B$ all belong to $\S$;

A4. If $A_1, A_2, \ldots$ are in $\S$, and $A_i \cap A_j = \varnothing$ whenever $i \neq j$,
then

$$\bigcup_{i=1}^{\infty} A_i \in \S \text{ and } P \left(\bigcup_{i=1}^{\infty} A_i \right) = \sum_{i=1}^{\infty} P(A_i).$$

As indicated in one of the problems at the end of this chapter, the
axioms given above are "inefficient" in that the requirement in A3
that $A \cup B$ and $A \cap B$ be in $\S$ is automatically met if all the other
conditions hold. The given form was chosen as being a better description of the object of interest.

At this point we pause to introduce some terminology. Members of $\S$ will be called *events*, and the value of the set function P, at any member E of $\S$, will be called the *probability* of the event E and written $P(E)$. The members of Ω will be called *elementary events* or *sample points*. Since we now have different names for "real world" and "mathematical" objects we can alter our convention about use of the phrase "intuitively speaking" to the convention that *any statement in which the words "outcome" or "likelihood" appear is to be viewed as an intuitive statement*. The reader is warned that in most books the distinction between "real world" and "mathematics" must be deduced from the context, since the words "event" and "probability" are used as we use them *but also for "outcome" and "likelihood."*

Let us examine the axioms intuitively by using our table of correspondences to see what the associated "real world" statements would be. Axiom A1 simply says that "some outcome" is "almost certain" to occur every time the experiment is run. Axiom A3 says that if A and B are outcomes, then there exist as conceivable outcomes "one or the other (possibly both) occurred," "both occurred," and "A occurred but B did not." Axiom A2 can be viewed as a "convention" that "all likelihoods shall be expressed as nonnegative real numbers."

Axiom A4 appears rather mysterious at first glance, but we note that, since $\Omega \in \S$ by A1 and $\varnothing (=\Omega \ominus \Omega) \in \S$ by A3, we can "try out" axiom A4 in the case $A_1 = \varnothing, A_2 = \varnothing, \ldots$. (Clearly $\varnothing \cap \varnothing = \varnothing$.) We find that

$$\sum_{i=1}^{\infty} P(\varnothing)$$

is a real number, hence that $P(\varnothing) = 0$. This fact gives us more information about A4; to see this, suppose A_1 and A_2 are in $\S$ and that $A_1 \cap A_2 = \varnothing$. Put $A_3 = A_4 = \cdots = \varnothing$, and apply axiom A4. Since in this case

$$\bigcup_{i=1}^{\infty} A_i = A_1 \cup A_2$$

and

$$\sum_{i=1}^{\infty} P(A_i) = P(A_1) + P(A_2),$$

we find that

$$P(A_1 \cup A_2) = P(A_1) + P(A_2),$$

i.e., our set function P is *additive*. Thus in real-world terms, we are claiming that "likelihood" is similar to "mass" in the sense that the likelihood of any outcome is the sum of the likelihood of "part of it" plus the likelihood of "the rest of it."

So far we have only examined, truly, the "watered down" version of A4, which results from replacing the upper limit ∞ by some integer n. (That we have gotten as far as n, and not just 2, is shown in the problems.) *This is all of* A4 *that need concern us in this book.* The additional features supplied by an upper limit of ∞ are purely technical. Later on, of course, when we are trying to construct probability spaces that model certain phenomena, we shall want to check that axiom A4 does indeed hold. In certain cases, however, this would lead us too far afield. As a compromise we state, without proof, the following theorem to which we shall appeal for assistance in verifying axiom A4. In essence this theorem states that if we can verify axioms A1 through A4 when only finite upper limits in A4 are considered, and if one other condition holds (condition 5 below), then we may assume that A4 holds with the infinite upper limit, since this can always be assured by "enlarging" our collection of events (going from $\mathcal{F}$ to $\mathcal{S}$ below).

THEOREM

If Ω *is a set,* $\mathcal{F}$ *a collection of subsets of* Ω, Q *a set function defined on the members of* $\mathcal{F}$, *and*

1. $\Omega \in \mathcal{F}, Q(\Omega) = 1;$

2. $Q(E) \geq 0$ *for every* $E \in \mathcal{F};$

3. If $A \in \mathcal{F}$ *and* $B \in \mathcal{F}$ *then* $A \cup B$, $A \cap B$, $A \ominus B$ *all belong to* $\mathcal{F};$

4. If $A_1, A_2, \ldots, A_n$ *are in* $\mathcal{F}$, *and* $A_i \cap A_j = \varnothing$ *whenever* $i \neq j$, *then*

$$\bigcup_{i=1}^{n} A_i \in \mathcal{F} \text{ and } Q\left(\bigcup_{i=1}^{n} A_i\right) = \sum_{i=1}^{n} Q(A_i);$$

5. If $A_0, A_1, \ldots$ *are in* $\mathcal{F}$, *and*

$$A_0 \subset \bigcup_{i=1}^{\infty} A_i,$$

then

$$Q(A_0) \leq \sum_{i=1}^{\infty} Q(A_i);$$

Then *there exists a collection* $\mathcal{S}$ *of subsets of* Ω *and a set function* P *defined on* $\mathcal{S}$ *such that*

1. $\mathcal{F} \subset \mathcal{S}$ *and* $P(E) = Q(E)$ *for each* E *in* $\mathcal{F}$.
2. $P(E) \geq 0$ *for every* $E \in \mathcal{S}$.
3. *If* $A \in \mathcal{S}$ *and* $B \in \mathcal{S}$ *then* $A \cup B$, $A \cap B$, $A \ominus B$ *all belong to* $\mathcal{S}$.
4. *If* A_1, A_2, . . . *are in* $\mathcal{S}$ *and* $A_i \cap A_j = \varnothing$ *whenever* $i \neq j$, *then*

$$\bigcup_{i=1}^{\infty} A_i \in \mathcal{S} \ and \ P\left(\bigcup_{i=1}^{\infty} A_i\right) = \sum_{i=1}^{\infty} P(A_i).$$

2.4 Laws of Probability

In this subsection we shall derive some elementary consequences of axioms A1 through A4. Let $(\Omega, \mathcal{S}, P)$ be a probability space, and let A and B be members of $\mathcal{S}$. Define A^c to be $\Omega \ominus A$. We first claim that

$$P(A) + P(A^c) = 1. \tag{2.1}$$

In the first place, A^c is certainly in $\mathcal{S}$ since A is in $\mathcal{S}$ by assumption, Ω is in $\mathcal{S}$ by axiom A1, and $\Omega \ominus A = A^c$ is in $\mathcal{S}$ by A3. Thus $P(A^c)$ is meaningful, and the left side of Eq. 2.1 makes sense. To see that the equality holds, note that $\Omega = A \cup A^c$ and $A \cap A^c = \varnothing$. By A1 and A4, then, $1 = P(\Omega) = P(A) + P(A^c)$.

Next we claim that

$$P(A \cup B) = P(A) + P(B) - P(A \cap B). \tag{2.2}$$

This is usually called the "law of total probability." It is easy to see that all of the sets appearing in Eq. 2.2 are in $\mathcal{S}$; to check the equality we note that

$$A = (A \ominus B) \cup (A \cap B) \ and \ (A \ominus B) \cap (A \cap B) = \varnothing,$$

and that

$$A \cup B = (A \ominus B) \cup B \ and \ (A \ominus B) \cap B = \varnothing,$$

so that by two applications of A4

$$P(A \cup B) = P(A \ominus B) + P(B)$$
$$= P(A) - P(A \cap B) + P(B).$$

Equation 2.2 can be generalized to the case of n events A_1, A_2, . . . ,

A_n, as is indicated in the exercises. Here we shall just give the formula for three events A, B, C:

$$P(A \cup B \cup C) = P(A) + P(B) + P(C) - P(A \cap B)$$
$$- P(A \cap C) - P(B \cap C) + P(A \cap B \cap C). \quad (2.3)$$

Another law of probability is that

$$\text{if } A \subset B, \text{ then } P(A) \leq P(B). \quad (2.4)$$

We have $B = (B \ominus A) \cup (B \cap A)$, and $(B \ominus A) \cap (B \cap A) = \varnothing$. Thus $P(B) = P(B \ominus A) + P(B \cap A)$. Since $P(B \ominus A) \geq 0$ and $B \cap A = A$,

$$P(B) \geq P(B \cap A) = P(A).$$

2.5   Exercises

2.1   Label the vertices of a square a, b, c, and d. Label the midpoint of side $\overline{ab}$ e, the midpoint of side $\overline{bc}$ f, that of $\overline{cd}$ g, and that of $\overline{ad}$ h. Let m be the center of the square and represent sets A, B, C, and Ω as follows:

Ω = the set of all points in the square $abcd$,

A = the set of all points in the rectangle $aegd$,

B = the set of all points in the rectangle $abfh$,

C = the set of all points in the triangles abm and cdm.

Let $A^c = \Omega \ominus A$, $B^c = \Omega \ominus B$, $C^c = \Omega \ominus C$, and describe the following sets: $A \cap B \cap C$, $A^c \cap B^c \cap C^c$, $(A \cup B) \ominus C$, $A \cup B \cup C$. (Notice that this exercise provides a Venn diagram for the study of *any* four sets A, B, C, Ω such that $A \subset \Omega$, $B \subset \Omega$, $C \subset \Omega$.)

2.2   By using the Venn diagram of Exercise 2.1, or otherwise, show that for any sets A, B, and C

$$A \cup (B \cup C) = (A \cup B) \cup C,$$
$$A \cap (B \cap C) = (A \cap B) \cap C,$$
$$A \cap (B \cup C) = (A \cap B) \cup (A \cap C),$$
$$A \cup (B \cap C) = (A \cup B) \cap (A \cup C),$$
$$A \cup (B \ominus C) = [(A \cup B) \ominus C] \cup (A \cap C),$$
$$(A \ominus B) \cup (B \ominus A) = (A \cup B) \ominus (A \cap B).$$

2.3   Let A be the set of integers $\{1, 3, 5, 7, 9\}$, B the set $\{2, 4, 6, 8, 10\}$, C the set $\{6, 7, 8, 9, 10\}$. Write out all the sets appearing in Exercise 2.2.

2.4 State the results of Exercise 2.2 if A, B, and C are viewed as outcomes of an experiment.

2.5 (a) By using the Venn diagram of Exercise 2.1, or otherwise, show that if A, B, and C are subsets of a given set Ω,

$$A \cup B \cup C = (A \cap B \cap C) \cup (A \cap B \cap C^c) \cup (A \cap B^c \cap C)$$
$$\cup (A \cap B^c \cap C^c) \cup (A^c \cap B \cap C)$$
$$\cup (A^c \cap B \cap C^c) \cup (A^c \cap B^c \cap C),$$

where complements are with respect to Ω. Show too that the sets in the union are disjoint.

(b) Assume that Ω is the sample space and that A, B, and C are events, in some probability space $(\Omega, \mathcal{S}, P)$. Show that

$$P(A) = P(A \cap B \cap C) + P(A \cap B \cap C^c) + P(A \cap B^c \cap C)$$
$$+ P(A \cap B^c \cap C^c),$$

$$P(B) = P(A \cap B \cap C) + P(A \cap B \cap C^c) + P(A^c \cap B \cap C)$$
$$+ P(A^c \cap B \cap C^c),$$

$$P(C) = P(A \cap B \cap C) + P(A \cap B^c \cap C) + P(A^c \cap B \cap C)$$
$$+ P(A^c \cap B^c \cap C),$$

$$P(A \cap B) = P(A \cap B \cap C) + P(A \cap B \cap C^c),$$

$$P(A \cap C) = P(A \cap B \cap C) + P(A \cap B^c \cap C),$$

$$P(B \cap C) = P(A \cap B \cap C) + P(A^c \cap B \cap C).$$

(c) Show that

$$P(A \cup B \cup C) = P(A) + P(B) + P(C) - P(A \cap B) - P(A \cap C)$$
$$- P(B \cap C) + P(A \cap B \cap C).$$

2.6 Use the result of Exercise 2.5 to compute the probability of $(A \cup B \cup C)$ given that $P(A) = \frac{1}{2}, P(B) = \frac{1}{2}, P(C) = \frac{1}{3}, P(A \cap B) = \frac{1}{9}, P(A \cap C) = \frac{1}{9}, P(B \cap C) = \frac{1}{6}, P(A \cap B \cap C) = \frac{1}{54}.$

2.7 Suppose that A and B are subsets of a given set Ω, and that $\mathcal{S}$ is a collection of sets, which contains A, B, and Ω and, in addition, contains the set $Y \ominus X$ whenever it contains the sets X and Y. Show that $\mathcal{S}$ contains $A \cup B$ and $A \cap B$, and thus show that axiom A3 of Section 2.3 could be "streamlined" to read

A3'. If $A \in \mathcal{S}$ and $B \in \mathcal{S}$, $A \ominus B \in \mathcal{S}$.

Hint: Show that $A \cup B = [(\Omega \ominus A) \ominus B]^c$.

2.8 Suppose that it is known for a given triple $(\Omega, \mathcal{S}, P)$ that axioms A1, A2, and A3 hold, and that axiom A4 holds if the upper limit ∞ is replaced by 2. Show that it follows that axiom A4 holds with an upper limit of n.

2.9 Show that if $\mathcal{S}$ has only finitely many distinct members, the infinite upper limit in axiom A4 is equivalent to an upper limit of 2, in that no additional restriction on $\S$ is implied by the infinite upper limit. *Hint:* If $\S$ has only finitely many distinct members, how can one find an infinite collection of *disjoint* members?

2.10   Let $(\Omega, \S, P)$ be a probability space, and let $E_1, E_2, E_3, \ldots$ be a sequence of events such that

$$E_1 \supset E_2 \supset E_3 \supset \cdots \text{ and } \bigcap_{i=1}^{\infty} E_i = \varnothing.$$

Show that

$$\lim_{i \to \infty} P(E_i) = 0.$$

Hint: Let $A_1 = E_1 \ominus E_2$, $A_2 = E_2 \ominus E_3$, $\ldots$, $A_n = E_n \ominus E_{n+1}$, $\ldots$. Show that the A_i are disjoint events and that

$$\bigcup_{i=k}^{\infty} A_i = E_k.$$

Use axiom A4 to show that

$$P(E_k) = \sum_{i=k}^{\infty} P(A_i),$$

and obtain the desired result from the convergence of this series when $k = 1$.

*2.11   Let Ω be the set of all points in the x-y plane for which $0 \leq x \leq 1$, $0 \leq y \leq 1$. Let $\mathfrak{F}$ be the collection of all subsets of this square which are themselves squares with sides parallel to the axes, or are the union of finitely many such squares. Define a set function P on the members of $\mathfrak{F}$ by $P(E)$ = area of E. Show that the triple $(\Omega, \mathfrak{F}, P)$ satisfies axioms A1, A2, and A3, and satisfies axiom A4 with an upper limit of 2 but *not* ∞. Show too that for this triple all the conditions of the theorem are met. *Hints:* Use the result of Exercise 2.7, and the fact that the difference of two squares can be "chopped up" into a finite union of squares by extending all the sides of both squares. Observe that a circular disk is not a finite union of squares, but *is* the limit of a sequence of such finite unions.

*2.12   *General Law of Total Probability*
1. Let $E_1, E_2, \ldots, E_n$ be n events in some probability space $(\Omega, \S, P)$, and let $E_i{}^1 = E_i$, $E_i{}^0 = \Omega \ominus E_i$. Notice that any integer k, where $0 \leq k < 2^n$, can be written in one and only one way in the form

$$k = b_{1k}2^{n-1} + b_{2k}2^{n-2} + \cdots + b_{nk}2^0$$

with each b_{ik} either 0 or 1. (This is the binary representation of k.) For any such k define

$$S_k = E_1^{b_{1k}} \cap E_2^{b_{2k}} \cap \cdots \cap E_n^{b_{nk}}.$$

Show that S_k is an event for each k $(0 \leq k < 2^n)$ and that $S_m \cap S_n = \varnothing$ if $m \neq n$.

2. Show that for any i

$$E_i = \bigcup_{k|i} S_k,$$

where $k|i$ denotes that the union is to be taken over all those subscripts k for which b_{ik} is a 1. Show that for any i and j

$$E_i \cap E_j = \bigcup_{k|i,j} S_k,$$

where here we require that both b_{ik} and b_{jk} be 1's in the binary representation of any subscript k appearing in the union. Finally, show that in general, for any $m \leq n$ of the E_i, say $E_{i1}, E_{i2}, \ldots, E_{im}$, we have

$$E_{i1} \cap E_{i2} \cap \cdots \cap E_{im} = \bigcup_{k|i1,i2,\ldots,im} S_k$$

and thus

$$P(E_{i1} \cap E_{i2} \cap \cdots \cap E_{im}) = \sum_{k|i1,i2,\ldots,im} P(S_k). \qquad (\psi)$$

Notice that all we have done is generalize the procedure of Exercise 2.5(b).

3. Consider the result of summing both sides of equation ψ over all possible choices of the subscripts $i1, i2, \ldots, im$. To clarify what is meant here, let us say that a *choice* is a set of m distinct integers $i1, i2, \ldots, im$ with $1 \leq i1 < i2 < \cdots < im \leq n$; and let us say that two choices are *distinct* if they have a different number in at least one position. As a notation for this scheme of summing over all the choices we use the symbol $\widetilde{\mathfrak{S}}_m$. Thus, summing both sides of equation ψ:

$$\widetilde{\mathfrak{S}}_m[P(E_{i1} \cap E_{i2} \cap \cdots \cap E_{im})] = \widetilde{\mathfrak{S}}_m \left[\sum_{k|i1,i2,\ldots,im} P(S_k) \right]. \quad (\psi\psi)$$

Denote by μ_{mk} the number of times $P(S_k)$ appears in the sum on the right of equation $\psi\psi$, and rewrite $\psi\psi$ as

$$\widetilde{\mathfrak{S}}_m[P(E_{i1} \cap E_{i2} \cap \cdots \cap E_{im})] = \sum_{k=0}^{2^n-1} \mu_{mk} P(S_k).$$

For convenience, abbreviate the left side of this equation as $\widetilde{\mathfrak{S}}_m$, and form T:

$$T = \sum_{m=1}^{n} (-)^{m+1} \widetilde{\mathfrak{S}}_m = \sum_{m=1}^{n} (-)^{m+1} \sum_{k=0}^{2^n-1} \mu_{mk} P(S_k).$$

4. Show that $P(E_{\cdot} \cup E_2 \cup \cdots \cup E_n) = \sum_{k=1}^{2^n-1} P(S_k).$

5. Assume the result, to be proved in Exercise 3.23, that

$$\sum_{m=1}^{n} (-)^{m+1} \mu_{mk} = 1$$

and show that

$$P(E_1 \cup E_2 \cup \cdots \cup E_n) = \sum_{m=1}^{n} (-)^{m+1} \tilde{\mathfrak{S}}_m,$$

the general law of total probability. Write out this formula in full for the cases $m = 3$ and 4.

*2.13   Go over Exercise 2.12 and observe that the result holds for any nonnegative additive set function that is defined on the sets in question.

*2.14   Use the result of Exercise 2.13, and the result of Exercise 2.12 repeatedly (first with $n = 4$ and then with $n = 3, 2$) to show that for any nonnegative set function ϕ

$$\begin{aligned}
\phi(A \cup B \cup C \cup D) = {} & \phi(A) + \phi(B) + \phi(C) + \phi(D) \\
& + \phi(A \cup B \cup C) + \phi(A \cup C \cup D) + \phi(A \cup B \cup D) \\
& + \phi(B \cup C \cup D) \\
& - \phi(A \cup B) - \phi(A \cup C) - \phi(A \cup D) - \phi(B \cup C) \\
& - \phi(B \cup D) - \phi(C \cup D) \\
& - \phi(A \cap B \cap C \cap D).
\end{aligned}$$

Use this result to show that

$$\begin{aligned}
\phi(A \cap B \cap C \cap D) \geq {} & \phi(A) + \phi(B) + \phi(C) + \phi(D) \\
& - 3\phi(A \cup B \cup C \cup D).
\end{aligned}$$

*2.15   (a) In a very hotly fought battle, at least 70 percent of the combatants lost an eye, at least 75 percent an ear, at least 80 percent an arm, and at least 85 percent a leg. How many lost all four? (Lewis Carroll).

(b) Show that the estimate in Exercise 2.14 is the best possible in that there exist sets A, B, C, D and a set function ϕ for which equality holds.

CHAPTER 3 CONSTRUCTION OF

PROBABILITY SPACES

IN THIS CHAPTER WE SHALL INVESTIGATE SOME TECHNIQUES FOR THE construction of a mathematical model of a given random phenomenon in the form of a probability space. All of these techniques, of course, presuppose that the random phenomenon of interest has been viewed as an "experiment" and that a collection of elementary outcomes has been chosen.

When the collection of elementary outcomes is not finite, additional concepts, to be introduced in Chapter 5, permit a simpler discussion. Thus, our treatment of such cases in this chapter will be brief.

The construction of a probability space for a given experiment is obviously essential if one wishes to obtain mathematical results. In addition, however, the construction process often pinpoints subtle questions that arise in apparently simple problems, and can help resolve these questions. In other words, the mathematical structure, in addition to giving "answers," provides a frame of reference from which to view random phenomena.

3.1 Finite Sample Spaces

If the set of elementary outcomes is finite we take as our sample space Ω a finite collection of objects, one for each elementary outcome. Now, it is customary to think of outcomes of an experiment as being themselves objects; hence we might say, "Take Ω to be the collection of all elementary outcomes." Let us agree to do this, since we thereby avoid the use of the phrase, "The object⸺in Ω corresponding to the elementary outcome⸺."

As our collection of events, $\mathcal{S}$, we take the collection of all subsets of Ω. If A and B are events, then so are $A \cup B$, $A \cap B$, $A \ominus B$; in fact, each of these is a subset of Ω and hence an event by definition. For the same reason $\varnothing$ and Ω are events, and so is

$$\bigcup_{i=1}^{\infty} A_i$$

if each of the A_i is an event, so we see that our choice of $\mathcal{S}$ is compatible with the axioms of a probability space. It remains to choose the set function P on $\mathcal{S}$—i.e., the probabilities.

To this end, let the members of Ω be $\omega_1, \omega_2, \ldots, \omega_n$; and let $p_1, p_2, \ldots, p_n$ be nonnegative real numbers such that

$$\sum_{i=1}^{n} p_i = 1.$$

Now, any event is a finite collection of the ω_i, that is, if E is an event there exists a subset J_E of the set of integers $1, 2, \ldots, n$ such that $E = \{\omega_i : i \in J_E\}$. Let us assign to any such E the probability

$$P(E) = \sum_{i \in J_E} p_i,$$

where the sum is taken over those subscripts i which belong to J_E. In particular we are taking $P(\omega_i) = p_i$ for each i, and

$$P(\Omega) = P(\omega_1, \omega_2, \ldots, \omega_n) = \sum_{i=1}^{n} p_i = 1.$$

Since all of the p_i are nonnegative, all of our probabilities are nonnegative, and, as we have just seen, $P(\Omega) = 1$. Moreover, if $A_i \in \mathcal{S}$ $(i = 1, 2, 3, \ldots)$ and $A_i \cap A_j = \varnothing$ when $i \neq j$, all but a finite number of the A_i must be the empty set. (Why?) The probability of the empty set is 0, however; no ω_i is in $\varnothing$, so we sum none of the p_i in forming $P(\varnothing)$. We conclude that only the case of a finite upper limit need be considered in verifying that axiom A4 holds (see Exercise 2.11), and the verification in this case is easy (see Exercise 3.15). *Thus, $(\Omega, \mathcal{S}, P)$ is a probability space.*

Our discussion to this point can be summarized as follows:

If a finite collection of elementary outcomes exists, take Ω to be the collection of all elementary outcomes and $\S$ the collection of all subsets of Ω. Assign to each member ω_i of Ω a nonnegative number p_i such that

$$\sum_i p_i = 1,$$

and define probabilities on $\S$ by

$$P(E) = \sum_{i \varepsilon J_E} p_i$$

where

$$E = \{\omega_i : i \varepsilon J_E\}.$$

So far we have not specified the p_i other than to require that they be nonnegative and sum to 1. Indeed we have seen that "as far as mathematics is concerned" any such set will do! A moment's thought will show that this "ambiguity" is quite reasonable, since we have not yet examined the physical experiment we are trying to model (other than to count its number of elementary outcomes). Presumably the choice of the p_i will determine how well our probability space models the physical experiment, and on intuitive grounds we claim that we should choose each p_i so that it is in some way related to the likelihood of the elementary outcome ω_i. In Chapter 1 we saw some ways of finding such numbers, but we wish to reemphasize here that this is a nonmathematical problem—the p_i must be chosen intuitively. Thus in what follows the reader may not complain of "unconvincing proofs" when we choose such p_i, since the proof is "in the eating." As it happens, the schemes of Chapter 1 have been found to give good results. Some additional ideas which have been found to "work" will be given below.

3.2   An Example

At this point we should like to discuss ways of applying the results of Section 3.1 to physical problems. Since a consideration of the many types of problems that could arise is clearly impossible, we shall confine ourselves to the treatment of a single example. This example is chosen to illustrate some of the ramifications of the classical theory of Chapter 1; the reader will find that the ideas within the following subsections can be applied to many of the problems he encounters (in particular, to the exercises).

Experiment 3.1.   An urn contains two red balls and one white ball. Two balls are selected from the urn at random.

Here and later we use the phrase "at random" to indicate that the experiment is conducted in such a way that it is intuitively plausible that arguments based on the idea of "equal likelihood" are valid. Here, for instance, we mean that the urn is well stirred and the selector is blindfolded.

THE DISTINGUISHABLE SPACE

Assume for the moment that the red balls in Experiment 3.1 are numbered 1 and 2, so that they can be told apart. An outcome of Experiment 3.1 can then be described by an ordered pair of subscripted letters—e.g., (R_1, W) for "the first ball selected was the red one labeled 1, the second was the white ball." In filling in the blanks in such an ordered pair (,   ), we can choose any one of the three symbols R_1, R_2, W for the first slot and either of the remaining two for the second. Thus we have six elementary outcomes: (R_1, W), (R_2, W), (W, R_1), (W, R_2), (R_1, R_2), (R_2, R_1). We take Ω to be this set of six ordered pairs, and $\mathcal{S}$ the set of all subsets of Ω.

Since Experiment 3.1 is supposed to have been conducted "at random," we argue intuitively that each of the above outcomes is equally likely: any ball could have been selected first, one being just as likely as any other, and then either of the remaining two could have been selected second, again without prejudice. Using the scheme of Chapter 1, then, we assign to each pair in Ω a probability of $\frac{1}{6}$; in terms of Section 3.1 we set $p_i = \frac{1}{6}$ for $i = 1, 2, \ldots, 6$. Since

$$p_i \geq 0 \text{ and } \sum_i p_i = 1,$$

we have arrived at a probability space once we assign to all other members of $\mathcal{S}$ the probability

$$P(E) = \sum_{i \in J_E} \left(\tfrac{1}{6}\right).$$

Let us call this probability space the *distinguishable* space.

THE ORDERED SPACE

So far we have assumed that the red balls in Experiment 3.1 were distinguishable. If this is not the case the only outcomes we can distinguish are ordered pairs such as (R, W)—for "first ball selected was red, second was white." There are only three such pairs—(R, W), (W, R), (R, R)—so we take Ω to be these three pairs. Again $\mathcal{S}$ is the set of all subsets of Ω, and as before we shall have determined a probability space once we assign probabilities to the three elementary events.

Notice that our three outcomes would be the same if the urn contained n red balls and one white, and that it is intuitively clear that if n were very large, the outcome (R, R) would be far more likely than either of the outcomes (R, W) or (W, R). Thus there is some question as to whether or not we should view our three pairs as equally likely. A procedure for avoiding this question, and which has been found to "work," is to *assign to each of the elementary events a probability equal to the probability of the corresponding* event in the distinguishable space.* The event (R, W) in the present space, for instance, corresponds to the event $(R_1, W) \cup (R_2, W)$ in the distinguishable space, and the latter event has in its space a probability of $\frac{1}{6} + \frac{1}{3} = \frac{1}{3}$. Thus, in the present space we put $P(\,(R, W)\,) = \frac{1}{3}$. A similar computation gives

$$P(\,(W, R)\,) = P(\,(R, R)\,) = \tfrac{1}{3},$$

so that we actually do end by assigning equal probabilities to our three elementary events. In the exercises we shall see that this would not be the case if there were more than three balls, however.

Since Ω contains only three points, $\mathcal{S}$ has only 8 members. For this very simple case we can easily list every event and its probability, as follows:

EVENT	PROBABILITY
$\varnothing$	0
$\{(R, W)\}$	$\frac{1}{3}$
$\{(W, R)\}$	$\frac{1}{3}$
$\{(R, R)\}$	$\frac{1}{3}$
$\{(R, W), (W, R)\}$	$\frac{2}{3}$
$\{(R, W), (R, R)\}$	$\frac{2}{3}$
$\{(W, R), (R, R)\}$	$\frac{2}{3}$
$\{(W, R), (R, W), (R, R)\} = \Omega$	1

* This is an intuitive word!

We shall call the probability space constructed in this subsection the *ordered* space.

In the preceding subsection we supposed that the outcomes (R, W) and (W, R) were distinguishable, that is, that the *order* in which the balls were picked from the urn was known. If this had not been the case, we could only have distinguished two outcomes: W—for "the white ball was one of those picked," and R—for "both balls were red." Here we take Ω to be the set of two points R and W and $\mathcal{S}$ the set of all subsets of Ω, namely $\{R\}$, $\{W\}$, $\varnothing$, $\{R, W\}$. Now, our elementary outcomes are not equally likely (intuitively), but by comparing with the "corresponding" events in the ordered space we arrive at the values $P(R) = \frac{1}{3}$ and $P(W) = \frac{2}{3}$; the same result would be obtained by comparing with the distinguishable space, as is easily seen.

In the three preceding subsections we have constructed three probability spaces for Experiment 3.1. These were different because the reported outcomes were assumed to differ, so the sample spaces were not the same. *The essential idea in all cases*, however, was to *reduce the problem to a point where one of the schemes of Chapter 1* (in this case the classical theory) *applied*.

3.3   Elementary Combinatorics

Experiment 3.1 was deliberately chosen so that the problem of enumerating outcomes was trivial. Before leaving the subject of finite sample spaces, we wish to work a more involved example, one which will require two of the most important formulas that are used when the enumeration problem ceases to be trivial. The development of these formulas is the domain of *combinatorial analysis* or *combinatorics*.

Experiment 3.2.   An urn contains k red balls and $(n - k)$ white balls, $0 < k < n$; m balls $(0 < m \leq n)$ are selected at random.

We wish to construct an unordered probability space for this experiment. As elementary events we can take the symbols $0, 1, 2,$ $\ldots, m$, where the symbol j stands for the outcome "of the balls selected, j were red." To assign probabilities to these elementary events we seek the probabilities of the corresponding events in the distinguishable space. To form *that* space we first suppose that the red balls are numbered from 1 to k, the white from 1 to $(n - k)$. An elementary event in the distinguishable space, then, can be viewed as an ordered m-tuple of subscripted symbols, such as $(R_2, W_5, \ldots, W_{12})$ for "the first ball selected was the red one numbered 2, the second was the white one numbered 5, . . . , the last was the white one numbered 12." Now (intuitively) the probability associated with each of these points should be one over the total number of points, since no outcome seems more or less likely than any other. Thus we are faced with the problem of counting the number of points in the distinguishable space.

To perform this count we use the "*mn* rule" of Chapter 1 m times. Thus, there are available a total of n distinct symbols—k symbols of the form R_i and $(n - k)$ of the form W_i. We can construct an ordered m-tuple of these symbols, such as $(R_2, W_5, \ldots, W_{12})$, by putting any one of the n available symbols in the first slot, any one of the remaining $(n - 1)$ in the second slot, . . . , any one of the remaining $(n - m + 1)$ symbols in the last slot, giving us

$$n(n - 1) \cdots (n - m + 1) = \frac{n!}{(n - m)!}$$

ways to form a set of m symbols. Thus, there are $n!/(n - m)!$ points in the distinguishable space.

Each choice of a set of m of the available n symbols, of the type discussed above, is called a *permutation* of size m of the n symbols. Thus we have derived the following formula:

Permutation Formula.   *There are precisely* $P_m^n = n!/(n - m)!$ *permutations of size m that can be formed from n distinguishable objects* $(0 < m \le n)$.

Now that we have counted the points in the distinguishable space, we can assign probabilities to all events in that space in the familiar way. Each such event will have a probability of $(n - m)!/n!$ times the number of elementary events it contains. Our next goal is to find those events in the distinguishable space which correspond to the events j (where $j = 0, 1, \ldots, m$) in the unordered space.

We proceed in two steps; first we shall find the event in the *ordered* space corresponding to j, and then we shall find the event in the distinguishable space to which *that* corresponds.

Now, a point in the ordered space is an ordered m-tuple of unsubscripted symbols R and W, such as $(R, R, \ldots, W)$ for "the first ball selected was red, the second was red, $\ldots$, the last was white." Corresponding to the event j in the unordered space, then, we have the set of all such m-tuples containing precisely j symbols R. To count these we note that their number is the number of distinct ways in which to pick j slots in $(\quad , \quad , \ldots, \quad)$ in which to put symbols R. Notice that if $j = 2$, for example, we do not wish to count the choices "first slot, second slot" and "second slot, first slot" separately, since these each lead to the same m-tuple $(R, R, W, \ldots, W)$. Thus we are interested here in what is called the number of *combinations* of j objects that can be selected from m. The appropriate formula is this:

Combination Formula.   *From n distinguishable objects one can form* $C_j^n = n!/j!(n - j)!$ *combinations of j objects* $(0 < j \leq n)$.

To derive this formula, notice that any set of j distinct objects can be reordered in $j!$ ways. (This is the number of permutations of size j from a collection of size j.) Therefore, corresponding to every *combination* of j objects selected from n there are $j!$ *permutations* of j objects selected from n and so

$$j!\,C_j^n = P_j^n = \frac{n!}{(n - j)!}.$$

(Notice that C_j^n is simply the binomial coefficient $\binom{n}{j}$. We shall see in the exercises that this is no coincidence.)

Our next objective is to choose, by examining the distinguishable space, the probability of an event $(R, R, \ldots, W)$, in the ordered space, which contains j symbols R. There are k subscripts available to attach to the j R's, and $(n - k)$ to attach to the $(m - j)$ W's, and hence there are

$$P_j^k P_{m-j}^{n-k} = \frac{k!}{(k - j)!} \frac{(n - k)!}{(n - k - m + j)!}$$

ways in which to convert the ordered m-tuple $(R, R, \ldots, W)$ into a *subscripted* one. Each of these ways leads to a point in the distinguishable space, and those points each have the same probability of $(n - m)!/$

$n!$. We conclude that *the probability to assign to a point in the ordered space containing j symbols R is*

$$\frac{\dfrac{k!}{(k-j)!}\dfrac{(n-k)!}{(n-k-m+j)!}}{\dfrac{n!}{(n-m)!}}. \tag{3.1}$$

Notice that this result is easily remembered, since it is simply $P_j^k P_{m-j}^{n-k}/P_m^n$—i.e., the number of ways to select j red balls from k, *in order*, times the number of ways to select $(m-j)$ white balls from $(n-k)$, *in order*, divided by the number of ways to select m balls from n, *in order*. Notice too that if we agree that, for negative integers n, $1/n! = 0$, as is customary, our formula takes account of the fact that one cannot extract more red balls from the urn than it contains, nor more white balls than it contains.

We have seen that the event j in the unordered space corresponds to C_j^m events in the ordered space, and that each of those has a probability given by Eq. 3.1. We conclude that *the probability to assign to a point j in the unordered space is*

$$\begin{aligned}
P(j) &= \frac{C_j^m P_j^k P_{m-j}^{n-k}}{P_m^n}\\
&= \frac{m!}{j!(m-j)!}\frac{k!}{(k-j)!}\frac{(n-k)!}{(n-k-m+j)!}\frac{(n-m)!}{n!}\\
&= \frac{C_j^k C_{m-j}^{n-k}}{C_m^n} \tag{3.2}
\end{aligned}$$

Again the result is easily remembered, since it is the number of ways to choose j red balls from k (without counting reorderings) times the number of ways to choose $(m-j)$ white balls from $(n-k)$ (without counting reorderings) divided by the number of ways to choose m objects from n (without counting reorderings). The reader is warned of the common error of using the numerator from Eq. 3.2 with the denominator from Eq. 3.1, or vice versa!

In closing this discussion, let us note that in our example we assumed that when balls were selected from the urn they were not replaced. A different problem arises when balls are selected one at a time, with the selected ball being replaced before each new drawing. Problems of the latter type will be found in the exercises. The two cases are frequently called "sampling without replacement" and "sampling with replacement," respectively.

3.4   Infinite Sample Spaces

So far in this chapter we have assumed that the random phenomenon of interest had only a finite number of elementary outcomes. We now consider the contrary case. As a first step we shall show that there are "different sizes" of infinity in a certain sense.

Let us assign to each positive integer $n = 1, 2, 3, \ldots$ a number $g(n)$, by the rule

$$g(n) = \begin{cases} n/2 \text{ if } n \text{ is even} \\ -(n-1)/2 \text{ if } n \text{ is odd.} \end{cases}$$

We note that the set of values of $g(n)$, as n ranges over the positive integers, is precisely the set of *all* integers $0, \pm 1, \pm 2, \ldots$. In fact, given an integer m (not necessarily positive), we can find a unique positive integer n such that $m = g(n)$, namely

$$n = \begin{cases} 2m \text{ if } m \text{ is positive} \\ 1 - 2m \text{ if } m \text{ is negative or zero.} \end{cases}$$

Thus we have succeeded in giving a rule that "matches" the positive integers and the set of all integers "one for one" in that to every positive integer there corresponds one and only one integer, and conversely. Now, *any set for which such a correspondence with the positive integers can be set up will be said to be "countably infinite," or simply "countable."*

Not every infinite set is countable. As an example, let $\mathcal{G}$ be the set of all subsets of the positive integers, and suppose $\mathcal{G}$ is countable. Every member of $\mathcal{G}$ is a set of positive integers and, since we are assuming $\mathcal{G}$ is countable, every member of $\mathcal{G}$ "corresponds to" some positive integer. Let us say that a member of $\mathcal{G}$ is "good" if it contains the positive integer to which it corresponds, and "bad" otherwise. Thus if the member $\{1, 2, 3\}$ of $\mathcal{G}$ corresponds to 2 it is "good," whereas if the member $\{1, 3, 5, 7, 9, \ldots\}$ of $\mathcal{G}$ corresponds to 4 it is "bad." So far so good, but now we look at the subset h of the positive integers defined as follows:

$h = \{n: n$ is a positive integer for which the corresponding member of $\mathcal{G}$ is bad$\}$.

Since h is a set of positive integers it is certainly a member of $\mathcal{G}$. The question is: is h "good" or "bad"? If h is "good" then some one of its members is its correspondent among the positive integers, and that integer corresponds to a "good" set—namely h—hence should not be in h by definition! If h is "bad" then its corresponding integer is related to a "bad" set—namely h—hence is in h by definition, making h "good"! This contradiction leads us to conclude that $\mathcal{G}$ is not countable. Sets that are not countable will be called "uncountable."

COUNTABLE SAMPLE SPACES

Suppose that for some random phenomenon of interest the collection of all elementary outcomes is countably infinite. We may then list these outcomes in the form $(\omega_1, \omega_2, \omega_3, \ldots)$ where ω_n stands for "that elementary outcome which was associated with the positive integer n when the set of elementary outcomes was shown to be countable." (Notice that any countable set can be listed or "enumerated" by this scheme.)

In this case the attack we developed for a finite collection of elementary events can be used with little change. *We take Ω to be the (countable) collection of all elementary outcomes ω_i and $\mathcal{S}$ to be the set of all subsets of Ω. We then choose a countable collection of nonnegative numbers p_i $(i = 1, 2, 3, \ldots)$ such that*

$$\sum_{i=1}^{\infty} p_i = 1,$$

and assign to any event E the probability

$$P(E) = \sum_{i \varepsilon J_E} p_i$$

where

$$E = \{\omega_i : i \varepsilon J_E\}.$$

Here of course the set J_E may be infinite, since it is a subset of the positive integers, but the sum in the definition of $P(E)$ is well-defined because the sum of *all* the p_i is finite. It is easy to see, using the arguments of Section 3.1, that $(\Omega, \mathcal{S}, P)$ is compatible with axioms A1, A2, and A3 of a probability space. Thus we need only check that A4 holds. This can be done by using properties of infinite series (see Exercise 3.16), or by appealing to the theorem of Chapter 2: if $A \varepsilon \mathcal{S}$, $A_i \varepsilon \mathcal{S}$ for $i = 1, 2, \ldots$, and

$$A \subset \bigcup_{i=1}^{\infty} A_i,$$

then every member of A is a member of some A_i and hence

$$P(A) = \sum_{i \varepsilon J_A} p_i \leq \sum_{i \varepsilon J_{A_1}} p_i + \sum_{i \varepsilon J_{A_2}} p_i + \cdots = \sum_j P(A_j).$$

EXAMPLE

Experiment 3.3.   A balanced coin is tossed until a head appears.

Here we read "balanced" as an assurance that "equally likely" intuition applies. As a set of elementary events for this experiment we take the positive integers $1, 2, 3, \ldots$, with the positive integer n corresponding to the outcome "head appeared for the first time on the nth toss." Clearly this collection is countable, hence it only remains to choose the p_i. To this end we construct a probability space $(\Omega_m, \mathcal{S}_m, P_m)$ for the experiment consisting of a *finite* number m of tosses (this is left as an exercise), and note that the event "corresponding" to the outcome "tail on the first k tosses and head on the $(k+1)$st (where $k \leq m-1$)" has a probability of $1/2^{k+1}$, *independent* of m. Thus it is suggestive, and experience has shown that it is fruitful, to take $p_i = 1/2^i$. We note that these p_i do indeed sum to 1.

UNCOUNTABLE SAMPLE SPACES

We have seen that there exist sets that are not countable, hence we might expect that probability spaces in which the sample space is uncountable can arise. This is indeed the case. Unfortunately a complete treatment of these spaces is not possible here. We confine ourselves to a single example which, we assure the reader, is "typical," although we do not have the "vocabulary" to describe the general situation it typifies!

For our example we can use Example 1.4 of Chapter 1. As Ω we take the set of all points in the rectangle $0 \leq r \leq L$, $0 \leq \theta < \pi$. As $\mathcal{F}$ we take the collection of all subsets of this rectangle that are themselves rectangles, or finite unions of rectangles. Since we know how to define areas for such sets, we define a set function Q on $\mathcal{F}$ by

$$Q(T) = \text{area of } T \quad (T \varepsilon \mathcal{F}).$$

As our notation indicates, the proper move here is to appeal to our theorem in order to find an enlargement $\mathcal{S}$ of $\mathcal{F}$, and a set function P

on $\mathcal{S}$, such that $(\Omega, \mathcal{S}, P)$ is a probability space. To this end it is necessary to check that $(\Omega, \mathcal{F}, Q)$ satisfies all the hypotheses of the theorem. Even this step is involved; the interested reader will find an outline of the procedure in the problems. We content ourselves with remarking that, while the resulting collection $\mathcal{S}$ will not consist of *all* subsets of the rectangle, it is a very difficult problem to prove that there are indeed subsets not in $\mathcal{S}$!

3.5   Exercises

3.1   Construct probability spaces for each of the experiments of Exercise 1.1.

3.2   Two cards are drawn at random, and without replacement, from a deck of cards labeled 1 through 5. Construct a probability space for this experiment and give probabilities for the events (a) first card selected was odd, (b) second card selected was odd, (c) both cards odd.

3.3   In how many ways can two rooks of different colors be put on a chess board so that they can take each other?

3.4   Attach the same probability to each permutation of the digits 1, 2, 3, 4. Let A_i be the event the digit i appears in its normal place $(i = 1, 2, 3, 4)$. Describe a probability space and find the probabilities of A_1, $A_2 \cup A_3$, $A_3 \cap A_4$.

3.5   Describe the distinguishable space, the ordered space, and the unordered space for each of the following experiments. State carefully any intuitive arguments you have used in your construction. (a) A well-balanced coin is tossed twice and the up faces recorded. (b) Two balls are selected at random, and without replacement, from an urn containing three red balls and one white ball. (c) Two balls are selected, with replacement, from an urn containing three red balls and one white ball.

3.6   An urn contains n red balls numbered from 1 to n, and n white balls numbered from 1 to n. $2r$ balls $(0 < r < n)$ are selected at random and without replacement. What is the probability that of the $2r$ balls selected no two have the same number? (Notice that this exercise can be put in more practical terms, such as pulling sox from a drawer to get a pair, or selecting nuts and bolts from a box of assorted sizes.)

3.7   The dial of a combination lock has numbers from 1 through 25. Give the number of possible combinations if: (a) All sets of three numbers are possible combinations. (b) No number may be used more than once in a combination. (c) The numbers in a combination must be increasing. (d) No number appears twice in a row in a combination; e.g., 1–1–5 and 3–2–2 are not combinations. (e) The numbers in a combination must not form either a decreasing or increasing sequence; e.g., 1–2–3 or 3–2–1.

DEFINITION OF A BRIDGE DECK

A *bridge deck* is defined here as a set of 52 cards, on each of which there appear two symbols. One symbol, which defines the *suit* to which the card belongs, is one of these four: spades, hearts, diamonds, clubs. The second symbol, which defines the *denomination* of the card, is one of the following: A(ace), K(king), Q(queen), J(jack), 10, 9, . . . , 3, 2. There is precisely one card with each choice of a suit and a denomination. Individual cards are referred to as the "ace of diamonds," the "ten of clubs," etc. In a *bridge game* this deck is shuffled and thirteen cards are dealt to each of four players.

3.8   In the course of a bridge game one player knows the location of 26 cards: the 13 that he was dealt and the 13 from another player's hand. Suppose that between these hands there are m spades ($0 \leq m \leq 13$), so that the remaining two players (*opponents*) have between them $(13 - m)$ spades. For each value of m list the possible ways the opponents' spades could be divided, along with the probability of each way. *Example:* For $m = 10$ the possibilities are (3, 0) and (2, 1) with probabilities

$$2 \frac{\binom{23}{13}}{\binom{26}{13}} \text{ and } 2 \frac{\binom{23}{12}\binom{3}{1}}{\binom{26}{13}}.$$

3.9   Refer to Exercise 3.8 and suppose that $m = 9$ and one of the opponents' spades is the queen. What is the probability that the opponent holding the queen holds at most one other spade? *Hint:* Assume that one opponent has been given the queen of spades, and count the number of ways to complete his set of thirteen cards by selecting twelve of the remaining 25.

3.10   Five cards are selected at random from a bridge deck, without replacement. Find the probabilities of the following events: (a) All five cards of the same suit. (b) All five cards in sequence; e.g., 3, 4, 5, 6, 7. (c) Both of these. (d) All in one suit, and denominations 10, J, Q, K, A. (e) Four cards of one denomination. (f) At least three cards of one denomination. (g) Precisely three cards of one denomination and two of another. (h) At least two cards of each of two denominations.

3.11   Let $A, B, C, \ldots, H$ be the events corresponding to parts $a, b, c, \ldots, h$ of Exercise 3.10. Find the probabilities of the following events (which are of interest in the game of *poker*, where they have the names given in italics): (a) $A \ominus B$, *flush*, (b) $B \ominus A$, *straight*, (c) $C \ominus D$, *straight flush*, (d) $[F \ominus G] \ominus E$, *three of a kind*, (e) $H \ominus F$, *two pair*.

*3.12   (a) Attach the same probability to each permutation of the 52 digits 1, 2, 3, . . . , 52. Let A_i be the event that the digit i appears in its natural place. Show that $P(A_i) = \frac{1}{52}$, $P(A_i \cap A_j) = 1/(52)(51)$ $(i \neq j)$, and

$$P(A_{i1} \cap A_{i2} \cap \cdots \cap A_{im}) = \frac{1}{(52)(51) \cdots (52 - m + 1)} = \frac{(52 - m)!}{52!}$$

where here $(i1, i2, \ldots, im)$ are supposed to be a set of m distinct integers chosen from $(1, 2, \ldots, 52)$, $1 < m \leq 52$.

  (b) Show that, in the notation of Exercise 2.12,

$$\widetilde{\mathfrak{S}}_m = \binom{52}{m} \frac{(52 - m)!}{52!} = \frac{1}{m!}.$$

  (c) Use the law of total probability to show that the probability of *at least one* digit being in its correct position is

$$P(1+) = 1 - \frac{1}{2!} + \frac{1}{3!} - \cdots + \frac{(-)^{m+1}}{m!} + \cdots - \frac{1}{52!} \doteq 1 - e^{-1}.$$

3.13   In Exercise 3.8 evaluate numerically the two most probable cases (splits) for $m = 7, 8, 9$.

3.14   Suppose that one computes $(1 + x)^n$ by direct multiplication: $(1 + x)^n = (1 + x)(1 + x) \cdots (1 + x)$. Clearly the result will be of the form $a_0 + a_1x + \cdots + a_nx^n$. By noticing that there will be one term in x^j, for each choice of a set of j of the factors $(1 + x)$ from which to use the x term, deduce that $a_j = C_j^m$.

3.15   Consider the experiment of tossing a balanced coin m times. Construct for this experiment the ordered space, using as sample points the ordered m-tuples of symbols H and T, such as $(H, H, T, \ldots, H)$, and assuming that these are equally likely. Find the probabilities of the events "tail on the first k tosses and head on the $(k + 1)$st" for $k = 0, 1, \ldots, (m - 1)$.

3.16   In a certain gambling game the likelihood of a player winning n dollars $(n = 0, 1, 2, \ldots)$ is inversely proportional to $n!$. What is the probability of a player winning at least five dollars? Describe your probability space in detail.

*3.17   An unbalanced coin has been found experimentally to give a head about $\frac{1}{3}$ of the time. A player flips this coin until the first appearance of a head. What is the probability that he will never stop? Describe your probability space.

3.18   A point P is chosen at random in the rectangle $0 < x < 2$, $0 < y < 3$. Let A be the event "$xy < 1$" and B the event "$y < x^2$." Find the probabilities of A, B, $A \cap B$, $A \cup B$, and $A \ominus B$. Describe your probability space (possibly with a certain vagueness about $\mathcal{S}$).

3.19   A number x, in the interval $0 \leq x \leq 1$, is selected in such a way that the probability of x lying in an interval $[x_1, x_2]$ is proportional to the length of that part of the curve $y = \cosh x$ between x_1 and x_2. What is the probability that $x > \frac{1}{2}$? Describe your probability space.

*3.20   The set of all sequences $(H, T, T, H, \ldots)$ can be associated with the set of all sequences $(1, 0, 0, 1, \ldots)$, and hence with the set of all binary fractions .1001 . . . . This last set, however, is the same as the set of all real numbers between zero and one. Assuming that sequences of coin tosses are such that for the corresponding binary numbers equal lengths are equally likely, compute the probability that in coin tossing the first head will appear on the kth toss ($k = 1, 2, 3, \ldots$).

THEORETICAL EXERCISES

3.21   (a) Let Ω be a set with finitely many members $\omega_1, \omega_2, \ldots, \omega_n$. Let $p_1, p_2, \ldots, p_n$ be nonnegative numbers such that

$$\sum_{i=1}^{n} p_i = 1.$$

Define a set function ϕ, on the subsets of Ω, by

$$\phi(E) = \sum_{i \in E} p_i,$$

where the summation is to be taken over all those subscripts i for which $\omega_i \in E$. Show that ϕ is nonnegative and additive. (b) Show that there are precisely 2^n distinct subsets of Ω.

3.22   Recall that a convergent series

$$\sum_{i=1}^{\infty} a_i$$

is said to be absolutely convergent if

$$\sum_{i=1}^{\infty} |a_i|$$

converges, and that in an absolutely convergent series the terms may be rearranged (taken in different order) without affecting either the convergence or the sum. Use this fact to show that axiom A4 holds for the probability space constructed in Section 3.4.

*3.23   (a) Let k be a positive integer, $0 \le k < 2^n$, and let the binary representation of k be $b_{1k}b_{2k} \cdots b_{nk}$. Let $N(k)$ be the number of b_{ik} which are ones (so that $0 \le N(k) \le n$). Recall from Exercise 2.12 that the notation $k|i1, i2, \ldots, im$ means that $b_{jk} = 1$ for $j = i1, i2, \ldots, im$. Show that

there are precisely $\binom{N(k)}{m}$ *distinct choices* (cf. Exercise 2.12) of the $i1, i2,$
$\ldots, im$ such that $k|i1, i2, \ldots, im$. Thus show that in Exercise 2.12
$\mu_{mk} = \binom{N(k)}{m}$. (b) Observe that

$$0 = -(1 - 1)^n = \sum_{m=0}^{n} (-)^{m+1} \binom{n}{m},$$

and thus show that

$$\sum_{m=1}^{n} (-)^{m+1} \binom{n}{m} = 1.$$

(c) Use the results of steps (a) and (b) to show that

$$\sum_{m=1}^{n} (-)^{m+1} \mu_{mk} = \sum_{m=1}^{n} (-)^{m+1} \binom{N(k)}{m} = \sum_{m=1}^{N(k)} (-)^{m+1} \binom{N(k)}{m} = 1.$$

3.24   By the binomial theorem

$$(1 + t)^m = \sum_{r=0}^{m} \binom{m}{r} t^r,$$

$$(1 + t)^n = \sum_{r=0}^{n} \binom{n}{r} t^r,$$

$$(1 + t)^{m+n} = \sum_{k=0}^{m+n} \binom{m + n}{k} t^k.$$

Multiply the polynomials on the right sides of the first two of these equations, and compare terms with the right side of the third equation, to deduce that

$$\sum_{r=0}^{k} \binom{m}{r} \binom{n}{k - r} = \binom{m + n}{k}.$$

CHAPTER 4 CONDITIONAL PROBABILITY

AND INDEPENDENCE

IN CHAPTER 1 WE EXAMINED CERTAIN OF OUR INTUITIVE IDEAS ABOUT random phenomena. One of those that was *not* mentioned might be called the (intuitive) notion of "unrelatedness": if a man in New York conducts Experiment 1.1 at the same time as another experimenter in Boston, we feel that the outcomes of the two experiments will be "unrelated" in that knowledge of the outcome of one is "no help" in learning the outcome of the other.

In this chapter we introduce the mathematical concept of *independence*, a concept that permits us to take account of intuitive feelings about "unrelatedness" in our models of random phenomena. We also introduce the concept of a *conditional probability*, which allows us to deal with problems where there is an intuitive "relation" among certain outcomes.

4.1 Conditional Probability

Given a probability space $(\Omega, \mathcal{S}, P)$, let B be an event (member of $\mathcal{S}$) with $P(B) > 0$, and A any event. We define $P(A|B)$—the *conditional probability* of A given B—by

$$P(A|B) = P(A \cap B)/P(B). \tag{4.1}$$

Notice that if we multiply through by $P(B)$ this formula becomes

$$P(A|B)P(B) = P(A \cap B), \tag{4.2}$$

which we may consider true regardless of whether or not $P(B) = 0$. If $P(B) \neq 0$, Eq. 4.2 follows from the definition of $P(A|B)$ in Eq. 4.1.

If $P(B) = 0$ (so that $P(A|B)$ is *not defined*) we have $P(A \cap B) = 0$, hence Eq. 4.2 reads "$0 = 0$" regardless of how one chooses to define $P(A|B)$. (To see that $P(A \cap B) = 0$ when $P(B) = 0$, note that $A \cap B \subset B$ and thus, by Eq. 2.4, $P(A \cap B) \leq P(B)$; since *all* probabilities are nonnegative this gives $0 \leq P(A \cap B) \leq 0$.)

The reason we are interested in conditional probabilities is that they give a precise way of treating situations where the outcome of an experiment is partially known or prescribed.

Example 4.1. In a certain game two dice are thrown, one onto a table where its upper horizontal (hereinafter abbreviated "up") face can be seen, and the other into a box where its up face is concealed. Players bet whether the number on the concealed die is greater or less than the number on the exposed die. In case of a tie the house collects all bets.

Here we all agree that if the die on the table reads "six" it would be madness to bet that the concealed one is "high," and that if the exposed die reads "two" we should demand odds before betting "low." In deciding just *what* odds to demand in this latter case we might reason intuitively as follows: the concealed die could show any one of six faces, presumably all six being equally likely, and in only one case ("one" face up) does the "low" bet win; thus the likelihood of "low" is $\frac{1}{6}$ *when a two is showing on the exposed die.*

Let us construct a probability space for this game by taking as a sample space the set of all ordered pairs $(i, j), i = 1, 2, \ldots 6$; $j = 1, 2, \ldots, 6$, the pair (i, j) corresponding to the outcome "concealed face i and exposed face j." Let us also agree to say "the event . . . ." when we mean "the event corresponding to the outcome . . . ."* It is intuitively clear that the event "low bets win" is the collection of pairs (i, j) with $i < j$—i.e., $\{(1, 2), (1, 3), \ldots, (1, 6), (2, 3), \ldots, (5, 6)\}$, and that the event "two on the exposed die" is $\{(1, 2), (2, 2), (3, 2), (4, 2), (5, 2), (6, 2)\}$ with probability of $\frac{1}{6}$. The intersection of these events is $\{(1, 2)\}$, with probability $\frac{1}{36}$. By our definition of conditional probability, then,

$$P(\text{"low bets win"}|\text{"exposed die two"}) = \frac{\frac{1}{36}}{\frac{1}{6}} = \frac{1}{6},$$

in accordance with the preceding intuitive argument.

* Finally, let us agree that we need no longer call attention to this convention every time it is used.

Mathematically speaking, discussion of conditional probabilities amounts to construction of a new probability space. In $(\Omega, \mathcal{S}, P)$ let $E \in \mathcal{S}$ and $P(E) > 0$. Define a new collection of subsets of E, $\mathcal{S}'$, by

$$\mathcal{S}' = \{A': A' = A \cap E \text{ for some } A \in \mathcal{S}\},$$

and define a set function P' on $\mathcal{S}'$ by

$$P'(A') = P(A')/P(E).$$

(Notice that P' is well-defined on $\mathcal{S}'$ because every A' in $\mathcal{S}'$ is the intersection of two members of $\mathcal{S}$, hence in $\mathcal{S}$, so that $P(A')$ is meaningful.)

We claim that $(E, \mathcal{S}', P')$ is a probability space—what one might call the "probability space given E." The proof is outlined in the exercises. Frequently it is helpful to refer to the new and old spaces in order to resolve or expose ambiguities in problem statements.

Example 4.2.   A box contains six good radio tubes and four bad ones. Two tubes are selected at random, and one of these is tested and found to be good. What is the likelihood that the other is also good?

As a sample space for the experiment of drawing two tubes, we take the four symbols GG, GB, BG, and BB; the symbol BG, for instance, corresponding to the outcome "first tube selected was bad, second was good." The considerations of Section 3.4 lead us to assigning probabilities of $\frac{15}{45}$, $\frac{12}{45}$, $\frac{12}{45}$, and $\frac{6}{45}$ to these elementary events. The question we have to answer now is that of what outcome is known to have occurred. If it is "at least one good," with corresponding event $\{GG, GB, BG\}$, then our new sample space consists of the points GG, GB, BG with probabilities $\frac{15}{39}$, $\frac{12}{39}$, and $\frac{12}{39}$, respectively, as the reader can show, and our answer to the problem is $\frac{15}{39} = \frac{5}{13}$. If, however, the problem statement is to be interpreted as assuring that the outcome "first tube was good" occurred, we find that our new sample space consists of the two points GG and GB, with probabilities $\frac{15}{27}$ and $\frac{12}{27}$, yielding an answer of $\frac{15}{27} = \frac{5}{9}$.

There are other possible interpretations of this problem, for instance, "one of the two tubes taken from the box was selected at random, tested, and found to be good." (In this case we have a "compound" experiment: first two tubes are selected, then one of *them* is selected.) We shall discuss this case shortly, but for the moment we can be satisfied with having made our point that reference to the sample space can expose ambiguities in a problem statement.

4.2   Stochastic Independence

Two events A and B are said to be *stochastically independent* (or *statistically independent* or simply *independent*) if

$$P(A \cap B) = P(A)P(B). \tag{4.3}$$

By comparing this equation with Eq. 4.1 we see that if A and B are independent, then $P(A|B) = P(A)$ whenever $P(A|B)$ is defined; i.e., whenever $P(B) > 0$. Conversely, if $P(A|B)$ is defined and equal to $P(A)$, equation 4.2 shows that A and B are independent. (Clearly the roles of A and B can be interchanged in these statements.) Notice, however, that our definition of independence makes sense even if neither of the conditional probabilities $P(A|B)$ and $P(B|A)$ are defined.

The definition of independence for more than two events, say for the n events $A_1, A_2, \ldots, A_n$, is more complicated than a simple extension of equation 4.3 to

$$P(A_1 \cap A_2 \cap \cdots \cap A_n) = P(A_1)P(A_2) \cdots P(A_n). \tag{4.4}$$

We require that this equality *and others* hold. To be precise, we require that for each integer k, where $2 \leq k \leq n$, every set of k different A_i (e.g., $A_{n1}, A_{n2}, \ldots, A_{nk}$) satisfies

$$P(A_{n1} \cap A_{n2} \cap \cdots \cap A_{nk}) = P(A_{n1})P(A_{n2}) \cdots P(A_{nk}). \tag{4.5}$$

Notice that for each k there are C_k^n choices of the k different events $A_{n1}, A_{n2}, \ldots, A_{nk}$, hence C_k^n equations such as equation 4.5 to satisfy. Thus when all the values of k are considered, a totality of

$$\sum_{k=2}^{n} C_k^n = 2^n - (n+1)$$

equations must hold if $A_1, A_2, \ldots, A_n$ are to be independent.

Let us write all of the equations corresponding to Eq. 4.5 for the case of three events A, B, C:

$(k = 2):$ $P(A \cap B) = P(A)P(B),$

               $P(A \cap C) = P(A)P(C),$

               $P(B \cap C) = P(B)P(C),$

$(k = 3):$ $P(A \cap B \cap C) = P(A)P(B)P(C).$

In elementary applications one rarely has to verify that all of the relations indicated in Eq. 4.5 are satisfied. The usual situation is that one *postulates* the independence of the given events, for intuitive reasons, and *uses* the relations in Eq. 4.5. One does frequently have to verify Eq. 4.3 directly, however.

As mentioned in the introduction, the concept of independence is important because it gives a mathematical model for an intuitive feeling we have in many situations. To see this, let us return to Example 4.2 and take the statement "one of the two tubes taken from the box was selected at random, tested, and found to be good" as the interpretation of the (ambiguous) statement that "one was tested and found to be good."

As a sample space Ω for this experiment we take the collection of symbols $GG1$, $GG2$, $BB1$, $BB2$, $GB1$, $GB2$, $BG1$, $BG2$, where, for instance, the symbol $BG1$ is supposed to correspond to the outcome "the first tube selected was *bad*, the second tube selected was *good*, the *first* tube selected was the one tested." Let us introduce an abbreviated notation for certain events of this sample space as follows:

$$XX1 = \{BB1, BG1, GB1, GG1\},$$
$$XX2 = \{BB2, BG2, GB2, GG2\},$$
$$GBX = \{GB1, GB2\},$$
$$BGX = \{BG1, BG2\},$$
$$BBX = \{BB1, BB2\},$$
$$GGX = \{GG1, GG2\}.$$

Here, for instance, the event $XX1$ corresponds to the outcome "the first tube taken from the box was the one tested," and GBX corresponds to the outcome "the first tube selected was good, the second bad."

Now, we *postulate* that the events $XX1$ and GBX are *independent*. The intuitive reason for introducing this mathematical postulate is that the likelihood of the *first* tube from the box being selected for testing seems "unrelated" to the *nature* of the two tubes from which the selection is made. Notice that if the tube tester "picks what appears to be the worse of the two tubes and tests it" it would be (intuitively) wrong to postulate independence of $XX1$ and GBX, since in this case there is reason to believe that the likelihood of the outcome [for which the corresponding event is]* $XX1$ is decreased when the outcome GBX is known to have occurred.

Since the tube for testing was selected "at random" we assign equal probabilities to $XX1$ and $XX2$. Since $XX1 \cap XX2 = \varnothing$ and $XX1 \cup XX2$ is Ω, these numbers must be $\frac{1}{2}$. Reasoning as in Chapter 3 we find that the probabilities of the events GBX, BGX, BBX, GGX should be in the proportion (12, 12, 6, 15), and arguments as in the preceding sentence show that the probabilities should be $\frac{12}{45}$, $\frac{12}{45}$, $\frac{6}{45}$, $\frac{15}{45}$, respectively. *By independence*, then,

$$P(GB1) = P(GBX \cap XX1) = P(GBX)P(XX1) = \tfrac{12}{90}.$$

Independence arguments similar to the foregoing give the following probabilities for our elementary events:

$$P(GG1) = \tfrac{15}{90}, \ P(GG2) = \tfrac{15}{90}, \ P(GB2) = \tfrac{12}{90},$$
$$P(BG1) = \tfrac{12}{90}, \ P(BG2) = \tfrac{12}{90}, \ P(BB1) = \tfrac{6}{90},$$
$$P(BB2) = \tfrac{6}{90}.$$

The event "the tube selected for testing was good" is $\{GG1, GG2, GB1, BG2\}$ with probability $\frac{3}{5}$. The event "both tubes good" is $\{GG1, GG2\}$, and the intersection of these is also $\{GG1, GG2\}$, with probability $\frac{1}{3}$. Thus the desired conditional probability is

$$P(\{GG1, GG2\}|\{GG1, GG2, GB1, BG2\}) = \frac{\frac{1}{3}}{\frac{3}{5}} = \tfrac{5}{9}.$$

We close this section with the remark that the concept of independence is of basic importance in the study of successive trials of an experiment, and will be used for this purpose in Section 7.1 and in Chapters 10 through 12.

4.3 Problem Formulation Using Conditional Probability

The purpose of this section is simply to call to the reader's attention the fact that many problems are most easily reduced to mathematical terms by using the ideas of conditional probability, and to indicate the procedure. To begin, let us extend Eq. 4.2 to the case of three events A, B, C. Assuming that the events A and $A \cap B$ have nonzero

---

* We hereby extend our convention to allow omission of this phrase in future.

probabilities, we have

$$P(C|A \cap B) = \frac{P(A \cap B \cap C)}{P(A \cap B)}$$

and

$$P(A \cap B) = P(A)P(B|A);$$

hence

$$P(A \cap B \cap C) = P(A)P(B|A)P(C|A \cap B). \qquad (4.6)$$

The reader can easily generalize this result to the case of n events $A_1, A_2, \ldots, A_n$, and obtain

$$P(A_1 \cap A_2 \cdots \cap A_n)$$
$$= P(A_1)P(A_2|A_1) \cdots P(A_n|A_1 \cap A_2 \cdots \cap A_{n-1}) \quad (4.7)$$

under the assumption that all of the conditional probabilities that appear are defined.

Now, suppose one wishes to compute the probability of some event of the form $A \cap B \cap C$. It may happen that considerable calculation can be saved by appealing to Eq. 4.6 rather than taking a direct approach.

Example 4.3.   An urn contains seven balls: two red and five white. Three balls are selected at random. What is the likelihood that the last two balls selected are red?

As a sample space for this experiment we take the collection of all possible ordered triples of the symbols R and W; for example, (R, W, W) for "the first ball selected was red, the next two white." Using a notation similar to that in Section 4.2 we define the events WXX, XRX, and XXR by

$$XXR = \{(W, R, R), (R, W, R), (W, W, R)\}$$

and so on. The corresponding outcomes are "the first ball selected was white," "the second ball selected was red," and "the last ball selected was red." Using Eq. 4.6 with A replaced by WXX, B by XRX, and C by XXR gives

$$P(\{(W, R, R)\}) = P(WXX \cap XRX \cap XXR)$$
$$= P(WXX)P(XRX|WXX)P(XXR|WXX \cap XRX).$$

The probabilities appearing here, however, are easily assigned on intuitive grounds:

$P(WXX) = \frac{5}{7}$—the likelihood that a ball selected from an urn containing five white and two red balls is white.

$P(XRX|WXX) = \frac{2}{6}$—the likelihood of selecting a red ball from an urn which originally contained five white and two red balls but has had one white ball removed.

$P(XXR|WXX \cap XRX) = \frac{1}{5}$ (why?).

Thus the desired probability is $(\frac{5}{7})\,(\frac{2}{6})\,(\frac{1}{5}) = \frac{1}{21}$. Of course the reader can solve this problem by the methods of Chapter 3, but if he does so the efficiency of the present scheme will be apparent.

4.4   Bayes' Theorem

Let $(\Omega, \mathcal{S}, P)$ be a probability space, and let $A_1, A_2, \ldots , A_n$ be n members of $\mathcal{S}$ such that

$$\bigcup_{i=1}^{n} A_i = \Omega,$$

$$P(A_i) > 0 \ (i = 1, 2, \ldots , n),$$

$$A_i \cap A_j = \varnothing \ (i \neq j).$$

Let $E \,\varepsilon\, \mathcal{S}$ and $P(E) > 0$. We claim that for any $j = 1, 2, \ldots , n$

$$P(A_j|E) = \frac{P(A_j)P(E|A_j)}{\sum\limits_{i=1}^{n} P(A_i)P(E|A_i)}. \tag{4.8}$$

To see this, note that by definition

$$P(A_j|E) = \frac{P(A_j \cap E)}{P(E)}, \tag{4.9}$$

but since

$$E = \Omega \cap E = (\bigcup_{i=1}^{n} A_i) \cap E = \bigcup_{i=1}^{n} (A_i \cap E),$$

and

$$(A_i \cap E) \cap (A_k \cap E) = \varnothing \quad (i \neq k),$$

we may replace $P(E)$ in Eq. 4.9 by using axiom A4:

$$P(E) = \sum_{i=1}^{n} P(A_i \cap E).$$

We obtain

$$P(A_j|E) = \frac{P(A_j \cap E)}{\sum\limits_{i=1}^{n} P(A_i \cap E)}. \tag{4.10}$$

On the other hand, by Eq. 4.2,

$$P(A_j \cap E) = P(A_j)P(E|A_j) \qquad (j = 1, 2, \ldots, n). \tag{4.11}$$

Use of Eq. 4.11 in the right side of Eq. 4.10 gives Eq. 4.8. This result (either in the form of Eq. 4.8 or of 4.10) is called Bayes' Theorem.

In the usual use of Bayes' theorem the A_i correspond to outcomes at some intermediate stage of a compound experiment, and E to some final outcome which is readily observed; the conditional probability of E given that A_i occurred is easily assigned on intuitive grounds for each i, and one wishes to know how likely it is that some particular intermediate result A_j occurred (given that E is known to have occurred). One can wax metaphysical and call the A_i "causes" and E an "effect" and say that Bayes' theorem allows one to "deduce causes from effects," but of course one can also laugh at this viewpoint.

The following example is designed to illustrate the use of Bayes' Theorem and also to show a much-frequented pitfall.

Example 4.4. An urn is known to contain 100 balls, of which some are red and some white. An observer selects ten balls from this urn at random and discovers that all ten are red. What is the probability that the urn contains all red balls?

As a sample space for this experiment we take the collection of all ordered pairs (i, j), where $i = 0, 1, 2, \ldots, 100$ and $j = 0, 1, 2, \ldots,$ 10—with the pair $(10,5)$, for instance, corresponding to the outcome "urn contained ten red balls, the selection of ten balls contained five red ones." Let the event E be defined by

$$E = (X, 10) = \{(0, 10), (1, 10), \ldots, (100, 10)\}$$

and the A_i by

$$A_i = (i, X) = \{(i, 0), (i, 1), \ldots, (i, 10)\}.$$

Thus E is the event "all ten balls selected were red" and A_i is the event "urn contained i red balls." By the methods of Chapter 3

$$P(E|A_i) = \frac{\binom{i}{10}}{\binom{100}{10}},$$

and thus, using Eq. 4.8, our answer is

$$P(A_{100}|E) = \frac{P(A_{100}) \cdot \binom{100}{10}}{\sum\limits_{i=0}^{100} \binom{i}{10} P(A_i)}. \qquad (4.12)$$

It remains, then, to choose the $P(A_i)$'s. Now *there is no way to do this from the problem statement.* If the problem statement began "From 101 urns, each containing 100 balls either red or white and no two containing the same number of red balls, an urn is selected at random . . . ," we could take $P(A_i) = \frac{1}{101}$, since then there would be an intuitive reason for assuming all possible numbers of red balls in the urn to be equally likely. In the present case we have no such assurance, and in fact if one equates ignorance and equal likelihood in situations such as this, as is sometimes done, it is possible to arrive at absurdities.

4.5   Exercises

4.1   Assuming that sexes of offspring are equally likely, what is the probability that a family with two children, one a boy, has two boys? What is the probability that a boy from a family with two children has a brother? Describe your probability spaces in detail.

4.2   Three balanced coins are tossed. What is the probability that the third coin is a head, given that the first two agree?

4.3   A white die and a red die are tossed simultaneously. Let A be the event "white die came up 1," B the event "sum of faces was seven." Compute the probabilities of A, B, $A \cap B$, $A|B$, $B|A$. Are A and B independent? Why?

4.4   Two dice are tossed six times. Let A be the event "sum seven on the first toss," B the event "sum even on each of the last four tosses." Find the probability of $A \cup B$.

4.5   Refer to Exercises 1.8 and 1.9, and compute the probability that every solution of the differential equation shall tend to zero as $t \to +\infty$, given that the roots are real.

4.6   Refer to Exercise 3.9, and compute the probability that one opponent holds the queen and one other spade, given that each opponent holds at least one spade other than the queen.

4.7   Two dice are thrown. (a) What is the probability that both faces are fours, given that the sum is eight or seven? (b) What is the probability that both faces are twos, given that the sum is four or seven?

4.8   Five cards are drawn at random from a bridge deck, without replacement, one at a time. Find the probabilities of: (a) Fifth card a spade, given that the first four cards are spades. (b) Fifth card a seven, given that the first four cards are 5, 6, 8, 9.

4.9   Which is more likely; at least one six in four throws of one die, or at least one pair of sixes in 24 throws of two dice?

4.10   An n-digit binary number is formed by a computer. The probability of the erroneous formation of any digit is p, and errors in different digits are independent. What is the probability of forming an erroneous number?

4.11   Four years after its launch date an artificial satellite falls to earth. Assuming that equal areas on the surface of the earth are equally likely, find the probability that the satellite lands in a latitude between 40°N and 50°N, given that it lands in a longitude between 50°W and 60°W.

4.12   Refer to Exercise 1.11 and compute the probability that the three pieces can be formed into a triangle given that $A^2 + B^2 > 1$.

4.13   In a bolt factory, machines A, B, C manufacture respectively 25, 35, and 40 percent of the output. Of their respective products 5, 4, and 2 percent are defective. A bolt is drawn at random and found to be defective. What are the probabilities that it was made by machines A, B, C?

4.14   A box of ten bolts is filled from the output of the factory of Exercise 4.13. (a) Compute the probability that all bolts in the box are good, assuming independence. (b) Compute the probability that two bolts selected at random from this box are good. (c) Compute the probability that all bolts in the box are good, given that two were selected at random, tested, and found to be good. (d) Compare this last answer with the result obtained by using Bayes' theorem and assuming that all numbers of defective bolts are equally likely.

4.15   An urn U_1 contains two red and three white balls, and another urn U_2 contains four red and five white balls. One ball is transferred at random from U_1 to U_2. Then one ball is drawn from U_2, and it happens to be red. What is the probability that a white ball was transferred?

4.16 Let $E_1, E_2, \ldots, E_n$ be independent events each with probability p. Use the law of total probability, and the definition of independence, to check that the probability of the occurrence of at least one of these events is $1 - (1 - p)^n$.

THEORETICAL EXERCISES

4.17 Show that if $E_1, E_2, \ldots, E_n$ are independent events then so are the events $E_1^*, E_2^*, \ldots, E_n^*$, where the asterisk indicates that the complement with respect to Ω may or may not be taken. *Hint:* Show that if *one* of the n independent events is complemented the resulting events are independent. Then simply introduce the desired number of complements one by one.

*4.18 (a) Show that $(A \cap C) \ominus (B \cap C) = (A \ominus B) \cap C$. (b) Use this result, and the results of Exercise 2.7, to show that $(E, \mathcal{S}', P')$ in Section 4.1 is a probability space.

*4.19 In Example 4.2 we found that the two interpretations "first tube good" and "one of the two tubes taken from the box was selected at random, tested, and found to be good" led to the same numerical result. Show that this was bound to happen by developing the following ideas. For a compound experiment where the two steps are independent, one can construct a probability space as follows: Let $(\Omega_1, \mathcal{S}_1, P_1)$ be a probability space for the first step, $(\Omega_2, \mathcal{S}_2, P_2)$ a probability space for the second step, and let the sample space for the entire experiment, Ω, be the collection of all ordered pairs (ω_1, ω_2) where ω_1 is a sample point of Ω_1 and ω_2 a sample point of Ω_2. Some collections of these ordered pairs will have the property that the collection of all their first coordinates is in $\mathcal{S}_1$ and the collection of all their second coordinates is in $\mathcal{S}_2$. These subsets of Ω can be assigned probabilities equal to the product of the probabilities of their coordinate sets. (The theorem in Chapter 2 is needed to extend the events so found to a suitable collection.)

CHAPTER 5 RANDOM VARIABLES AND

PROBABILITY DISTRIBUTIONS

SO FAR, THE BASIC CONCEPTS OF PROBABILITY THEORY HAVE BEEN developed and illustrated in terms of qualitative outcomes, such as "good or bad," "heads or tails," and finite sequences of symbols. Frequently, however, we are interested in the numerical values assumed by certain "variables" associated with an experiment. The notions of *random variable* and *probability distribution* permit a mathematical description and analysis of problems of this sort, and hence they will be introduced in this chapter, along with some techniques for their manipulation. As will be seen, these notions also greatly simplify certain problems in which the sample space contains an infinite number of points.

5.1 Random Variables

In the past, natural scientists aimed primarily at the discovery of laws which "deterministically" described natural phenomena in that the value of any particular variable was to be uniquely determined when specific values were assigned to all other relevant variables. However, there are many natural phenomena that seem to defy interpretation in terms of such deterministic laws. The variables associated with such phenomena usually appear to depend on the interplay of a very complex system of deterministic causes but seem to elude all attempts to predict which one of their various possible values will be assumed. Some typical examples of such variables are: the number of heads obtained when a coin is tossed n times, the weekly expenses of a family, and the number of alpha particles emitted from a radioactive source. Intuitively speaking, any such variable is called a *random variable*, or sometimes a *variate*.

To abstract a precise mathematical concept from this vague notion of a random variable, we use the general concept of a function. First, recall from calculus that a function f of a numerical variable x is defined to be any rule which assigns a unique numerical value $f(x)$ to each value of x in some prescribed domain of numbers. This definition can be extended to cases where the independent variable x takes values in any well-defined set of objects. For example, the length of an interval is a function on the set of all intervals, and the depth of craters on the moon can be defined as a function on the set of all moon craters. In the same sense, the number X of heads occurring when a coin is tossed twice can be viewed as a function on the sample space Ω composed of the four points: $\omega_1 = (T, T)$, $\omega_2 = (T, H)$, $\omega_3 = (H, T)$, and $\omega_4 = (H, H)$; clearly, $X(\omega_1) = 0$, $X(\omega_2) = X(\omega_3) = 1$, and $X(\omega_4) = 2$. *A random variable can thus be defined roughly as a numerical-valued function on a sample space.*

To be more precise, let Ω be a given sample space, and let $\mathcal{S}$ be a collection of subsets of Ω that satisfies the axioms of Chapter 2. Then, *a function X on the sample space Ω is defined to be a random variable if for every fixed real number x the subset $\{\omega: X(\omega) \leq x\}$ of Ω is a member of the given collection $\mathcal{S}$.* Here, $\{\omega: X(\omega) \leq x\}$ of course denotes the collection of all points in Ω for which X assumes some value equal to or less than x. (Mathematicians call a function having the above property a *measurable function* with respect to $\mathcal{S}$.)

As will be seen in the next two sections, it is logically necessary that for every real number x the set $\{\omega: X(\omega) \leq x\}$ be an event; that is, a member of $\mathcal{S}$ in accordance with the axioms of Chapter 2. The purpose of the restriction in the above definition is to satisfy this requirement.

For a trivial illustration, consider the example near the end of the third preceding paragraph. There, $\Omega = \{\omega_1, \omega_2, \omega_3, \omega_4\}$, and the set $\{\omega: X(\omega) \leq x\}$ is $\varnothing$ if $x < 0$, $\{\omega_1\}$ if $0 \leq x < 1$, $\{\omega_1, \omega_2, \omega_3\}$ if $1 \leq x < 2$, Ω if $x \geq 2$. If $\mathcal{S}$ is the set of all 16 subsets of Ω including the empty set $\varnothing$, then the four sets $\{\omega: X(\omega) \leq x\}$ are members of $\mathcal{S}$, and X is a random variable. However, one could legitimately take $\mathcal{S}$ to be the set $\{\varnothing, \Omega\}$; but then two of the sets $\{\omega: X(\omega) \leq x\}$ would not be members of $\mathcal{S}$, and X would *not* be a random variable.

Random variables will be denoted in this book by capital letters

$X, Y, \ldots$, whereas specific values that they assume will be denoted by small letters $x, y, \ldots$.

5.2   Probability Distributions

Let a probability space $(\Omega, \mathcal{S}, P)$ and a random variable X defined on Ω be given. The *probability distribution* or simply *distribution* of the random variable X is defined to be the set function Q that assigns to "practically every" set A of real numbers the probability that X assumes a value in A; that is, $Q(A) = P(\{\omega: X(\omega) \text{ in } A\})$. (The meaning of the phrase "practically every" in this definition is discussed in the last two paragraphs of this section.) By using advanced methods, it can be shown that this set function is actually completely determined by the values it takes on a certain "small" collection of subsets of real numbers, namely the subsets of the form $\{\alpha: \alpha \leq x\}$. In other words, the distribution of a random variable is completely determined when one specifies the probability of the event $\{\omega: X(\omega) \leq x\}$ for every real number x. Our axioms and our definition of a random variable assure that each of these probabilities is well defined when a probability space $(\Omega, \mathcal{S}, P)$ is given, and hence that every random variable then has a distribution.

Henceforth, we will use a simpler but more ambiguous notation. Thus, we define $P(X \leq x)$ by the relation

$$P(X \leq x) = P(\{\omega: X(\omega) \leq x\}) = Q(\{\alpha: \alpha \leq x\}).$$

For fixed x, $P(X \leq x)$ can be viewed as a value of a function on either subsets of the sample space Ω or subsets of real numbers. Such symbols as $P(X = x)$, $P(X > x)$, and $P(x_1 < X \leq x_2)$ will be used in a similar way. Also, we will usually write $\{X \leq x\}$ instead of $\{\omega: X(\omega) \leq x\}$. Furthermore, every reference to a random variable X is to convey the implicit assumption that a probability space $(\Omega, \mathcal{S}, P)$ is given and that Ω is the domain of X.

To clarify the above material and to provide examples for future use, we now briefly consider special cases of the two basic types of probability distributions. First, suppose the random variable X may assume only a finite number n of distinct values, and denote these values by $x_1, x_2, \ldots, x_n$. Then the n events $\{X = x_1\}, \{X = x_2\}$,

. . . , $\{X = x_n\}$ are disjoint, and their union is the whole sample space Ω. Thus, there are n nonnegative numbers p_1, p_2, . . . , p_n such that

$$p_i = P(X = x_i),$$

$$p_1 + p_2 + \cdots + p_n = 1,$$

and

$$P(X \leq x) = \sum_{x_i \leq x} p_i$$

for every fixed value of x, where the summation extends over all values of i for which $x_i \leq x$.

When X may assume any value in an interval $a \leq x \leq b$ with $a < b$, one cannot construct the distribution of X by using numbers p_i as in the preceding paragraph, since the numbers in an interval cannot be enumerated in a sequence. In such cases, one must use some other method to compute the value of $P(X \leq x)$, such as that used in Example 5.3.

Example 5.1. Suppose an ideal coin is tossed three times. Let Ω be the set of eight ordered 3-tuples $(E_1, E_2, E_3,)$ where E_i denotes the outcome (head or tail) of the ith toss; (let $\mathcal{S}$ be the set of all 256 subsets of Ω;) let P be the set function (on $\mathcal{S}$) that assigns the probability $\frac{1}{8}$ to each 3-tuple in Ω; and let the random variable X denote the number of heads that occur. Then X may assume only the values 0, 1, 2, and 3. Letting $p_i = P(X = i)$, one easily sees that $p_0 = p_3 = \frac{1}{8}$ and $p_1 = p_2 = \frac{3}{8}$ and that

$$P(X \leq x) = \begin{cases} 0 & (-\infty < x < 0) \\ \dfrac{1}{8} & (0 \leq x < 1) \\ \dfrac{4}{8} & (1 \leq x < 2) \\ \dfrac{7}{8} & (2 \leq x < 3) \\ 1 & (3 \leq x < \infty). \end{cases} \tag{5.1}$$

Example 5.2. Suppose an ideal die is tossed three times. Let Ω be the set of all 216 ordered 3-tuples (E_1, E_2, E_3), where E_i denotes the outcome (1, 2, 3, 4, 5, or 6 dots appeared on the upturned face) of the ith toss; (let $\mathcal{S}$ be the set of all subsets of Ω;) let P be the set function (on $\mathcal{S}$) which assigns the probability $\frac{1}{216}$ to each 3-tuple in Ω; and let X

denote the number of occurrences of the event "an even number of dots appeared on the upturned face." Then one can see that X and p_i take the same values as in Example 5.1, and also that $P(X \leq x)$ is given by Eq. 5.1.

Obviously, reference to the set $\mathcal{S}$ is not necessary in the solution of simple problems such as the two foregoing examples.

These same two examples illustrate the important fact that many random variables have the same distribution. Thus, probability distributions are more basic than random variables.

Example 5.3.   Suppose a point Q is chosen at random inside or on a circle C of radius r with its center at the point O. Let Ω be the set of all points inside or on C; (let $\mathcal{S}$ be the set of practically all subsets of Ω;) let P be the set function (on $\mathcal{S}$) that assigns equal probabilities to sets having equal areas; and let X be the distance from O to Q. For $0 \leq x \leq r$, the event $\{X \leq x\}$ then occurs when Q lies inside or on a circle of radius x, center O, and area πx^2 and hence has the probability $\pi x^2 / \pi r^2$, since the area of C is πr^2. Thus,

$$P(X \leq x) = \begin{cases} 0 & (-\infty < x < 0) \\ x^2/r^2 & (0 \leq x \leq r) \\ 1 & (r < x < \infty). \end{cases} \tag{5.2}$$

For the more sophisticated reader, we briefly consider here, as promised earlier, a more careful description of the distribution of a random variable. Thus, momentarily let R denote the set of all real numbers α, and let $\mathcal{B}$ denote the smallest set of subsets of R that satisfies the two conditions: (1) for every real number x, the set $\{\alpha : \alpha \leq x\}$ of real numbers is a member of $\mathcal{B}$, and (2) with Ω and $\mathcal{S}$ replaced by R and $\mathcal{B}$, $\mathcal{B}$ satisfies the axioms of Chapter 2. (Mathematicians call $\mathcal{B}$ a *Borel field* and its members *Borel sets* of real numbers.) We also assume that a probability space $(\Omega, \mathcal{S}, P)$ and a random variable X on Ω are given. Now, by using advanced methods, it can be shown that there is a unique set function Q that assigns to each set A in $\mathcal{B}$ the probability that X assumes a value in A; that is,

$$Q(A) = P(\{\omega : X(\omega) \text{ in } A\}).$$

The content of all this is that the function X relates the probability space $(\Omega, \mathcal{S}, P)$ with a new probability space $(R, \mathcal{B}, Q)$ which has the set R of all real numbers as its sample space. This function Q is properly defined as the probability distribution of X.

For a final remark on terminology, let f be a given numerical-valued function which satisfies the two conditions: (1) $f(x)$ is uniquely defined for every real number x, and (2) for every real number x, the set $\{\alpha : f(\alpha) \leq x\}$ of real numbers is a Borel set; that is, a member of the collection $\mathcal{B}$ described in the preceding paragraph. Such a function is often called a *Borel function* or a measurable function with respect to $\mathcal{B}$. Thus, if the sample space Ω for a random variable X is the set of all real numbers, and $\mathcal{S}$ is the collection $\mathcal{B}$, then X is a Borel function. It can be shown that every function that is continuous or "piecewise" continuous for all x's is a Borel function, although mathematicians can construct functions that are not Borel functions. Nevertheless, practically every function encountered in practice is a Borel function; similarly, practically every conceivable set of real numbers is a Borel set. We will occasionally use such phrases as practically every (all, etc.) function or set in this sense; the more sophisticated reader may wish to substitute "every Borel" for "practically every," "all Borel" for "practically all," etc.

5.3   The Distribution Function

Since it is generally easier to work with ordinary functions of numerical variables than with set functions, we next consider how to describe probability distributions in terms of functions of numerical variables.

Let X be a given random variable. Note that the event $\{X \leq x\}$, and hence $P(X \leq x)$, depends only on the numerical value of x, since X is a fixed random variable. Therefore, we can introduce the function F defined for all real values of x by

$$F(x) = P(X \leq x) \qquad (-\infty < x < \infty). \qquad (5.3)$$

This function F uniquely determines the distribution of X and is called the *distribution function* of X or of the distribution of X. Instead of F, the notation F_X is used by some authors. With $F(x) = P(X \leq x)$, Eqs. 5.1 and 5.2 show two examples of distribution functions. As shown in Eq. 5.1, a distribution function is not necessarily a continuous function.

To facilitate the development of the properties of F as well as for later use, we also introduce the function g, defined for all real values of x by

$$g(x) = P(X = x) \qquad (-\infty < x < \infty) \qquad (5.4)$$

and called the *probability function* of X or of the distribution of X. Clearly, $0 \leq g(x) \leq 1$ for every x. To evaluate this function when F is given, first note that, when $a < b$,

$$P(X \leq b) = P(X \leq a) + P(a < X \leq b),$$

since the event $\{X \leq b\}$ is the union of the two disjoint events $\{X \leq a\}$ and $\{a < X \leq b\}$, and hence that

$$P(a < X \leq b) = F(b) - F(a) \qquad (a < b). \qquad (5.5)$$

It is plausible that a single value of X can be treated as a limit of intervals containing and shrinking to that value and hence from Eqs. 5.4 and 5.5 that

$$g(b) = \lim_{a \to b-} P(a < X \leq b) = F(b) - \lim_{a \to b-} F(a), \qquad (5.6)$$

where $a \to b-$ indicates that a approaches b from the left (with a always less than b). (A rigorous proof can be based on axiom A4, which basically implies all of the continuity properties of F.)

If F is continuous at $x = b$, Eq. 5.6 shows that $g(b) = 0$. Otherwise, $g(b)$ is the amount of the jump in $F(x)$ from the limiting value of $F(x)$ as x approaches b from the left up to the value of $F(b)$. In Example 5.3, $g(x) = 0$ for every x since F is continuous at every x; this does not mean that the event $\{X = x\}$ is necessarily impossible but merely that this event must be truly insignificant when compared with the very large number of elementary events. This example also shows that a probability function does not necessarily determine a distribution. For Example 5.1,

$$g(1) = F(1) - \lim_{x \to 1-} F(x) = \tfrac{4}{8} - \tfrac{1}{8} = \tfrac{3}{8},$$

and the function g has the values $g(0) = g(3) = \tfrac{1}{8}$ and $g(1) = g(2) = \tfrac{3}{8}$ and is otherwise 0.

The function F can be used to compute the probability that X takes a value in any sufficiently nice set of real numbers. For example, when $a < b$, use of the equation

$$P(X \leq b) + P(X = a) = P(X \leq a) + P(a \leq X \leq b)$$

and other similar ones leads to the following equations:

$$P(a \leq X \leq b) = F(b) - F(a) + g(a),$$
$$P(a < X < b) = F(b) - F(a) - g(b), \qquad (5.7)$$
$$P(a \leq X < b) = F(b) - F(a) + g(a) - g(b).$$

For Example 5.1, Eqs. 5.5 and 5.7 show that $P(2 < X \leq 3) = \frac{1}{8}$, $P(2 \leq X \leq 3) = \frac{4}{8}, P(2 < X < 3) = 0$, and $P(2 \leq X < 3) = \frac{3}{8}$. For Example 5.3,

$$P(r/4 < X \leq r/2) = P(r/4 \leq X \leq r/2) = P(r/4 < X < r/2)$$
$$= P(r/4 \leq X < r/2) = \frac{3}{16}.$$

Obviously, F cannot be any function but must satisfy certain conditions. Since a probability must be a number between 0 and 1, Eqs. 5.3 and 5.5 show that

$$0 \leq F(x) \leq 1 \qquad (-\infty < x < \infty), \qquad (5.8)$$
$$F(a) \leq F(b) \qquad (-\infty < a \leq b < \infty). \qquad (5.9)$$

The latter relation means that F must be a monotonic nondecreasing function. Since $X \leq -\infty$ is impossible and $X \leq +\infty$ is certain, it is plausible that

$$F(-\infty) = 0 \text{ and } F(+\infty) = 1, \qquad (5.10)$$

where

$$F(\pm\infty) = \lim_{x \to \pm\infty} F(x).$$

It is also plausible that

$$\lim_{h \to 0+} F(x + h) = \lim_{h \to 0+} P[X \leq (x + h)] = P(X \leq x) = F(x),$$

where $h \to 0+$ indicates that h approaches 0 from the right, and hence that

$$\lim_{h \to 0+} [F(x + h) - F(x)] = 0 \qquad (5.11)$$

for every fixed x; this means that F must be continuous from the right.* (A rigorous proof of Eqs. 5.10 and 5.11 can be based on axiom A4.)

In summary, when a random variable X is given, the function F defined in Eq. 5.3 is the distribution function of X, and it satisfies

---

* Some authors use the definition $F(x) = P(X < x)$ instead of Eq. 5.3; in this case, F is continuous from the left. Adoption and consistent usage of either one of these equally good conventions is necessary in probability theory.

relations 5.8 to 5.11. Conversely, if any function F that satisfies relations 5.8 to 5.11 is initially given, one can construct in many ways a probability space and a random variable X such that $F(x) = P(X \leq x)$. In fact, this can be done by choosing Ω to be the set of all real numbers x, X to be the function such that $X(x) = x$ for every x in Ω, and P to be the set function for which $P(X \leq x) = F(x)$. For this reason, one can often study distribution functions without reference to the underlying sample spaces and random variables. In the construction of possible mathematical models for complex physical problems, it is often expedient to do this.

5.4   Discrete Distributions

In this section and the next, we will study two basic types of probability distributions; these contain most distributions encountered in practice. Several important special cases are described in Chapters 7 and 8.

We define a *discrete distribution* to be a probability distribution whose probability function g has the following property: there is a countable (finite or countably infinite) number of values of x, to be denoted by $x_1, x_2, x_3, \ldots$ or simply by $\{x_i\}$, for which the (finite or infinite) series $\sum_i g(x_i)$ has the sum 1, where the summation extends over all members of the sequence $\{x_i\}$. A random variable is called discrete if its distribution is discrete. Of course, the numbers $g(x_i)$ are given by

$$g(x_i) = P(X = x_i) \qquad (i = 1, 2, 3, \ldots)$$

and must satisfy the relations

$$g(x_i) \geq 0 \text{ and } \sum_i g(x_i) = 1. \tag{5.12}$$

For example, the random variables and the distribution of Examples 5.1 and 5.2 are discrete, since

$$g(0) + g(1) + g(2) + g(3) = 1.$$

However, the random variable of Example 5.3 is not discrete, since $g(x) = 0$ for every x.

Let X be a discrete random variable. Since

$$\Sigma g(x_i) = 1,$$

the probability is 0 that X does not assume one of the values x_i; in other words, the probability is 0 that X assumes any values other than those in the sequence $\{x_i\}$. Therefore, $g(x) = 0$ when $x \neq x_i$ for all values of i. Hence, the probability function is completely known when the sequence $\{x_i\}$ is known, so that Eq. 5.12 is satisfied.

Since the total probability 1 is distributed among the points $x_1, x_2, x_3, \ldots$, these numbers are often called "possible values" or "mass points" or "probability points." In practice, these numbers are usually known before either the probability function or the distribution function is evaluated, as in Examples 5.1 and 5.2. There are frequently only a finite number of these possible values, or the countably infinite number of them usually do not have a finite limit point (such as the sequence $\{1/i\}$ has at 0).

For a discrete random variable X with distribution function F, we see from Eq. 5.6 that

$$g(x_i) = F(x_i) - \lim_{x \to x_i-} F(x) \qquad (i = 1, 2, 3, \ldots). \qquad (5.13)$$

Also,

$$F(x) = P(X \leq x) = \sum_{x_i \leq x} g(x_i) \qquad (-\infty < x < \infty), \qquad (5.14)$$

where the summation extends over all values of i for which $x_i \leq x$. This expression shows that the distribution function of a discrete distribution can be computed when the probability function is known, and hence that the probability function of a discrete distribution uniquely determines the distribution. When the sequence $\{x_i\}$ does not have a finite limit point, this expression also shows that the distribution function is a step function, a function which increases only in finite jumps.

In summary, when a discrete distribution function F is given, the probability function g is defined by Eq. 5.13 at its possible values and satisfies Eq. 5.12. Conversely, when any function g is defined on a countable set of real numbers and satisfies Eq. 5.12, the corresponding discrete distribution function F can be obtained from Eq. 5.14.

When working problems involving a discrete random variable, it is usually more convenient to work with the probability function g than with the distribution function F. For example, if A is an event that occurs when X assumes a value in a given subset $\{x_{i_1}, x_{i_2}, \ldots\}$ of the x_i's, then

$$P(A) = g(x_{i_1}) + g(x_{i_2}) + \cdots.$$

For Example 5.1, if A is the event "either 0 or 3 heads occur," then $P(A) = P(X = 0) + P(X = 3) = g(0) + g(3) = \frac{1}{4}$.

5.5   Continuous Distributions

We will call a probability distribution a *continuous distribution* if its distribution function is continuous at every real value of its argument. We will call a probability distribution an *absolutely continuous distribution** if it is a continuous distribution and if also its distribution function F has the property that there is some nonnegative function f such that

$$F(x) = \int_{-\infty}^{x} f(x')\, dx' \qquad (-\infty < x < \infty) \qquad (5.15)$$

for every real value of x. Such a function f is called a (probability) *density function* of the distribution. A random variable is called continuous or absolutely continuous if its distribution is continuous or absolutely continuous. (While we can view the integral in Eq. 5.15 as an ordinary Riemann integral in this book, a completely general development would treat it as a Lebesgue integral and f as a Lebesgue-measurable function.)

For example, the random variable of Example 5.3 is absolutely continuous because it has the density function defined by

$$f(x) = \begin{cases} 2x/r^2 & (0 \le x \le r) \\ 0 & (-\infty < x < 0,\, r < x < \infty), \end{cases} \qquad (5.16)$$

since substitution of this function in the integral of Eq. 5.15 gives the distribution function defined by $F(x) = P(X \le x)$ given in Eq. 5.2. Note that f is not uniquely defined by Eq. 5.15, since other values— e.g., 0—could be assigned to $f(r)$ than the value $2/r$ used here.

Virtually every continuous distribution encountered in practical applications is absolutely continuous. For this reason and because absolutely continuous distributions are mathematically much simpler

---

* Some authors call an absolutely continuous distribution just a continuous distribution.

than continuous distributions, very little will be said in this book about continuous distributions that are not absolutely continuous.

An absolutely continuous probability distribution is analogous to a mass distribution obtained by smearing (sufficiently smoothly) a unit mass of matter along an axis of real numbers, whereas a discrete distribution is analogous to the mass distribution obtained by distributing a unit mass in lumps along an axis of real numbers. The probability function g of a discrete distribution specifies how (where and how much) the lumps are distributed, while the density function f of an absolutely continuous distribution specifies the linear mass density at each point.

By differentiating each side of Eq. 5.15, we find that

$$f(x) = \frac{d}{dx} F(x). \tag{5.17}$$

From Eq. 5.15, we also see that, for $a < b$,

$$\int_a^b f(x) \, dx = F(b) - F(a). \tag{5.18}$$

Combining this with Eq. 5.5 shows that

$$P(a < X \le b) = \int_a^b f(x) \, dx \tag{5.19}$$

and hence that the probabilities of various events can be obtained by integrating f. Since F is a nondecreasing function, its slope f must be nonnegative. This, $F(+\infty) = 1$, and Eq. 5.15 imply that every density function must satisfy the two conditions

$$f(x) \ge 0 \text{ and } \int_{-\infty}^{\infty} f(x) \, dx = 1. \tag{5.20}$$

Thus, when the distribution function F of an absolutely continuous distribution is given, the density function can be obtained from Eq. 5.17 and satisfies Eqs. 5.15 and 5.18 to 5.20. Conversely, when any function f is initially given so that it satisfies Eq. 5.20, the corresponding distribution function F can be obtained from Eq. 5.15.

It was remarked in Section 5.2 that the probability function g has the value $g(b) = 0$ at $x = b$ if the distribution function F is continuous at $x = b$. It follows that the probability function for a continuous distribution is identically equal to 0 and is therefore useless.

Since $P(X = x) = 0$ for every x when X is continuous, the signs

$<$ and $\leq$ can be freely interchanged when describing events without changing the numerical values of probabilities of events. For example, since $\{a \leq X \leq b\}$ is the union of the three disjoint events $\{a < X < b\}$, $\{X = a\}$, and $\{X = b\}$, we have

$$P(a \leq X \leq b) = P(a < X < b).$$

Given F, the derivative f of Eq. 5.17 does not always exist for all values of x in the ordinary sense of calculus. For example, the density function of Eq. 5.16 has a discontinuity at $x = r$, so that F does not have an ordinary derivative at $x = r$. However, one can assign any finite nonnegative value to $f(r)$ without affecting the probabilities of any events. The same remarks apply to any piecewise continuous density function (one that is continuous except at each of a countable number of simple discontinuities having no finite limit point) so that F is a differentiable function except at the discontinuities of f.

Since $f(x) = dF(x)/dx$, we can intuitively write

$$dF(x) = f(x)\, dx = P[x < X < (x + dx)],$$

when f is continuous at x and when dx is viewed as a very small positive number. The quantity $f(x)\, dx$ is often called the (infinitesimal) *probability element* and approximately represents the probability that X will assume a value between x and $(x + dx)$. Geometrically, $f(x)\, dx$ can of course be viewed as the area bounded by a graph of f, the x axis, and lines perpendicular to the x axis at x and $(x + dx)$.

In the solution of problems involving an absolutely continuous random variable, it is usually more convenient to work with the density function f than with the distribution function F. For example, if A is an event that occurs when X assumes a value in a given set B of real numbers, then

$$P(A) = \int_B f(x)\, dx,$$

where the integral extends over the set B.

5.6   Mixed Distributions

Let a and b be numbers for which $a \geq 0$, $b \geq 0$, and $a + b = 1$; and let F_d and F_{ac} be given discrete and absolutely continuous distribution functions. Then, the reader can show that the function F defined by

$$F(x) = aF_d(x) + bF_{ac}(x) \qquad (5.21)$$

for every x is a probability distribution function. The distribution represented by such a distribution function will be called a *mixed discrete–absolutely continuous distribution*. Analysis of such distributions can be easily accomplished by combining the results of the two preceding sections. Such distributions occasionally occur in practical applications.

By the use of advanced methods, it can be shown that every distribution function has discontinuities (jumps) at no more than a countable number of points x_i and is continuous at every other value of x. From this fact, it is plausible (and can be proved) that every distribution function can be written in the form

$$F(x) = aF_d(x) + bF_c(x), \qquad (5.22)$$

where $a \geq 0$, $b \geq 0$, and $a + b = 1$, and F_d and F_c are discrete and continuous distribution functions. Thus every distribution can be viewed as a *mixed distribution*, a mixture of a discrete and a continuous distribution.

Equations 5.21 and 5.22 are not identical because a continuous distribution is not necessarily absolutely continuous. In fact, there is another kind of continuous distribution, which is called a *singular continuous distribution*. Furthermore, it can be shown that every distribution function F can be written in the form

$$F(x) = aF_d(x) + bF_{ac}(x) + cF_{sc}(x),$$

where $a \geq 0$, $b \geq 0$, $c \geq 0$, and $a + b + c = 1$, and F_d, F_{ac}, and F_{sc} are, respectively, discrete, absolutely continuous, and singular continuous distribution functions. Singular continuous distributions rarely, if ever, arise in practice, and examples of them have been constructed only by means of involved analytic operations. Therefore, Eq. 5.21 represents the most general type of distribution explicitly considered hereafter in this book.

5.7 Derived Distributions

A general problem that frequently arises can be stated as follows: Given a random variable X and a function h, derive some function that describes the distribution of the random variable Y defined by $Y(\omega) = h[X(\omega)]$ for every ω in the sample space Ω of X. Of course, one cannot correctly call Y a random variable unless h satisfies some regularity condition; it can be shown that Y is rigorously a random variable on Ω if h is a piecewise continuous function (or, in general, if h is a so-called Borel function). This problem amounts basically to a transformation of independent real variables. Although no general computational method can be given for solving this strictly analytical problem, detailed methods for several special types of problems can be based on calculus, the theory of integral transforms (as indicated in Section 6.5), and other branches of mathematics. In this section, we will briefly consider a few elementary special cases.

Hereafter, when two or more random variables X, Y, . . . appear in a discussion, the various functions associated with these random variables will be distinguished by using subscripts—for example, F_X, F_Y, ...

To describe the distribution of Y, it is often best to obtain first its distribution function F_Y, from which one can find the density function f_Y and the probability function g_Y when these functions exist. Since X and Y are random variables on the same sample space Ω, we can denote the event $\{\omega : Y(\omega) \leq y\}$ by $\{Y \leq y\}$ or by $\{h(X) \leq y\}$ if $Y = h(X)$ and can hence write

$$F_Y(y) = P[h(X) \leq y] \quad \text{if} \quad Y = h(X). \tag{5.23}$$

As will be seen later, an important special case is that of a linear function $h(x) = cx + d$, in which c and d are given real numbers for which $c > 0$ and $-\infty < d < \infty$. For the random variable $Y = cX + d$, Eq. 5.23 shows that

$$F_{cX+d}(y) = P[(cX + d) \leq y] = P\left(X \leq \frac{y - d}{c}\right) = F_X\left(\frac{y - d}{c}\right). \tag{5.24}$$

If X is absolutely continuous, then $Y = cX + d$ is absolutely continuous, and differentiation of Eq. 5.24 shows that

$$f_{cX+d}(y) = \frac{1}{c} f_X\left(\frac{y - d}{c}\right). \tag{5.25}$$

If X is discrete, then $Y = cX + d$ is discrete and has the probability function given by

$$g_{cX+d}(y) = g_X\left(\frac{y-d}{c}\right). \tag{5.26}$$

Equation 5.25 is a special case of the following theorem:

Let: (1) *X be an absolutely continuous random variable,* (2) *a and b be two numbers (possibly, with* $a = -\infty$ *and/or* $b = \infty$*) such that*

$$P(a < X < b) = 1,$$

(3) *h be a differentiable function of x for all x in the open interval* (a, b)*,* (4) *for all x in* (a, b)*, either* $h'(x) > 0$ *or* $h'(x) < 0$*, and* (5) α *and* β *be the numbers (possibly, with* $\alpha = -\infty$ *and/or* $\beta = \infty$*) defined by*

$$\alpha' = \lim_{x\to a+} h(x), \qquad \beta' = \lim_{x\to b-} h(x),$$
$$\alpha = \min(\alpha', \beta'), \qquad \beta = \max(\alpha', \beta'). \tag{5.27}$$

Then $Y = h(X)$ *is an absolutely continuous random variable and has the density function given by*

$$f_Y(y) = \begin{cases} f_X[h^{-1}(y)]\left|\dfrac{d}{dy}h^{-1}(y)\right| & (\alpha < y < \beta) \\ 0 & (y < \alpha \text{ or } y > \beta). \end{cases} \tag{5.28}$$

In this theorem, (a, b) denotes the set of all real numbers x for which $a < x < b$, h' denotes the derivative of h, h^{-1} denotes the inverse function of h, and $|z|$ denotes the magnitude of the real number z. When $h'(x) > 0$ for all x in (a, b), h is a strictly increasing monotonic function whose values increase from $\alpha = \alpha'$ to $\beta = \beta'$ as x increases from a to b; and hence, for every value of y with $\alpha < y < \beta$, there is exactly one value of $x = h^{-1}(y)$ such that $y = h(x)$. For example, when $h(x) = cx + d$ with $c > 0$, we can choose $a = \alpha = -\infty$ and $b = \beta = \infty$ and can note that substitution of $h^{-1}(y) = (y - d)/c$ and $dh^{-1}(y)/dy = 1/c$ in Eq. 5.28 gives Eq. 5.25. Discussion of the case when $h'(x) < 0$ for all x in (a, b) is left for the reader.

To prove Eq. 5.28, we consider two cases: the case in which h is an increasing function on (a, b) and that in which h is a decreasing function on (a, b). For $\alpha < y < \beta$, the distribution function of Y can be written respectively for these cases as

$$F_Y(y) = P[h(X) \le y] = P[X \le h^{-1}(y)] = F_X[h^{-1}(y)],$$
$$F_Y(y) = P[h(X) \le y] = P[X \ge h^{-1}(y)] = 1 - F_X[h^{-1}(y)].$$

If a or b is finite, note that we can define h to be any continuous function (e.g., $h(x) = 0$) on $x \leq a$ and $x \geq b$, since $P(X \leq a \text{ or } X \geq b) = 0$. Use of the so-called chain rule (of calculus) for differentiating a function of a function to differentiate the above two relations with respect to y will give Eq. 5.28 when $\alpha < y < \beta$. Since $P[h(X) \leq \alpha] = 0$ and $P[h(X) \geq \beta] = 1$, $F_Y(y) = 0$ for $y \leq \alpha$, $F_Y(y) = 1$ for $y \geq \beta$, and hence $f_Y(y) = 0$ for $y < \alpha$ and for $y > \beta$. (Any finite values can be assigned to $f_Y(\alpha)$ and $f_Y(\beta)$.)

Example 5.4.   Find the density function for the area $Y = \pi X^2$ of the circle of radius X, where X is the random variable of Example 5.3. Clearly, we can let $a = 0$, $b = r$, $h(x) = \pi x^2$, $\alpha = 0$, and $\beta = \pi r^2$; then $h^{-1}(y) = (y/\pi)^{1/2}$ and $dh^{-1}(y)/dy = (1/4\pi y)^{1/2}$ for $0 < y < \pi r^2$. Since $f_X(x) = 2x/r^2$ for $0 \leq x \leq r$, Eq. 5.28 now shows that

$$f_Y(y) = \begin{cases} 1/\pi r^2 & (0 \leq y \leq \pi r^2) \\ 0 & (\text{otherwise}). \end{cases}$$

Of course, the above theorem is not directly applicable to many special problems that arise. Here, we briefly consider one such important special case in which $h(x) = x^2$ and hence $Y = X^2$. Since, for $y < 0$, the event $\{X^2 \leq y\}$ is empty,

$$F_{X^2}(y) = 0 \qquad (y < 0). \tag{5.29}$$

For $y \geq 0$,

$$\begin{aligned} F_{X^2}(y) = P(X^2 \leq y) &= P(-\sqrt{y} \leq X \leq \sqrt{y}) \\ &= F_X(\sqrt{y}) - F_X(-\sqrt{y}) + g_X(-\sqrt{y}). \end{aligned} \tag{5.30}$$

When X is absolutely continuous, Eqs. 5.29 and 5.30 imply that X^2 is absolutely continuous and has the density function given by

$$f_{X^2}(y) = \begin{cases} \dfrac{1}{2\sqrt{y}} [f_X(\sqrt{y}) + f_X(-\sqrt{y})] & (y > 0) \\ 0 & (y < 0). \end{cases} \tag{5.31}$$

When X is discrete, X^2 is discrete and has the probability function given by

$$g_{X^2}(y) = g_X(-\sqrt{y}) + g_X(\sqrt{y}). \tag{5.32}$$

THE PROBABILITY TRANSFORMATION

A variable transformation of basic importance in the theory of distributions is known as the *probability (integral) transformation* and is defined by

$$Y = F_X(X), \qquad (5.33)$$

where F_X is the distribution function of any given random variable X. Since F_X is a nondecreasing right-continuous function, we can define a sort of inverse function F_X^{-1} on $0 \le y \le 1$ by setting $F_X^{-1}(y)$ equal to the smallest value of x for which $F_X(x) \ge y$. Then, if X is *continuous*,

$$F_Y(y) = P(F_X(X) \le y) = P(X \le F_X^{-1}(y)) = y,$$

for $0 \le y \le 1$. (If F_X has a discontinuity and jumps from y_1 to $y_2 > y_1$ at $x = x_0$, then note that $F_Y(y) = y_2$ for $y_1 \le y < y_2$ while $F_Y(y) \to y_1$ as $y \to y_1-$.) Hence Y is an absolutely continuous random variable for which

$$f_Y(y) = \begin{cases} 1 & (0 \le y \le 1) \\ 0 & \text{(otherwise)}. \end{cases} \qquad (5.34)$$

If we call the distribution having the density function given by Eq. 5.34 the *normalized uniform distribution*, we have just proved the fundamentally important fact that *every continuous probability distribution can be transformed into the normalized uniform distribution*. This curious fact is of great usefulness both in theory and in practice because it forms a theoretical link between every pair of continuous distributions in that every continuous distribution can be transformed at least theoretically into every other continuous distribution by applying the transformation of Eq. 5.33 to each and thus establishing a one-to-one correspondence between them. When X is not continuous, one can easily show that Y does not have a uniform distribution; but Y is of course always a random variable because F_X is a Borel function.

5.8 Exercises

Note: In these and later exercises, we use the following convention: Every probability function $g(x)$ or density function $f(x)$ has the value zero at every x except those for which other values are specified, and every distribution function $F(x)$ has the value zero (or one) at every x smaller (or larger) than those specified.

Some distributions appear so frequently that they are commonly known by special names. In the following exercises, a name, say A, in parenthesis at the end of an exercise indicates that the distribution in that exercise is a special case of the A distribution.

In Exercises 5.1–5.10, construct an appropriate sample space Ω, express the given random variable X as a function on Ω, and assign an appropriate definition to the probability function $g(x) = P(X = x)$ in Exercises 5.1–5.6 and to the distribution function $F(x) = P(X \leq x)$ in Exercises 5.7–5.10.

5.1 X is the number on the showing face of the icosahedron in Experiment 1.1 of Section 1.2.

5.2   For the experiment of tossing two balanced dice described in Section 1.3, X is the total number of dots appearing on both dice.

5.3 X is the number of white balls selected in the experiment of Section 3.2. (Bernoulli)

5.4   If the likelihood of a salesman's making a sale on a single call is $\frac{1}{5}$, let X be the number of sales made during five independent calls. (binomial)

5.5   If a balanced coin is tossed successively (as described in Section 3.4), let X be the number of the toss at which a head first appears.

5.6   From a box containing 8 good radio tubes and 1 defective tube, the tubes are withdrawn at random and tested one at a time. If a tube (a) is not, (b) is, replaced in the box after it is tested, let X be the number of the test in which the defective tube is first tested. (c) For each of these cases, what is the probability that the defective tube will be tested during the first test? At least once during the first three tests? At least once during the first nine tests?

5.7   In Experiment 1.3 of Section 1.3, X is the distance between the point of impact and the center of the target. (beta)

5.8   In Buffon's needle problem of Section 1.3, X is the distance r between the center of the stick and the nearest ruled line. (rectangular or uniform)

5.9   (a) A lost child has wandered randomly for two days in a forest having approximately the shape of an equilateral triangle whose sides each have length 2 miles. Let X be the perpendicular distance from the child to one fixed side of the triangle. (b) What is the probability that X is less than $\frac{1}{2}$ mile? (beta)

5.10   (a) A cylindrical rod has length L and radius R, where L is chosen at random between π and 4π, and R is chosen at random between 1 and 2. Let X be the volume of the rod. (b) Evaluate $P(4\pi^2 < X \leq 9\pi^2)$.

5.11   Verify that each given function is a probability distribution function, sketch its graph, and find the corresponding probability function. If the random variable X has the given distribution function, compute the probability that each of the following relations is satisfied: $X = 1$, $X < 1$, $X \leq 1$, $X = 0$, $0 < X < 1$, $|X| \leq 1$. [In (a), our convention means that $F(x) = 0$ for $x < 0$ and $F(x) = 1$ for $x \geq 1$.]

(a) $$F(x) = \frac{1}{6} + \frac{x}{2} \qquad (0 \le x < 1).$$

(b) $$F(x) = \begin{cases} \frac{1}{4}e^x & (-\infty < x < 0) \\ \frac{1}{2} & (0 \le x < 1) \\ 1 - \frac{1}{2}e^{-(x-1)} & (1 \le x < \infty). \end{cases}$$

5.12   As parts (a), (b), . . . , (f), show respectively that the random variables of Exercises 5.1, 5.2, . . . , 5.6 have discrete distributions.

5.13   Use the probability function of Exercise 5.2 to compute the probability that the total number of dots appearing when two dice are tossed is (a) even, (b) odd, and (c) divisible by 4.

5.14   For each of the following functions g, evaluate the constant c so that g is a probability function, find the corresponding distribution function F, and sketch the graphs of g and F:

(a) $\qquad\qquad g(x) = cx \qquad\qquad (x = 0, 1, \ldots, 6).$

(b) $\qquad\qquad g(x) = c2^x/x! \qquad (x = 0, 1, 2, \ldots).$

(c) $\qquad g(1/n) = c(\frac{1}{3})^n \qquad (n = 1, 2, 3, \ldots).$

(b: Poisson)

5.15   As parts (a), (b), (c), and (d), show respectively that the random variables of Exercises 5.7, 5.8, 5.9, and 5.10 have absolutely continuous distributions, and find their density functions.

5.16   For each of the following functions f, evaluate the constant c so that f is a density function, find the corresponding distribution function F, and sketch the graphs of f and F:

(a) $\qquad f(x) = cx(12 - x^2) \qquad (0 < x < \sqrt{12}).$

(b) $\qquad f(x) = cx \exp[-\pi x^2/4] \qquad (0 \le x < \infty).$

(c) $\qquad f(x) = c[1 + (x - 1)^2]^{-1} \qquad (-\infty < x < \infty).$

(b: Rayleigh, c: Cauchy)

5.17   Verify that each given function is a distribution function, find the corresponding probability function g or density function f, and sketch the graphs of F and g or f. Here, a and p are positive constants with $0 \le p < 1$.

(a) $F(x) = k/10 \qquad (k \le x < k + 1; k = 1, 2, \ldots, 9).$

(b) $F(x) = 1 - p^{n+1} \qquad (n \le x < n + 1; n = 0, 1, 2, \ldots).$

(c) $F(x) = x^a \qquad (0 < x \le 1).$

(d) $F(x) = 1 - \exp[-a(x-5)] \qquad (5 \le x < \infty).$

(e) $F(x) = \frac{1}{2}(1 - \cos \pi x) \qquad (0 \le x < 1).$

(b: geometric, d: exponential)

5.18   If X has the (a) probability function, (b) density function, given below and if A and B are the events $A = \{0 \leq X < 3\}$ and $B = \{2 < X < 5\}$, compute the probability of each of the following events: A, B, $A \cup B$, $A \cap B$, A given B, B given A. Are A and B disjoint? Independent?

(a) $$g(x) = (\tfrac{1}{2})^{x+1} \qquad (x = 0, 1, 2, \ldots).$$

(b) $$f(x) = x^{-2} \qquad (1 < x < \infty).$$

(a: geometric, b: Pareto)

5.19   If the density function $f(x)$ is symmetric about some constant value μ of x so that $f(\mu - x) = f(\mu + x)$ for every x and if $a > 0$, derive the following results:

(a) $$F(\mu) = \tfrac{1}{2}.$$

(b) $$P(X > \mu + a) = \tfrac{1}{2} - \int_{\mu}^{\mu+a} f(x) \, dx.$$

(c) $$F(\mu - a) + F(\mu + a) = 1.$$

(d) $$P(\mu - a < X < \mu + a) = 2F(\mu + a) - 1.$$

(e) $$P(|X - \mu| > a) = 2F(\mu - a) = 2[1 - F(\mu + a)].$$

5.20   Express each distribution function of Exercise 5.11 in the form of Eq. 5.21.

5.21   If the salesman of Exercise 5.4 receives a basic salary of two dollars per call and also a commission of one dollar for each sale made, express his income S for five calls as a function of X, and find its probability function g_S.

5.22   If the temperature T in degrees Fahrenheit of a certain object has the density function

$$f_T(t) = (6/9^3)(t - 68)(77 - t) \qquad (68 < t < 77),$$

find the density function for the temperature θ in degrees centigrade. [Note that $\theta = (\tfrac{5}{9})(T - 32)$.] (beta)

5.23   Let X have the rectangular density function $f_X(x) = \tfrac{1}{2}$ for $|x| < 1$. Find and sketch the density function for each of the following new random variables in which a is a positive constant: (a) $(aX)^2$, (b) $|aX|$, (c) $-a \log |X|$, (d) $a \sin (\pi X/2)$.

5.24   If X and Y have the exponential and Pareto density functions

$$f_X(x) = ae^{-ax} \qquad (0 < x < \infty)$$
$$f_Y(y) = a(y + 1)^{-(a+1)} \qquad (0 < y < \infty),$$

where a is a positive constant, find the function h so that $X = h(Y)$.

*5.25   (a) Suppose points are uniformly distributed on the perimeter of a hexagon (so that every two parts of the perimeter having equal lengths have equal probabilities). If a is the length of each side of the hexagon and if X is the distance from the center of the hexagon to a point on the perimeter, derive and sketch the density and distribution functions of X. (b) Instead of taking points on the perimeter to be uniformly distributed, suppose radial directions from the center of the hexagon are uniformly distributed, and repeat part (a).

5.26   The speed of a molecule in a uniform gas at equilibrium is a random variable V whose density function has the form

$$f(v) = av^2 e^{-bv^2} \qquad (0 < v < \infty),$$

where $b = m/2kT$ and k, T, and m denote Boltzmann's constant, the absolute temperature, and the mass of a molecule, respectively. (a) Use integration by parts and the fact (derived in Section 8.2) that

$$\int_0^\infty e^{-x^2}\, dx = \sqrt{\pi}/2$$

to evaluate the constant a. (b) Derive the distribution of the kinetic energy $W = mV^2/2$ of a molecule. (a: Maxwell, b: gamma)

APPLICATIONS IN ENGINEERING

The next five exercises are the first in the following series of more or less related exercises: 5.27–5.31, 6.30–6.38, 7.19, 8.18–8.19, 9.34–9.44, 10.28–10.30, and 12.20–12.21. These exercises illustrate (in a necessarily incomplete manner) some applications to the analysis of continuous-flow engineering processes, in which some material flows continuously through a piece of engineering equipment. Several of them, particularly those connected with Exercises 6.32, 6.36, and 6.37, are based on a particular approach, which apparently first appeared progressively in the recent engineering papers by Gilliland, Mason, and Oliver, by Danckwerts, and by Zwietering, which are listed in the bibliography. Also listed is a recent book by Levenspiel, who presents a more complete engineering development.

5.27   Give a more complete discussion of the physical situation and the mathematical model indicated below, including particularly the relevance of the intuitive interpretation of probabilities as relative frequencies.

As a first approximation, suppose that a fluid flows continuously at a constant rate of Q molecules (or atoms) per minute into and also out of a "reactor" (e.g., chemical reactor, automobile or rocket engine, water reservoir) and that negligible chemical reaction occurs. Then, there is always some number, say V, of molecules inside the reactor. (Of course, Q and V are normally very large numbers; e.g., 10^{25}.) Of the $Q\Delta\theta$ molecules that enter during a specified very short time interval $(\theta, \theta + \Delta\theta)$, some fraction $f_\theta(t)\Delta t$ will leave during the later very short time interval $(\theta + t, \theta + t + \Delta t)$, for each $t > 0$, where f_θ is some nonnegative function for which

$$\int_0^\infty f_\theta(t) \, dt = 1$$

(if no molecules become trapped, which we assume hereafter). Suppose that the reactor operates in such a manner that f_θ does not depend on θ (e.g., under "steady state" conditions), so that the (statistical) length of time that a molecule remains in the reactor does not depend on when it entered. Finally, suppose that the function f_θ has been measured experimentally, possibly in the form of a graph. (This can often be done by using a tracer, such as carbon-14.)

To form a mathematical model, let f be a given density function that approximates the measured function f_θ. Let $(\Omega, \, \mathcal{S}, \, P)$ be any continuous probability space and T be a continuous random variable defined on Ω so that T has f as its density function. Intuitively speaking, the random variable T represents the total time that a molecule remains in the reactor; that is, the "residence time" of a molecule in the reactor, or in other words, the "waiting time" for a molecule to leave the reactor, measured from the time it entered. Therefore, we may call T the *residence time* of a molecule and its distribution the *residence-time distribution*.

5.28   Experimentation has shown that the residence-time density function of Exercise 5.27 can often be satisfactorily approximated by a function of one of the following types:

(a) $f(t) = A \exp\left[-(t - a)/(\tau - a)\right]$ $(a \le t < \infty)$,

(b) $f(t) = A t^{n-1} \exp\left[-nt/\tau\right]$ $(0 \le t < \infty)$,

where $a < \tau$ and $\tau = V/Q$ are positive constants and n is a positive integer. In each case, evaluate A so that f is a probability density function. *Hint:* For every nonnegative integer n,

$$\int_0^\infty x^n e^{-x} \, dx = n!.$$

(a: exponential, b: gamma)

5.29   As parts (a) and (b), find the density function $f_r(s)$ of the new random variable $T_r = T/\tau$, where T has the density function of Exercise 5.28. (b: Erlang)

5.30   The reactor of Exercise 5.27 is said to be "well stirred" if the molecules inside it are always mixed in any manner such that the likelihood that any given molecule will leave the reactor during any very short time interval of length Δt is approximately $\Delta t/\tau$. Show that the residence-time distribution for a well-stirred reactor should have the exponential density function given by

$$f(t) = \tau^{-1} e^{-t/\tau} \qquad (0 \le t < \infty),$$

where $\tau = V/Q$. *Hint:* Show that

$$f(t)\Delta t = [1 - F(t)](Q\Delta t/V)$$

and therefore that $df/dt = -f/\tau$.

5.31 Suppose two well-stirred reactors (as described in Exercise 5.30), with each always containing V molecules, are connected in parallel so that the entering fluid splits between them. If the total flow rate is $2Q$ molecules per minute and if the fraction a $(0 < a \le \frac{1}{2})$ of this fluid flows through one of these reactors and the remainder $(1 - a)$ flows through the other, deduce that the residence-time distribution has the so-called hyperexponential density function

$$f(t) = \frac{2a^2}{\tau} \exp\left[-2at/\tau\right] + \frac{2(1-a)^2}{\tau} \exp\left[-2(1-a)t/\tau\right] \qquad (0 \le t < \infty)$$

where $\tau = V/Q$.

CHAPTER **6** EXPECTATION OF A

DISTRIBUTION

IN CHAPTER 5 WE SAW HOW TO DESCRIBE PROBABILITY DISTRIBUTIONS in terms of appropriate *functions*, just as mass distributions in one-dimensional mechanical systems can be described by analogous functions. In mechanics, it is useful to summarize some of the primary properties of mass distributions in terms of those few *numbers* that specify centers of mass and moments of inertia. The analogous numbers for probability distributions, which are likewise found to be very useful in probability theory, are described in this chapter. In addition, some integral transforms of distributions are discussed in the last two sections. These are useful in probability theory in somewhat the same way that Laplace transforms are useful in solving differential equations.

6.1   The Stieltjes Integral

The concept and notation of the Stieltjes integral is extremely useful in unifying probability theory. For example, when this notation is used, only one proof is required for a theorem that is equally true for discrete, continuous, and general distributions. This fact will be used later. However, use of the Stieltjes integral is rarely necessary in practical applications. Thus, the reader who wishes to be restricted to discrete or absolutely continuous distributions or to mixtures of these can view the Stieltjes integral merely as a concise notation that simultaneously denotes three equations 6.7, 6.9, and 6.10 and he can thus essentially omit this section.

A completely general treatment of the expectation of a distribution would require use of a certain generalized integral known as the Lebesgue-Stieltjes integral. However, since discussion of this integral requires methods more advanced than can be used in this book, we will limit ourselves to a plausible development based on the less general Riemann-Stieltjes integral. Except for certain improper integrals, it can be shown that the Lebesgue-Stieltjes integral of a function exists when the Riemann-Stieltjes integral exists, with the two integrals having the same value, and that the former integral has every property possessed by the latter. (Of course, the converse of these statements is false.)

For a general definition of the Riemann-Stieltjes integral, let there be given a closed interval $[a, b]$, i.e., the set of all real numbers x for which $a \leq x \leq b$; and let F and h be given numerical-valued functions that are defined for every x in $[a, b]$. By a partition of $[a, b]$, we mean a finite set of numbers $x_0, x_1, \ldots, x_n$ for which

$$a = x_0 \leq x_1 \leq \cdots \leq x_n = b.$$

For every partition of $[a, b]$, choose n points $x_1', x_2', \ldots, x_n'$ such that $x_{i-1} \leq x_i' \leq x_i$ for $i = 1, 2, \ldots, n$. If the limit in Eq. 6.1 exists as a finite number, the *Riemann-Stieltjes integral of h with respect to F over* $[a, b]$ can then be defined by

$$\int_a^b h(x) \, dF(x) = \lim_{\delta_n \to 0} \sum_{i=1}^n h(x_i')[F(x_i) - F(x_{i-1})], \qquad (6.1)$$

where the limit is taken over all partitions of $[a, b]$ as the maximum value $\delta_n = \max (x_i - x_{i-1})$ of $x_i - x_{i-1}$ for $i = 1, 2, \ldots, n$ tends to 0. [Of course, this requires that n approach ∞, since $\delta_n \geq \frac{1}{n} (b - a)$.]

In general, the limit and hence the integral in Eq. 6.1 will not exist unless F and h satisfy certain regularity conditions. Since we will be interested only in the case when F is a probability distribution function, we will assume henceforth that F is such a function and is therefore monotonic nondecreasing, continuous on the right, and bounded between 0 and 1 (even though these conditions are not necessary for existence of the integral). Then, for a given function h, it can be shown that the integral in Eq. 6.1 exists for *every* distribution function F if and only if h is continuous on $[a, b]$. Another sufficient condition is that F be continuous on $[a, b]$ and h be piecewise continuous on $[a, b]$.

Some special cases are treated in detail toward the end of this section. (We remark that the Lebesgue-Stieltjes integral of h with respect to F over $[a, b]$, also denoted by

$$\int_a^b h(x)\, dF(x),$$

can be defined in terms of a limit somewhat analogous to the limit in Eq. 6.1 and that it exists when h is a continuous or piecewise continuous function, or, in general, when h is a so-called Borel function.)

One can readily see that the Stieltjes integral is a generalization of the ordinary Riemann integral, which is studied in calculus. Replace F by the special function defined by $F(x) = x$, and note that Eq. 6.1 then becomes

$$\int_a^b h(x)\, dx = \lim_{\delta_n \to 0} \sum_{i=1}^n h(x_i')(x_i - x_{i-1}).$$

The Stieltjes and Riemann integrals have similar properties. Thus, using proofs similar to those used in calculus for Riemann integrals, one can show, for example, that

$$\int_a^b h(x)\, dF(x) = \int_a^c h(x)\, dF(x) + \int_c^b h(x)\, dF(x) \qquad (a < c < b), \quad (6.2)$$

$$\int_a^b [h_1(x) + h_2(x)]\, dF(x) = \int_a^b h_1(x)\, dF(x) + \int_a^b h_2(x)\, dF(x), \quad (6.3)$$

$$\int_a^b ch(x)\, dF(x) = c \int_a^b h(x)\, dF(x) \qquad (c = \text{constant}), \quad (6.4)$$

$$m \int_a^b dF(x) \le \int_a^b h(x)\, dF(x) \le M \int_a^b dF(x), \quad (6.5)$$

where m and M are constants such that $m \le h(x) \le M$ for $a \le x \le b$.

The Riemann-Stieltjes integral of h with respect to F over the whole real line is defined in terms of Eq. 6.1 by

$$\int_{-\infty}^{\infty} h(x)\, dF(x) = \lim_{\substack{a \to -\infty \\ b \to +\infty}} \int_a^b h(x)\, dF(x), \quad (6.6)$$

provided that the double limit exists and is finite. This integral is similar to and can be viewed in much the same way as the improper Riemann integral treated in calculus. Thus, it is said to be *absolutely convergent* if the Riemann-Stieltjes integral of the magnitude of h exists and is finite, i.e., if

$$\int_{-\infty}^{\infty} |h(x)|\, dF(x) < \infty.$$

Also, it can be shown that relations 6.2 to 6.5 remain valid when the limits a and b are replaced by $-\infty$ and ∞, provided that all of the resulting improper integrals are absolutely convergent.

Three special cases of Eq. 6.6 reduce to more familiar forms and are sufficient for most elementary work in probability theory. First, let F be the distribution function of a *discrete* random variable X, and let g be the probability function of X. Then, if (and only if) h is continuous at every "possible value" x_i of X, Eq. 6.6 takes the form

$$\int_{-\infty}^{\infty} h(x)\, dF(x) = \sum_i h(x_i)g(x_i), \tag{6.7}$$

where the summation extends over all of the possible values x_i of X. Of course, this integral exists or is absolutely convergent if and only if the (finite or infinite) series in Eq. 6.7 is, respectively, convergent or absolutely convergent. To prove Eq. 6.7 when the possible values of X are $x_1, x_2, \ldots, x_m$, with $x_i < x_j$ when $i < j$, note from Eq. 6.2 that

$$\int_{-\infty}^{\infty} h(x)\, dF(x) = \int_{-\infty}^{x_0} h(x)\, dF(x) + \sum_{j=1}^{m} \int_{x_{j-1}}^{x_j} h(x)\, dF(x)$$
$$+ \int_{x_m}^{\infty} h(x)\, dF(x), \tag{6.8}$$

where $x_0 = x_1 - 1$. The first and last integrals in Eq. 6.8 are 0, since $F(x) = 0$ for $-\infty < x \le x_0$ and $F(x) = 1$ for $x_m \le x < \infty$. Now let a and b be any two successive ones of the values $x_0, x_1, \ldots, x_m$. Using these numbers in Eq. 6.1 shows that

$$\int_a^b h(x)\, dF(x) = \lim_{x_{n-1} \to b} h(x'_n)[F(b) - F(x_{n-1})] = h(b)g(b),$$

since $F(x_i) - F(x_{i-1}) = 0$ for $a \le x_{i-1} \le x_i < b,$

$$F(b) - F(x_{n-1}) = g(b),$$

$$\lim_{x_{n-1} \to b} h(x'_n) = h(b).$$

Thus

$$\int_{x_{j-1}}^{x_j} h(x)\, dF(x) = h(x_j)g(x_j) \text{ for } j = 1, 2, \ldots, m;$$

and putting these values in Eq. 6.8 gives Eq. 6.7. When X has an infinite but countable number of possible values, Eq. 6.7 can be proved in a similar way.

Next, let F be the distribution function of an *absolutely continuous* distribution, and let f be its density function. Then, if f and h are sufficiently smooth—e.g., if f and h are piecewise continuous—Eq. 6.6 reduces to the Riemann integral

$$\int_{-\infty}^{\infty} h(x)\, dF(x) = \int_{-\infty}^{\infty} h(x)f(x)\, dx. \tag{6.9}$$

Of course, this integral exists or is absolutely convergent if and only if the (proper or improper) integral on the right side of Eq. 6.9, respectively, exists or is absolutely convergent. To indicate how Eq. 6.9 can be proved when f and h are continuous for all x, note that the mean value theorem of calculus implies that

$$F(x_i) - F(x_{i-1}) = f(x_i'')(x_i - x_{i-1})$$

for some x_i'' such that $x_{i-1} \leq x_i'' \leq x_i$. When the right side of this expression is placed in the right side of Eq. 6.1, we find that

$$\int_a^b h(x)\, dF(x) = \lim_{\delta_n \to 0} \sum_{i=1}^n h(x_i')f(x_i'')(x_i - x_{i-1}),$$

which is essentially equivalent to the definition of the Riemann integral

$$\int_a^b h(x)f(x)\, dx.$$

Loosely speaking, $h(x_i')f(x_i'')$ behaves like $h(x_i')f(x_i')$ when the above limit is taken, since x_i' and x_i'' both lie between x_{i-1} and x_i while

$$\lim_{\delta_n \to 0} (x_i - x_{i-1}) = 0.$$

Now, Eq. 6.9 follows from this fact and Eq. 6.6. For the more general case when f and h have only a finite number of simple discontinuities, one can write Eq. 6.6 as the sum of a finite number of integrals and can use the above procedure for each one of the summand integrals. No attempt will be made here to prove Eq. 6.9 under more general conditions on f and h.

Finally, let F be the distribution function of a *mixed discrete–absolutely continuous* distribution having the form $F = aF_d + bF_{ac}$ of Eq. 5.21, and let g and f be the probability function and the density function of F_d and F_{ac}. Then, by combining the results of the preceding two cases, one can show that

$$\int_{-\infty}^{\infty} h(x)\, dF(x) = a \sum_i h(x_i)g(x_i) + b \int_{-\infty}^{\infty} h(x)f(x)\, dx, \quad (6.10)$$

provided h is continuous at every x_i, and f and h are sufficiently smooth.

6.2   Expectation of a Distribution

The *expectation* or *mean of the random variable X*, to be denoted by $E(X)$ or by μ, is defined to be the Stieltjes integral of x with respect to the distribution function F of X; that is,

$$\mu = E(X) = \int_{-\infty}^{\infty} x\, dF(x), \quad (6.11)$$

provided this integral converges absolutely. For discrete, absolutely continuous, and mixed discrete–absolutely continuous distributions, Eqs. 6.7, 6.9, and 6.10 show that Eq. 6.11 reduces respectively to

$$E(X) = \sum_i x_i g(x_i), \quad (6.12)$$

$$E(X) = \int_{-\infty}^{\infty} xf(x)\, dx, \quad (6.13)$$

$$E(X) = a \sum_i x_i g(x_i) + b \int_{-\infty}^{\infty} xf(x)\, dx. \quad (6.14)$$

The *expectation of a distribution* is defined to be the expectation of any random variable having that distribution. In probability theory and its many applications, such names as *expectation, mathematical expectation, expected value, mean, average,* and *ensemble average* are often used for $E(X)$. While $E(X)$ is generally accepted notation in mathematics and statistics, $\bar{X}$ and $<X>$ are common substitutes in physics and engineering.

We say that the expectation of X exists or that X has a finite mean if and only if the integral in Eq. 6.11 converges absolutely; that is,

$$\int_{-\infty}^{\infty} |x|\, dF(x) < \infty.$$

Thus, the mean of a discrete random variable with probability function g exists if and only if the finite or infinite series in Eq. 6.12 converges absolutely; that is,

$$\sum_i |x_i| g(x_i) < \infty.$$

Similarly, the mean of an absolutely continuous distribution with density function f exists if and only if

$$\int_{-\infty}^{\infty} |x| f(x)\, dx < \infty.$$

Every bounded random variable has a finite mean. By definition, a random variable X is bounded if there is a constant A such that $|X(\omega)| = |x| < A$ for every ω in the sample space Ω. This implies that the distribution function F of X satisfies $F(x) = 0$ for $x \leq -A$ and $F(x) = 1$ for $x \geq A$. Therefore, Eqs. 6.2, 6.5, and 6.6 imply that

$$\int_{-\infty}^{\infty} |x|\, dF(x) = \int_{-A}^{A} |x|\, dF(x) \leq A \int_{-A}^{A} dF(x) = A.$$

While most interesting distributions have finite expectations, there are important ones that do not have this property. For example, the Cauchy distribution, which has the density function

$$f(x) = \pi^{-1}(1 + x^2)^{-1} \text{ for } -\infty < x < \infty,$$

does not have a finite mean, since

$$\int_{-\infty}^{\infty} |x|\, dF(x) = \lim_{a \to \infty} \frac{2}{\pi} \int_0^a \frac{x\, dx}{1 + x^2} = \frac{1}{\pi} \lim_{a \to \infty} \log\,(1 + a^2) = \infty.$$

The mean of a distribution is a measure of the "center" or "weighted average" of the distribution. For example, Eq. 6.13 is formally identical with the formula of mechanics for finding the center of mass of a one-dimensional continuous mass distribution having a total mass of 1. Also, Eq. 6.12 is analogous to a formula used to compute the arithmetic average of finite sets of numbers. Suppose there are n distinct values $x_1, x_2, \ldots, x_n$ which occur, respectively, $N_1, N_2, \ldots, N_n$ times; and we denote the total number of numbers by

$$N = N_1 + N_2 + \cdots + N_n.$$

Then the average is given by

$$\frac{1}{N} \sum_{i=1}^{n} N_i x_i = \sum_{i=1}^{n} x_i R_i,$$

where $R_i = N_i/N$ is the relative frequency of x_i.

It will be shown in Chapter 11 that the mean of a random variable also has the important property that will be indicated now. Suppose that X_i for $i = 1, 2, 3, \ldots$ is a random variable on the sample space Ω and that every X_i has exactly the same distribution as the given random variable X. Then the arithmetic averages

$$\bar{X}_1 = X_1, \bar{X}_2 = \tfrac{1}{2}(X_1 + X_2),$$
$$\bar{X}_3 = \tfrac{1}{3}(X_1 + X_2 + X_3), \ldots$$

are random variables on Ω. This infinite sequence of averages, $\bar{X}_1, \bar{X}_2, \bar{X}_3, \ldots$, will (with probability one) tend to a limiting value if and only if X has a finite mean. Furthermore, this limiting value will precisely equal the mean of X.

The expected value is one of several possible quantities that can be used to indicate the general location of a distribution along the x axis. Other similar quantities that have found limited usage (particularly, in statistics) are the *median* and the *mode*, which are defined in the exercises. We generally prefer the mean to these other quantities because it lends itself best to analytical manipulation and because it has the important property indicated in the preceding paragraph.

Example 6.1.   The mean of the random variables of Examples 5.1 and 5.2 is

$$\mu = E(X) = 0\left(\frac{1}{8}\right) + 1\left(\frac{3}{8}\right) + 2\left(\frac{3}{8}\right) + 3\left(\frac{1}{8}\right) = \frac{3}{2}.$$

The expected value of the distribution of Example 5.3 is

$$\mu = E(X) = \int_0^r x\,\frac{2x}{r^2}\,dx = \frac{2}{3}r.$$

6.3   Expectation of a Derived Distribution

In Section 5.7 we studied the distribution of the random variable Y given by
$$Y = h(X), \tag{6.15}$$
where X is some given random variable and h is practically any given

function. From Eq. 6.11, the expectation of Y is given by

$$E(Y) = E[h(X)] = \int_{-\infty}^{\infty} y \, dF_Y(y), \qquad (6.16)$$

where F_Y is the distribution function of Y.

On the other hand, it is natural to consider the Stieltjes integral of h with respect to F_X, the distribution function of X; this quantity may be called the *expectation of the function h with respect to X* and may be denoted by $E_X[h(X)]$. Thus,

$$E_X[h(X)] = \int_{-\infty}^{\infty} h(x) \, dF_X(x). \qquad (6.17)$$

We say that this expectation exists if and only if the integral is absolutely convergent.

Of great importance in probability theory is the striking fact that *for every random variable X and practically every (every Borel) function h*

$$E[h(X)] = E_X[h(X)] \qquad (6.18)$$

in the sense that if either of these expectations exists, then so does the other, and the two are equal. In other words, Eq. 6.18 says that the mean of the random variable $Y = h(X)$ is equal to the expectation of the function h with respect to X.

An extension of Eq. 6.18 is of even greater importance in probability theory. Given random variables X and Y related as in Eq. 6.15, one often wants the expectation of the function H with respect to Y, where H is some function such as $H(y) = (y - a)^n$ or $H(y) = e^{\theta y}$. The computation of such expectations is often facilitated by using the following extension of Eq. 6.18: *If h is practically any function, and if X and Y are random variables such that $Y = h(X)$, then for practically every function H*

$$E_Y[H(Y)] = E_X\{H[h(X)]\} \qquad (6.19)$$

or, in terms of integrals,

$$\int_{-\infty}^{\infty} H(y) \, dF_Y(y) = \int_{-\infty}^{\infty} H[h(x)] \, dF_X(x) \qquad (6.20)$$

if either of these expectations exist. If H is the function defined by $H(y) = y$, Eq. 6.19 reduces to 6.18.

We can easily prove Eq. 6.19, and hence 6.18, under those special conditions required for Eq. 5.28 in Section 5.7. Thus, use of Eq. 5.28

and the variable change $y = h(x)$ shows that

$$
\begin{aligned}
E_X\{H[h(X)]\} &= \int_a^b H[h(x)]f_X(x)\,dx \\
&= \int_\alpha^\beta H(y)f_X[h^{-1}(y)]\left|\frac{d}{dy}h^{-1}(y)\right|dy \\
&= \int_\alpha^\beta H(y)f_Y(y)\,dy \\
&= E_Y[H(Y)].
\end{aligned}
$$

Although no attempt can be made here to give general proofs of Eqs. 6.18 and 6.19, we remark that their validity requires that all integrals used to define expectations be absolutely convergent. (The reader should be able to provide proofs for some other special cases—e.g., when X is discrete.)

Given a random variable X and a function h, we thus have two distinct notions—those represented by $E[h(X)]$ and $E_X[h(X)]$. However, since these quantities are practically always numerically equal, they are both usually denoted by $E[h(X)]$, since this notation is more convenient. Nevertheless, the reader should keep both notions in mind, at least because they provide two distinct methods for computing $E[h(X)]$.

Of course, one can easily derive from Eqs. 6.18 and 6.19 important special cases. For example, if X is a given random variable, if h_1, h_2, . . . , h_n are practically any given functions, and if c_1, c_2, . . . , c_n are given constants, use of Eqs. 6.3, 6.4, 6.6, 6.17, and 6.18 shows that the random variable

$$
Y = c_1 h_1(X) + \cdots + c_n h_n(X)
$$

has the expectation given by

$$
E[c_1 h_1(X) + \cdots + c_n h_n(X)] = c_1 E[h_1(X)]
$$
$$
+ \cdots + c_n E[h_n(X)], \quad (6.21)
$$

which can also be written as

$$
E\left(\sum_{i=1}^n c_i Y_i\right) = \sum_{i=1}^n c_i E(Y_i) \quad \text{if} \quad Y_i = h_i(X). \quad (6.22)
$$

Similarly, if h is practically any function for which there are constants m and M such that $m \le h(x) \le M$ for all x, use of Eqs. 6.5, 6.6, 6.17, and 6.18 shows that

$$m \le E[h(X)] \le M. \tag{6.23}$$

Example 6.2.   Consider the random variable $Y = \pi X^2$ of Example 5.4. Use of Eqs. 6.16 and 6.17 shows in turn that

$$E(Y) = \int_0^{\pi r^2} y(1/\pi r^2)\, dy = \tfrac{1}{2}\pi r^2$$

and

$$E(Y) = \int_0^r \pi x^2 (2x/r^2)\, dx = \tfrac{1}{2}\pi r^2.$$

With $h(x) = \pi x^2$ and $H(y) = e^{\theta y}$, where θ is a real-valued parameter, Eq. 6.19 reduces here to the true equation

$$E(e^{\theta Y}) = \int_0^{\pi r^2} e^{\theta y}\, (1/\pi r^2)\, dy = \int_0^r e^{\theta \pi x^2}\, (2x/r^2)\, dx$$

$$= \frac{1}{\pi r^2 \theta}\, (e^{\pi r^2 \theta} - 1).$$

6.4   Variance of a Distribution

The *variance of the random variable* X, to be denoted by Var (X) or by σ^2, is defined to be the expectation of $(X - \mu)^2$; that is,

$$\sigma^2 = \text{Var}\ (X) = E[(X - \mu)^2], \tag{6.24}$$

where $\mu = E(X)$. The *variance of a distribution* is defined to be the variance of any random variable having that distribution. The positive square root σ of the variance is known as the *standard deviation;* it has the same units as X. By expanding the quadratic $(X - \mu)^2$ in Eq. 6.24 and by making use of Eq. 6.21, we find that

$$\text{Var}\ (X) = E(X^2) - \mu^2, \tag{6.25}$$

which often simplifies the computation of σ. (Of course, the usual remarks about existence apply to the variance.)

Although a more accurate interpretation of the variance is presented in Section 11.1, we remark here that the variance is the mean square deviation from the mean of a distribution and is formally analogous to the moment of inertia relative to the center of mass of a one-dimensional mass distribution with a total mass of 1. The standard deviation is a measure of the variability or dispersion of a distribution or of the possible departure of a random variable from its mean. It indicates the concentration of a distribution about its mean and the degree to which the mean represents the distribution as a whole. Although other measures of such variability have been proposed, the variance is the simplest useful one.

Example 6.3. For the random variables of Examples 5.1, 5.3, and 5.4, we find respectively that

$$E(X^2) = 0\left(\frac{1}{8}\right) + 1\left(\frac{3}{8}\right) + 4\left(\frac{3}{8}\right) + 9\left(\frac{1}{8}\right) = 3,$$

$$E(X^2) = \int_0^r x^2 \frac{2x}{r^2} \, dx = \frac{1}{2} r^2,$$

$$E(Y^2) = \int_0^{\pi r^2} y^2 \frac{1}{\pi r^2} \, dy = \frac{1}{3} \pi^2 r^4.$$

Use of Eq. 6.25, these results, and the means computed in Examples 6.1 and 6.2 shows that the respective variances are

$$\sigma^2 = 3 - \left(\frac{3}{2}\right)^2 = \frac{3}{4},$$

$$\sigma^2 = \frac{1}{2} r^2 - \left(\frac{2}{3} r\right)^2 = \frac{1}{18} r^2,$$

$$\sigma^2 = \frac{1}{3} \pi^2 r^4 - \left(\frac{1}{2} \pi r^2\right)^2 = \frac{1}{12} \pi^2 r^4.$$

6.5 Moments and Moment-Generating Functions

In this and the next section, we consider briefly certain generating functions and integral transforms of distributions that facilitate computations in probability theory in somewhat the same way as do Laplace transforms in the theory of differential equations.

MOMENTS

First, we note that, for every nonnegative integer n, the nth *moment*, if it exists, of the distribution of a random variable X (or simply of X) is defined to be the expected value $E(X^n)$ of X^n. For example, the zeroth and first moments of every distribution are 1 and its mean. Frequently, these moments are called *raw moments* or moments about the origin, to distinguish them from moments about other points. The nth moment about any point $x = a$, if it exists, is naturally defined as $E[(X - a)^n]$. If a is the mean μ of X, these moments are often called *central moments*. For example, the variance is the second central moment.

Rather standard symbols for the raw and central moments are μ'_n and μ_n; that is,

$$\mu'_n = E(X^n), \quad \mu_n = E[(X - \mu)^n]. \qquad (6.26)$$

In terms of this notation,

$$\mu = \mu'_1, \; \mu_1 = 0, \; \sigma^2 = \mu_2 = \mu'_2 - (\mu'_1)^2. \qquad (6.27)$$

The following fact about moments is noteworthy: *If the mth raw moment of a random variable X exists, then the mth and all preceding moments of X about any finite point all exist.* This follows from simple computations and the relation

$$E(|X|^{m-1}) \leq E(|X|^m) + 1,$$

which is true because

$$|x|^{m-1} \leq |x|^m + 1$$

for all real x and all $m \geq 1$.

MOMENT-GENERATING FUNCTIONS

Given a random variable X with distribution function F, suppose that the expected value of $e^{\theta X}$ has a finite value for every real value of θ satisfying $-h < \theta < h$ for some $h > 0$. Then, we say that X (or the distribution of X) has the *moment-generating function* M defined by

$$M(\theta) = E(e^{\theta X}) = \int_{-\infty}^{\infty} e^{\theta x} \, dF(x). \qquad (6.28)$$

This function is essentially a type of Laplace transform and is a function of the continuous variable θ for all θ in some neighborhood of $\theta = 0$.

Unfortunately, many distributions do not have moment-generating functions. For example, if X has the density function given by

$$f(x) = \begin{cases} (\alpha - 1)x^{-\alpha} & (1 \leq x < \infty) \\ 0 & (-\infty < x < 1) \end{cases}$$

for some $\alpha > 1$, then, for every $\theta > 0$, $e^{\theta x} f(x) \to \infty$ as $x \to \infty$ and thus $e^{\theta X}$ does not have a finite mean for any $\theta > 0$.

The usefulness of moment-generating functions depends partially on the following *uniqueness* theorem (whose proof must be omitted): *A probability distribution is uniquely determined by its moment-generating function, and conversely.* In other words, for those distributions which have moment-generating functions, there is a one-to-one correspondence between distributions and moment-generating functions, just as there is such a correspondence between distributions and distribution functions. Thus, knowledge of a moment-generating function is mathematically equivalent to knowledge of its corresponding distribution function and of its corresponding distribution.

If the random variable X has the moment-generating function M, one can use Eqs. 6.3, 6.4, 6.6, and 6.28, and the series

$$e^{\theta X} = 1 + \theta X + \frac{\theta^2}{2!} X^2 + \cdots + \frac{\theta^n}{n!} X^n + \cdots$$

to show that all moments of X exist, that the series

$$M(\theta) = 1 + \theta E(X) + \frac{\theta^2}{2!} E(X^2) + \cdots + \frac{\theta^n}{n!} E(X^n) + \cdots \quad (6.29)$$

converges absolutely for all θ in some neighborhood of $\theta = 0$, and hence that

$$\left. \frac{d^n M(\theta)}{d\theta^n} \right|_{\theta=0} = E(X^n) \quad (n = 0, 1, 2, \ldots). \quad (6.30)$$

This, and the uniqueness theorem, show that the sequence of all raw moments characterizes a distribution which *has* a moment-generating function, in terms of an infinite sequence of numbers—in somewhat the same way that the sequence of coefficients in a Maclaurin series characterizes an ordinary function.

Equations 6.29 and 6.30 show how the raw moments of a distribution can be obtained from the moment-generating function, if it exists, either by direct expansion in a Maclaurin series or by differentiation. It will be seen in Chapters 7 and 8 that this method for computing moments is often much more efficient than direct evaluations based on definitions such as Eq. 6.26. Incidentally, the name "moment-generating function" comes from the fact that moments can be "generated" in this way.

Another important use of the moment-generating function is in solving the following problem (also discussed in Section 5.7): Given a random variable X with distribution function F and practically any function h, derive the distribution of the random variable Y defined by $Y = h(X)$. To solve such a problem by using moment-generating functions, one first notes that the moment-generating function of Y can be written in the form

$$M_Y(\theta) = E(e^{\theta Y}) = E(e^{\theta h(X)}) = \int_{-\infty}^{\infty} e^{\theta h(x)} \, dF(x). \qquad (6.31)$$

Then, if evaluation of this integral gives a function M_Y, which one can recognize (from memory or a table) as the moment-generating function of a specific distribution, the uniqueness theorem assures that this specific distribution is the distribution of Y.

Two other very important properties of moment-generating functions are stated and illustrated in Sections 10.6 and 12.3.

Example 6.4.   The random variable X has the *continuous* distribution function F. Show that the random variable $Y = F(X)$ has the normalized uniform distribution having the density function given in Eq. 5.34, and compute the moments of Y. First, note that this uniform distribution has the moment-generating function

$$M(\theta) = \int_0^1 e^{\theta x} \, dx = \theta^{-1}(e^\theta - 1).$$

Use of Eq. 6.31 and the variable transformation $u = F(x)$ now shows that

$$M_Y(\theta) = \int_{-\infty}^{\infty} e^{\theta F(x)} \, dF(x) = \int_0^1 e^{\theta u} \, du = \theta^{-1}(e^\theta - 1)$$

and hence that Y has the normalized uniform distribution. Since

$$\theta^{-1}(e^\theta - 1) = \sum_{n=0}^{\infty} \frac{\theta^n}{(n+1)!},$$

Eqs. 6.26, 6.27, and 6.29 show that $\mu_n' = 1/(n+1)$, $\mu = \frac{1}{2}$, and $\sigma^2 = \frac{1}{12}$. To find the central moments μ_n of Y, note that, in general,

$$E(e^{\theta(X-\mu)}) = e^{-\mu\theta} M(\theta)$$

$$= \sum_{n=0}^{\infty} \frac{\theta^n}{n!} \mu_n.$$

Now, since $\mu = \frac{1}{2}$,

$$e^{-\mu\theta}M_Y(\theta) = \theta^{-1}(e^{\theta/2} - e^{-\theta/2}) = \sum_{m=0}^{\infty} \frac{\theta^{2m}}{(2m+1)!\,2^{2m}},$$

and therefore

$$\mu_{2m} = \frac{1}{(2m+1)2^{2m}}, \quad \mu_{2m+1} = 0 \qquad (m = 0, 1, 2, \ldots).$$

6.6   Other Integral Transforms

The *characteristic function* φ of a random variable X, or of the distribution of X, having the distribution function F is defined by

$$\varphi(u) = E(e^{iuX}) = \int_{-\infty}^{\infty} e^{iux}\,dF(x), \tag{6.32}$$

where $i = \sqrt{-1}$ and u is a continuous real variable. Since

$$e^{iux} = \cos ux + i \sin ux,$$

φ can also be written as

$$\varphi(u) = \int_{-\infty}^{\infty} \cos ux\,dF(x) + i \int_{-\infty}^{\infty} \sin ux\,dF(x). \tag{6.33}$$

Because the two integrals in Eq. 6.33 are absolutely convergent for every distribution function F, φ is a *complex*-valued function whose real and imaginary parts are finite for every real value of u. One can easily show that every characteristic function is continuous and satisfies $|\varphi(u)| \leq \varphi(0) = 1$ for every real u.

From Eq. 6.33, *every random variable (and therefore every distribution) has a characteristic function. Furthermore, it can be shown that a distribution is uniquely determined by its characteristic function, and conversely.* Therefore, there is a one-to-one correspondence between *all* distributions and their characteristic functions. For this reason, characteristic functions are much more powerful and are almost always used instead of moment-generating functions in advanced developments.

Of course, characteristic functions can be used for every purpose for which moment-generating functions are used. For example, one can apply the following theorem to evaluate moments: *If the mth moment of the random variable X exists, then the characteristic function φ of X*

can be expanded near $u = 0$ in the form

$$\varphi(u) = 1 + \sum_{n=1}^{m} \frac{(iu)^n}{n!} E(X^n) + o(u^m), \qquad (6.34)$$

where

$$\lim_{u \to 0} \frac{o(u^m)}{u^m} = 0.$$

Note that this theorem does not require existence of any moments higher than the mth.

A characteristic function is essentially a *Fourier transform* and therefore satisfies certain inversion formulas, two of which are merely stated here. *If X is a random variable having characteristic function φ and distribution function F and if a and b, where $a < b$, are finite real numbers at which F is continuous, then*

$$F(b) - F(a) = \lim_{A \to \infty} \frac{1}{2\pi} \int_{-A}^{A} \frac{e^{-iua} - e^{-iub}}{iu} \varphi(u)\, du. \qquad (6.35)$$

Furthermore, if φ is absolutely integrable, i.e., if

$$\int_{-\infty}^{\infty} |\varphi(u)|\, du < \infty,$$

then X is absolutely continuous and has the density function f given by

$$f(x) = \frac{1}{2\pi} \int_{-\infty}^{\infty} e^{-iux} \varphi(u)\, du \qquad (6.36)$$

for every real x.

As a final transform, we consider the special case of a discrete random variable X whose possible values are nonnegative integers and whose probability function is g. If we set $s = e^{\theta}$ in the moment-generating function of X, we obtain the function

$$A(s) = E(s^X) = \sum_{n} g(n)s^n. \qquad (6.37)$$

This function A is a polynomial or an infinite power series and always exists at least for $|s| \leq 1$, since

$$\sum_{n} g(n) = 1.$$

It may be called the *discrete generating function* of X.

Discrete generating functions are simpler than moment-generating functions and characteristic functions and are often used, instead of these functions, when only random variables with nonnegative integral possible values appear in an analysis. For example, considerable use is made of discrete generating functions in the book by Feller listed in the bibliography.

Discrete generating functions can, of course, be used for the same purposes as are the other integral transforms. For example, the reader can show that the mean and variance, if they exist, of a random variable X with discrete generating function, Eq. 6.37, are given by

$$E(X) = A'(1)$$
$$\text{Var } (X) = A''(1) + A'(1) - [A'(1)]^2,$$

(6.38)

where the "prime" symbol denotes differentiation with respect to s.

6.7   Exercises

6.1   If F is absolutely continuous so that $dF(x) = f(x)\, dx$, write Eqs. 6.2 through 6.5 in terms of Riemann integrals, and verify their validity when $F(x) = h(x) = h_1(x) = x^2$ and $h_2(x) = x$.

6.2   If F is a discrete distribution function with probability function g, write Eqs. 6.2 through 6.5 in terms of g and summations, and verify their validity when $g(x) = \frac{1}{5}$ for $x = 1, 2, \ldots, 5$, $h(x) = h_1(x) = x$, and $h_2(x) = 5$.

6.3   In Eq. 6.6, let F be the Cauchy distribution function so that $dF(x)/dx = 1/[\pi(1 + x^2)]$ for $-\infty < x < \infty$. If y is any real number and if $a \to -\infty$ and $b \to \infty$ in such a way that $1 + b^2 = (1 + a^2) \exp [2\pi y]$, show that

$$\int_a^b \pi^{-1}(1 + x^2)^{-1}x\, dx \to y$$

and that

$$\int_a^b \pi^{-1}(1 + x^2)^{-1}|x|\, dx \to \infty.$$

(In such cases, we say that the limit in Eq. 6.6 does not exist, since there is no one number which $\int_a^b h(x)\, dF(x)$ approaches as a and b approach their respective limits independently of each other.)

6.4   As Exercise 6.4.k for $k = 1, 2, \ldots, 10$, compute the mean of the random variable of Exercise 5.k. *Hint for Exercises* 6.4.5 *and* 6.4.6b: For

$|p| < 1$,

$$\sum_{n=1}^{\infty} np^{n-1} = \frac{d}{dp} \sum_{n=1}^{\infty} p^n = \frac{d}{dp}\left(\frac{p}{1-p}\right).$$

6.5 The *median* of a distribution, denoted by m_e, is defined as a number such that $P(X < m_e) \leq 0.5$ and also $P(X > m_e) \leq 0.5$, in which X is a random variable having the given distribution. When there is an interval of points satisfying these conditions, we take the mid-point of the interval as the median. (a) For a continuous distribution, show that m_e satisfies $F(m_e) = 0.5$. (b) Show that the median may be characterized as a number at which the function $h(c) = E(|X - c|)$ is minimized.

6.6 For an absolutely continuous (or discrete) distribution, a *mode* of the distribution is defined as a number m_o at which the density (or probability) function has a relative maximum. For example, if the density function has two derivatives near a point m_o, then m_o is a mode if $f'(m_o) = 0$ and $f''(m_o) < 0$. We say that a distribution is *unimodal* if it has one mode, *bimodal* if it has two modes, etc. If a unimodal density function satisfies $f(c - x) = f(c + x)$ for some constant c and all x and has a mean, show that the mean, median, and mode are identical and equal to c (cf. Exercise 5.19).

6.7 As parts (a), (b), and (c), find the mean, median, and mode for each density function in Exercise 5.16.

6.8 An ideal die is tossed once. A player wins one cent if 1, 3, or 5 dots appear and wins two cents if 2 or 4 dots appear, while he looses four cents if 6 dots appear. Find the *expected value* of the player's winnings.

6.9 If the distribution function F of X satisfies $xF(x) \to 0$ as $x \to -\infty$ and $x[1 - F(x)] \to 0$ as $x \to \infty$, use integration by parts to make the following true relation at least plausible:

$$E(X) = \int_0^\infty [1 - F(x)]\, dx - \int_{-\infty}^0 F(x)\, dx,$$

and interpret this relation in terms of certain areas in a graph of $F(x)$ versus x.

6.10 As parts (a), (b), (c), and (d), use Eqs. 6.16 and also 6.17 to find the expectations of the functions given in Exercise 5.23, and thus verify Eq. 6.18 in each case.

6.11 For the salesman of Exercise 5.21, use the distribution of (a) X, and (b) S, to find his average income per call.

*6.12 During a holiday season, a merchant will make a net profit of α dollars for each unit amount of some commodity sold and will lose β dollars for each unit amount left unsold at the end of the season. Suppose that the merchant can purchase this commodity only before the season starts, and that the total amount his customers will want to buy during the season can be viewed as a continuous random variable with a given density function $f(x)$ for $0 < x < \infty$. (a) Find a relation between α, β, and $F(y)$, where y is the number of units which the merchant should purchase in order to maximize the expected value of his profit P on this commodity. (b) Compute y when $\alpha = 1$, $\beta = 2$, and $f(x) = 2 \times 10^{-4}x \exp(-10^{-4}x^2)$ for $0 < x < \infty$.

6.13   As Exercise 6.10.k for $k = 1, 2, \ldots, 10$, use the result of Exercise 6.4.k in computing the variance of the random variable of Exercise 5.k.

6.14   (a) Find the mode (sometimes called the "most probable value"), average, and standard deviation of the speed of a molecule, under the conditions of Exercise 5.26. (b) Evaluate each of these quantities for nitrogen at 68 degrees Fahrenheit. (Then, for units of centimeters per second, $T = 293$, $k = 1.38 \times 10^{-16}$, and $m = 4.65 \times 10^{-23}$.)

6.15   Under the conditions of Exercise 5.26, use integration by parts and (1) the density function of V and (2) the derived density function of W to find (a) the mean and (b) the variance of the kinetic energy of a molecule, and thus verify Eq. 6.19 in this case.

*6.16   As parts (a) and (b), compute the mean and standard deviation of each density function found in Exercise 5.25. (c) Compare these means with the radius r that a circle must have in order to have the same area as the hexagon.

6.17   Let X have a finite mean μ, and let $h(c) = E(X - c)^2$ for every real c. Use Eq. 6.21 to show that $h(c) = E(X - \mu)^2 + (\mu - c)^2$, and therefore that $h(c)$ takes its minimum possible value, Var (X), when $c = \mu$.

6.18   Let X have a finite mean μ and variance σ^2. (a) If a and b are any constants, show that Var $(aX + b) = a^2$ Var (X). (b) If Y denotes the "standardized" random variable $(X - \mu)/\sigma$, show that the mean and variance of Y are 0 and 1. (c) If X also has a finite nth raw moment for a positive integer n, show that

$$E(X + c)^n = \sum_{k=0}^{n} \binom{n}{k} c^{n-k} E(X^k)$$

for every real c.

6.19   Find the moment-generating function for the distribution of Example 5.1, and use it to find the mean and variance.

6.20   As parts (a), (b), (c), (d), and (e), find the moment-generating function of the random variable of Exercises 5.1, 5.3, 5.5, 5.8, and 5.9. Use it to find the mean and variance, and compare these values with those obtained in Exercises 6.4 and 6.10.

6.21   As parts (a) and (b), find the moment-generating function, mean, and standard deviation of each distribution in Exercise 5.11.

6.22　　Let X have the exponential distribution with density function $\mu^{-1}e^{-x/\mu}$, where $\mu > 0$ is a constant. Find the moment-generating function, and use it to find the mean, standard deviation, and all raw moments of X.

6.23　　(a) Given $f(x) = 1$ for $0 < x < 1$, use Eq. 6.31 to derive the distribution of $Y = -5 \log X$. (b) If X has the continuous distribution function F, derive the distribution of $Y = -\mu \log [1 - F(X)]$, where μ is a positive constant.

6.24　　Let X have a so-called Poisson distribution, whose moment-generating function is $M(\theta) = \exp(-\mu + \mu e^{\theta})$ in which $\mu > 0$ is a constant. (a) Find the mean and variance of X. (b) Expand $M(\theta)$ in a series so that Eq. 6.28 can be used to find the probability function of X.

6.25　　Let X have a moment-generating function M_X, and let a and b be any two constants. Show that the moment-generating function of $Y = aX + b$ is $M_Y(\theta) = e^{b\theta} M_X(a\theta)$.

6.26　　Let p and q be constants such that $p \geq 0$, $q \geq 0$, and $p + q = 1$. (a) Given that X has the discrete generating function $A(s) = (q + ps)^n$, where n is a positive integer, use Eqs. 6.37 and 6.38 to find the probability function, mean, and variance of X. (b) Repeat part (a), for $A(s) = q/(1 - ps)$.

6.27　　Derive Eqs. 6.38.

6.28　　(a) If X has the moment-generating function M, show that the characteristic function φ of X is given by $\varphi(u) = M(iu)$. (b) Show that $|M(iu)| \leq M(0) = 1$ for every real u, even though $M(u)$ may take every real positive value as u varies over the real numbers.

*6.29　　Let X have the distribution function $F(x) = x$ for $0 < x < 1$. (a) Use Eq. 6.32 or 6.33 to show that X has the characteristic function $\varphi(u) = (e^{iu} - 1)/iu$. (b) Given this characteristic function φ, use Eq. 6.36 to find f.

APPLICATIONS IN ENGINEERING

6.30　　If T has the distribution of Exercises (a) 5.28(a), (b) 5.28(b), or (c) 5.31, compute the moment-generating function M_T, mean, and standard deviation of T.

6.31　　For the reactor of Exercise 5.27, show that

$$V = Q \int_0^{\infty} [1 - F(t)] \, dt$$

and therefore from Exercise 6.9 that $E(T) = \tau = V/Q$, if $t[1 - F(t)] \to 0$ as $t \to \infty$ (which we assume hereafter because every normal physical reactor must satisfy this condition). (Of course, V, Q, and hence τ can usually be measured experimentally, and therefore the residence time T can be treated in the normalized form T_r of Exercise 5.29.)

6.32   For each molecule in the reactor of Exercise 5.27 at any fixed instant of time, we define its *age* as the time that has elapsed since the molecule entered the reactor and its *future lifetime* as the time it will remain in the reactor until it leaves, and we wish to abstract these quantities as random variables X and Y, respectively. Denote their density and distribution functions by g_X, G_X, g_Y, and G_Y. Their distributions are to be defined so that, for example, $G_X(x)$ is approximately the fraction of the V molecules in the reactor at any fixed time θ which entered between $(\theta - x)$ and θ, and $g_Y(y)\Delta y$ is approximately the fraction of these V molecules that will leave between $(\theta + y)$ and $(\theta + y + \Delta y)$. If F is the distribution function of the residence time T, show that

$$g_X(x) = \tau^{-1}[1 - F(x)] \qquad (0 \le x < \infty)$$

$$g_Y(y) = \tau^{-1}[1 - F(y)] \qquad (0 \le y < \infty),$$

where $\tau = V/Q$. (Note that X and Y have the same distribution and that X refers to the past while Y refers to the future behavior of the molecules in the reactor at any instant of time.) *Hint:* See Exercise 6.31 and note that

$$g_X(x)\Delta x = V^{-1}[1 - F(x)]Q\Delta x.$$

6.33   (a) Express the mean μ_X, variance σ_X^2, and moment-generating function M_X (if they exist) of X and Y of Exercise 6.32 in terms of the moments and moment-generating function M_T of T. (b) If T has the distribution of Exercises 5.28(b) and 6.30(b), evaluate μ_X and σ_X^2.

6.34   For a well-stirred reactor as described in Exercise 5.30, show that T, X, and Y of Exercise 6.32 have the same exponential distribution.

6.35   If the residence time T of Exercise 5.27 has the distribution function defined by $F(t) = 0$ for $t < t_0$ and $F(t) = 1$ for $t \ge t_0$, for some constant $t_0 > 0$, compute the mean and variance of T. Conclude that every molecule remains in the reactor for exactly t_0 minutes (with probability one, and that the molecules must flow side by side through the reactor without any mixing. This corresponds to an extreme case often called "ideal piston flow.")

6.36   Let a specific residence-time density function f for the reactor of Exercise 5.27 be given. Suppose a combustion or other chemical reaction occurs in such a way that the rate of the reaction in any very small region inside the reactor depends only on the concentration c (in moles per cubic foot, say) in that region of one chemical species, say A, which is consumed by the reaction. Denote this rate by $R(c)$, where R is a given positive function. Let $c_0 > 0$ and $c_e (0 \le c_e < c_0)$ denote the concentrations of A in the fluid flowing, respectively, into and out of the reactor. For fixed c_0, the value of c_e usually (but not always) depends on the amount of molecular mixing that occurs inside the reactor; that is, on the amount of mixing of molecules having different ages. Under simplifying assumptions, it can be shown that the amount of such mixing is limited by the specified function f and therefore that, for fixed c_0, c_e must always be between two extreme limits. One of these limits, say c_e', is given by

$$c_e' = \int_0^\infty C(t)f(t)\, dt,$$

where $C(t)$ is the solution of the problem

$$\frac{dC}{dt} = -R(C), \qquad C(0) = c_0.$$

(a) If $f(t) = 0$ for $t < 0$ and if $R(c) = kc$ for a positive constant k, show that $c_e' = c_0 M_T(-k)$, where M_T is the moment-generating function (if it exists) of T. (b) Evaluate c_e' for each density function given in Exercise 5.28. (See Exercise 6.30.) (c) For every nonnegative random variable T and every constant $k > 0$, show that $0 < M_T(-k) < 1$ and therefore that $M_T(-k)$ exists, even when T does not have a moment-generating function, that is, even when $M_T(\theta)$ does not exist for any $\theta > 0$.

6.37   In the paper by Zwietering listed in the bibliography, it is shown that the other limit of c_e indicated in Exercise 6.36 is given by $c_e'' = c(0)$, where $c(t)$ is the *nonnegative* integral of the (nonlinear) differential equation

$$\frac{dc}{dt} = R(c) + \frac{f(t)}{1 - F(t)}\, (c - c_0)$$

which (for all normal cases) is bounded for all $t \geq 0$, so that usually $dc/dt \to 0$ as $t \to \infty$. If f and R are as in Exercise 6.36a, show at least by direct substitution that the solution of this problem is

$$c(t) = \frac{c_0 e^{kt}}{1 - F(t)} \int_t^\infty e^{-kx} f(x)\, dx$$

and therefore that $c_e' = c_e'' = c_0 M_T(-k)$ in this case (of a so-called first-order reaction).

6.38   In Exercises 6.36 and 6.37, let $f(t) = \tau^{-1} e^{-t/\tau}$ for $0 \leq t < \infty$ and $R(c) = kc^2$ for a positive constant k. So far as analytically possible, evaluate c_e' and c_e''. *Hint:* Solve the quadratic equation $dc/dt = 0$ for c_e''. (For all values of $kc_0\tau$, it can be shown in this case that $c_e' < c_e''$.)

CHAPTER 7   SPECIAL DISCRETE

DISTRIBUTIONS

IN THIS CHAPTER WE STUDY CERTAIN DISCRETE DISTRIBUTIONS THAT ARE encountered frequently in theory and practice. Two of these, the binomial and Poisson distributions, are two of the three principal distributions that appear throughout probability theory. (The normal distribution, the third principal one, is discussed in Chapter 8.)

7.1   The Binomial Distribution

Suppose that for some experiment there is a certain outcome E in which we are interested, so that we classify the outcome of any trial of this experiment as either "success" (if E occurs) or "failure" (if E does not occur). Suppose further that the probability space $(\Omega, \mathcal{S}, P)$ is an appropriate mathematical model for this experiment.

A frequently occurring situation is that in which one proposes to run the above experiment n times, and is intuitively satisfied that "the conditions of each trial will be the same" and "the chance of success at any trial is not related to the results of the other trials." The random variable of interest in this new experiment (which consists of running the original experiment n times) is the total number of successes.

As a sample space Ω_n for the new experiment, we can take the set of all ordered n-tuples of the symbols S and F; for example, $(S, S, F, \ldots, S)$—for "success on the first and second trials, failure on the third, $\ldots$, success on the last." The problem of interest can then be phrased mathematically as a determination of the distribution of

105

the random variable S_n, on Ω_n, defined by

$$S_n(\omega_j) = \text{Number of } S\text{'s in the ordered } n\text{-tuple } \omega_j.$$

Clearly S_n is discrete with possible values $0, 1, 2, \ldots, n$.

In order to determine the distribution of S_n (or even to talk about it, if one wishes to be very punctilious), it is necessary to select a probability space $(\Omega_n, \mathcal{S}_n, P_n)$ for the new experiment. The considerations of Chapter 3 show that we can take $\mathcal{S}_n$ to be the set of all subsets of Ω_n, and that our problem reduces to defining P_n on each of the elementary events ω_j in such a way that

$$P_n(\omega_j) \geq 0$$

and

$$\sum_j P_n(\omega_j) = 1.$$

Let us define events $A_1, A_2, \ldots, A_n$ in $\mathcal{S}_n$ by

$$A_1 = (S, *, *, \ldots, *),$$
$$A_2 = (*, S, *, \ldots, *),$$
$$\cdots \cdots \cdots \cdots \cdots \cdots,$$
$$A_n = (*, *, \ldots, *, S),$$

where

$$(S, *, *, \ldots, *) = \{(S, S, S, \ldots, S), (S, F, S, \ldots, S),$$
$$\ldots, (S, F, F, \ldots, F)\}$$

and so on. In words, A_j corresponds to the outcome "success at the jth trial" and is the collection of all those n-tuples in Ω_n having an S in the jth "slot."

To model mathematically the intuitive notion that "the conditions of each trial are the same," we *postulate* that

$$P_n(A_j) = P(E) \qquad (j = 1, 2, \ldots, n).$$

The intuitive idea here is that, since $(\Omega, \mathcal{S}, P)$ is supposed to be an appropriate probability space for the old experiment, $P(E)$ should measure the chance of success at each trial if all trials are identical.

To model the intuitive notion that "the chance of success at any trial is unrelated to the results of other trials," we *postulate* that the events A_1, A_2, . . . , A_n are independent. Recall that this means that

$$. P_n(A_1 \cap A_2) = P_n(A_1)P_n(A_2),$$
$$P_n(A_1 \cap A_5 \cap A_6) = P_n(A_1)P_n(A_5)P_n(A_6),$$

and so on—that is, the probability of the simultaneous occurrence of any k different A_i ($k \leq n$) is the product of the separate probabilities. Recall too that by an exercise in Chapter 4 this postulate implies that the events A_1^*, A_2^*, . . . , A_n^* are also independent, the event A_j^* being either A_j or A_j^c.

Now, let $(S, S, F, . . . , F, S)$ be an ordered n-tuple in Ω_n. Clearly this elementary event is the intersection

$$A_1 \cap A_2 \cap A_3^c \cap \cdots \cap A_{n-1}^c \cap A_n;$$

therefore by independence it has the probability

$$P_n[(S, S, F, . . . , F, S)]$$
$$= P_n(A_1)P_n(A_2)P_n(A_3^c) \cdots P_n(A_{n-1}^c)P_n(A_n). \quad (7.1)$$

We have already postulated that $P_n(A_j) = P(E)$, however, and this implies that $P_n(A_j^c) = 1 - P(E)$, so Eq. 7.1 becomes

$$P_n[(S, S, F, . . . , F, S)]$$
$$= P(E)P(E)[1 - P(E)] \cdots [1 - P(E)]P(E). \quad (7.2)$$

If our elementary event $(S, S, F, . . . , F, S)$ contains k symbols S ($0 \leq k \leq n$), and $(n - k)$ symbols F, we can collect factors in Eq. 7.2 and write

$$P_n[(S, S, F, . . . , F, S)] = [P(E)]^k[1 - P(E)]^{n-k}. \quad (7.3)$$

Let us abbreviate $P(E)$ by p and $[1 - P(E)]$ by q and summarize by saying *an elementary event $(S, S, F, . . . , S) = \omega_j$ containing k symbols S ($k \leq n$) is assigned the probability $P_n(\omega_j) = p^k q^{n-k}$.*

Clearly $P_n(\omega_j) \geq 0$. We leave as an exercise the verification that

$$\sum_j P_n(\omega_j) = 1,$$

and return to the problem of determining the distribution of the random variable S_n. We have seen that the probability of each sample point at which S_n takes the value k ($0 \leq k \leq n$) is $p^k q^{n-k}$. For any fixed k there are C_k^n sample points containing precisely k symbols S, since this is the number of distinct ways of choosing k "slots" out of n

in which to put S's. We conclude that S_n has the probability function g given by

$$g(k) = C_k^n p^k q^{n-k} \qquad (k = 0, 1, \ldots, n). \qquad (7.4)$$

If p is a given number between zero and one, and n is a positive integer, a discrete random variable with possible values $0, 1, \ldots, n$, and probability function given by Eq. 7.4, is said to be *binomially distributed with parameters* (n, p), or to have the *binomial distribution* $B(n, p)$. Thus we may loosely summarize our considerations to this point as follows:

The number of successes in n independent trials, with (constant) probability p of success at each trial, has the binomial distribution $B(n, p)$.

MOMENTS OF THE BINOMIAL DISTRIBUTION

Recall that the binomial theorem asserts that if n is a positive integer and x and y are real numbers

$$(x + y)^n = \sum_{k=0}^{n} \binom{n}{k} x^k y^{n-k}. \qquad (7.5)$$

By setting $x = p$ and $y = q = 1 - p$, we have

$$1 = \sum_{k=0}^{n} \binom{n}{k} p^k q^{n-k}.$$

This shows that the sum of the $g(k)$ in Eq. 7.4 is unity, so that Eq. 7.4 does determine a probability distribution (and the sum of the $P_n(\omega_j)$ is indeed one). The reason for the name "binomial distribution" is the frequent appearance of the binomial theorem in this subsection.

If X is a discrete random variable with probability function g given by Eq. 7.4—that is, if X has the binomial distribution $B(n, p)$—the moment generating function of X is given by

$$\begin{aligned}
M(\theta) = E(e^{\theta X}) &= \sum_{k=0}^{n} e^{k\theta} \binom{n}{k} p^k q^{n-k} \\
&= \sum_{k=0}^{n} \binom{n}{k} (pe^{\theta})^k q^{n-k} \\
&= (q + pe^{\theta})^n, \qquad (7.6)
\end{aligned}$$

again by the binomial theorem. Using the properties of the moment generating function, then,

$$\mu = E(X) = \frac{dM}{d\theta}\Big|_{\theta=0} = n(q + pe^\theta)^{n-1}pe^\theta\Big|_{\theta=0} = np \qquad (7.7)$$

and

$$E(X^2) = \frac{d^2M}{d\theta^2}\Big|_{\theta=0} = n^2p^2 + npq$$

and, finally,

$$\sigma^2 = E(X^2) - \mu^2 = npq. \qquad (7.8)$$

Thus the binomial distribution $B(n, p)$ has mean np and variance npq.

In the exercises the mean and variance of the binomial distribution are calculated directly instead of by using the moment-generating function. In Sections 10.1 and 10.4 a different calculation, based on a different interpretation of the random variable S_n, is made. In Section 10.6 this new interpretation of S_n is used to give another derivation of the binomial distribution.

7.2   The Poisson Distribution

A discrete random variable X, with possible values 0, 1, 2, . . . (all nonnegative integers) is said to have the *Poisson distribution with parameter* λ if its probability function g is given by

$$g(k) = \frac{\lambda^k}{k!} e^{-\lambda} \qquad (\lambda > 0; k = 0, 1, 2, . . .). \qquad (7.9)$$

To check that Eq. 7.9 does define a distribution, note that

$$\sum_{k=0}^{\infty} g(k) = \sum_{k=0}^{\infty} \frac{\lambda^k}{k!} e^{-\lambda} = e^{-\lambda} \sum_{k=0}^{\infty} \frac{\lambda^k}{k!} = (e^{-\lambda})(e^{\lambda}) = 1.$$

The computation of the mean, variance, and moment-generating function of this distribution is an easy exercise.

In Section 7.4 we shall see that the Poisson distribution is in a certain sense a "limit" of the binomial distribution. In the exercises we shall see that it can arise in physical problems in which there is a certain "linearity" or "density." As an example of this situation, we consider the experiment of throwing n raisins into a large batch of cookie dough of volume V, stirring, then scooping out a volume of dough v and baking it into a cookie. The number of raisins in the cookie, intuitively speaking, is proportional to v but can have chance fluctuations about its "nominal value" of nv/V. Experience has shown that the Poisson distribution with parameter nv/V gives a good model of this experiment. Here n/V is the "density" we spoke of, and the proportionality in v the "linearity."

7.3   The Hypergeometric Distribution

Let X be a discrete random variable with possible values 0, 1, 2, . . . , m, with m a positive integer, and let n and k be positive integers such that $k \leq (m + n)$. If X has the probability function g given by

$$g(r) = \frac{\binom{m}{r}\binom{n}{k-r}}{\binom{m+n}{k}} \qquad (r = 0, 1, \ldots, m), \qquad (7.10)$$

then X is said to have the *hypergeometric distribution* with parameters (m, n, k). Notice that if $r > k$ (which can happen if $k < m$) the factor $\binom{n}{k-r}$ is zero by definition, while if $(k - r) > n$ (which can happen if $k > n$) the same factor is again zero by definition.

Recall from Chapter 3 that, if k balls are selected from an urn containing m red balls and n white balls, the probability of the sample containing r red balls is given by the right side of Eq. 7.10 for $\max [0, k - n] \leq r \leq \min [k, m]$. Since we have just seen that the right side of Eq. 7.10 vanishes for other values of r or, in other words, that Eq. 7.10 takes account of the fact that no sample of size k can contain more than k red balls or more than n white balls, we conclude that the number of red balls has the hypergeometric distribution with parameters (m, n, k).

The mean of the hypergeometric distribution with parameters (m, n, k) is $km/(m + n)$ and the variance is

$$\frac{kmn}{(m + n)^2}\left(1 - \frac{k - 1}{m + n - 1}\right).$$

We defer the computation of these until the exercises of Chapter 10. The fact that

$$\sum_{r=0}^{m} g(r) = 1$$

was obtained in the exercises of Chapter 3.

7.4 Relations Between Distributions

In this chapter we have discussed three discrete distributions: the binomial, Poisson, and hypergeometric. These distributions are closely related, as we shall indicate in this section.

RELATION BETWEEN THE HYPERGEOMETRIC AND BINOMIAL DISTRIBUTIONS

Suppose an urn contains 10^6 red balls and 10^8 white ones, and five balls are selected at random. We know that the probability of finding r red balls in this sample is given by the hypergeometric formula:

$$P_H(r) = \frac{\binom{10^6}{r}\binom{10^8}{5-r}}{\binom{10^6 + 10^8}{5}}. \tag{7.11}$$

On the other hand, if we pick a ball from the urn five times, *replacing after each pick*, we have repeated independent trials with a constant probability $p = 10^6/(10^6 + 10^8)$ of success at each trial. The number of red balls obtained will have the binomial distribution

$$P_B(r) = \binom{5}{r} p^r (1 - p)^{5-r}. \tag{7.12}$$

Now, the ratio of red balls to white balls in the urn will not be changed significantly by removing as few as five balls, so we should expect that Eq. 7.11, which allows for nonreplacement, should be approximated very closely by Eq. 7.12. This is indeed so, as we now verify for a more general case. We have

$$
\frac{\dbinom{m}{r}\dbinom{n}{k-r}}{\dbinom{m+n}{k}}
$$

$$
= \frac{m(m-1)\ \cdots\ (m-r+1)}{r!}\ \frac{n(n-1)\ \cdots\ (n-k+r+1)}{(k-r)!}
$$
$$
\times \frac{k!}{(m+n)(m+n-1)\ \cdots\ (m+n-k+1)}
$$

$$
= \binom{k}{r}\frac{m(m-1)\ \cdots\ (m-r+1)n(n-1)\ \cdots\ (n-k+r+1)}{(m+n)(m+n-1)\ \cdots\ (m+n-k+1)}
$$

$$(7.13)$$

$$
> \binom{k}{r}\frac{m(m-1)\ \cdots\ (m-r+1)n(n-1)\ \cdots\ (n-k+r+1)}{(m+n)^k}
$$

$$
> \binom{k}{r}\left(\frac{m-r}{m+n}\right)^r\left(\frac{n-k+r}{m+n}\right)^{k-r};
$$

$$(7.14)$$

but also, since $\left(\dfrac{m-j}{m+n-j}\right) < \left(\dfrac{m}{m+n}\right)$ for any positive j,

$$
\frac{m(m-1)\ \cdots\ (m-r+1)}{(m+n)(m+n-1)\ \cdots\ (m+n-r+1)} < \left(\frac{m}{m+n}\right)^r \quad (7.15)
$$

and

$$
\frac{n(n-1)\ \cdots\ (n-k+r+1)}{(m+n-r)(m+n-r-1)\ \cdots\ (m+n-k+1)}
$$

$$
< \left(\frac{n}{n-r}\right)^{k-r}\frac{(n-r)(n-r-1)\ \cdots\ (n-k+1)}{(m+n-r)\ \cdots\ (m+n-k+1)}
$$

$$
< \left(\frac{n}{n-r}\right)^{k-r}\left(\frac{n-r}{m+n-r}\right)^{k-r} < \left(\frac{n}{n-r}\right)^k\left(\frac{n}{m+n}\right)^{k-r}. \quad (7.16)
$$

Thus, using Eqs. 7.15 and 7.16 in Eq. 7.13,

$$
\frac{\dbinom{m}{r}\dbinom{n}{k-r}}{\dbinom{m+n}{k}} < \binom{k}{r}\left(\frac{m}{m+n}\right)^r\left(\frac{n}{m+n}\right)^{k-r}\left(1-\frac{r}{n}\right)^{-k}. \quad (7.17)
$$

Combining Eqs. 7.17 and 7.14 gives

$$\binom{k}{r}\left(\frac{m-r}{m+n}\right)^r\left(\frac{n-k+r}{m+n}\right)^{k-r} < \frac{\binom{m}{r}\binom{n}{k-r}}{\binom{m+n}{k}}$$

$$< \binom{k}{r}\left(\frac{m}{m+n}\right)^r\left(\frac{n}{m+n}\right)^{k-r}\left(1-\frac{r}{n}\right)^{-k}, \quad (7.18)$$

so that *if k (hence r) is small compared to both m and n*

$$\frac{\binom{m}{r}\binom{n}{k-r}}{\binom{m+n}{k}} \doteq \binom{k}{r}\left(\frac{m}{m+n}\right)^r\left(\frac{n}{m+n}\right)^{k-r}, \quad (7.19)$$

where $\doteq$ denotes "approximately equal to." Equation 7.19, which is made precise by Eq. 7.18, can be read: "In a small sample of a large population, replacement and nonreplacement give approximately equivalent results."

RELATION BETWEEN THE BINOMIAL AND POISSON DISTRIBUTIONS

The Poisson and binomial distributions are related by a formula similar to Eq. 7.19; in fact *if n is large and p small*

$$\binom{n}{k}p^k(1-p)^{n-k} \doteq \frac{(np)^k}{k!}e^{-np}. \quad (7.20)$$

Of course, it is necessary to make precise what is meant here by "n large and p small" and "$\doteq$." We defer this to the exercises and content ourselves for the present with the following rule of thumb: If $n > 100$, $p < 0.01$, and $np < 1$, the two sides of Eq. 7.20 agree to approximately three decimal places for every k. In addition, for those values of k for which $(k - np)^2/n < 0.01$, the two sides of Eq. 7.20 agree to within one percent of either side.

Example. If $n = 100$, $p = \frac{1}{100}$, $k = 0$, the two sides of Eq. 7.20 are 0.3660 and 0.3678. For the same n and p, and $k \doteq 7$, the two sides are 0.000463 and 0.000511. In each case the two sides agree to approximately three decimal places, but if $k = 7$ the error in approximating

0.000463 by 0.000511 is 0.000048, or ten percent of 0.000463. Here of course $(k - np)^2/n$ is 0.36, which is much greater than 0.01. In the case of $k = 0$, the error in approximating 0.3660 by 0.3678 is 0.0018, or about half a percent of 0.3660; here $(k - np)^2/n = 0.01$.

7.5   Exercises

7.1   Compute the probabilities of: (a) Three heads in five tosses of a balanced coin. (b) At least two fives in six throws of a fair die. (c) More than one 19 in ten trials of Experiment 1.1. State any assumptions made.

7.2   If the experiment of Exercise 1.8 is repeated ten times, what is the probability distribution for the number of complex roots? What is the probability that there are complex roots at least eight times?

7.3   (a) When forming 36-digit binary numbers, a malfunctioning digital computer has been found to form a digit incorrectly about one time in a thousand. Assuming that errors in forming different digits are independent, find the probabilities of having zero, one, or more than one, incorrect digits in a given 36-digit number. (b) This computer forms 10^6 numbers per second. What is the probability of an erroneous number being formed during any one-second period of operation?

7.4   (a) Use the binomial theorem to show that

$$nx(x + y)^{n-1} = x \frac{\partial}{\partial x} [(x + y)^n] = \sum_{j=0}^{n} j \binom{n}{j} x^j y^{n-j}, \qquad (\psi)$$

and interpret the result of evaluating this formula at $x = p$, $y = q = 1 - p$. (b) Take the partial with respect to x of (ψ), multiply by x, and interpret when $x = p$, $y = q = 1 - p$.

7.5   Compute the mean, variance, and moment-generating function of the Poisson distribution.

7.6   A certain digital computer has been found to average about one transistor failure per hour, and experience shows that the Poisson distribution applies. Find the probability of the successful completion of a certain computation that takes three hours to perform. Assume that because of redundancy circuits the computer breaks down only if three or more transistors are inoperative.

7.7   A giant computer has ten times as many transistors as the computer of Exercise 7.6, and of the same type. This computer is 100 times faster than that of Exercise 7.6, but breaks down if two or more transistor failures occur. Find the probability of completion of the same problem as in Exercise 7.6.

7.8   A box contains 90 good and 10 defective screws. What is the probability that 10 screws selected for use are all good?

7.9   A room contains 50 smokers and 50 nonsmokers. What is the probability that if 30 of these people are selected at random none will be a smoker?

7.10   What is the probability that 300 different people, from a city of 5000 smokers and 5000 nonsmokers, are all smokers? (Use the binomial approximation.)

7.11   A box contains 900 good and 100 defective screws. Find approximately the probability that ten screws selected for use are good.

7.12   A game consists of shuffling a bridge deck, removing a card at random, and challenging the opponent to guess the card. Find approximately the probability of more than one correct guess in 50 games. (Use the Poisson approximation.)

7.13   Find approximately the probability of two sevens in 25 trials of Experiment 1.1.

7.14   (a) The number of misprints on a page has been found empirically to have the Poisson distribution. Assuming an average of one misprint per page, what is the probability of more than one misprint on any given page? (b) Estimate the probability of one or more pages, in a 300-page book, having more than five misprints.

7.15   Show that for large t, $e^{-t} \doteq e^{-t} + 1/t$ in the sense that for every $\epsilon > 0$ there exists a T such that

$$\left| e^{-t} - \left(e^{-t} + \frac{1}{t} \right) \right| < \epsilon \qquad (t \geq T).$$

Show, however, that the error in using the right side, as an approximation to the left side, gets larger and larger *in comparison to the left side* as t increases; that is, that the "relative" error becomes infinite.

*7.16   (a) By writing

$$\binom{n}{k} p^k (1 - p)^{n-k} = \frac{(np)^k}{k!} \left(\frac{n}{n} \right) \left(\frac{n-1}{n} \right) \cdots \left(\frac{n-k+1}{n} \right) (1 - p)^{n-k},$$

show that

$$\left| \binom{n}{k} p^k (1 - p)^{n-k} - \frac{(np)^k}{k!} e^{-np} \right| = \left| \frac{(np)^k}{k!} e^{-np} \right| \cdot \left| \binom{n}{n} \left(\frac{n-1}{n} \right) \cdots \right.$$
$$\left. \left(\frac{n-k+1}{n} \right) (1 - p)^{n-k} e^{np} - 1 \right|.$$

Show that the first term on the right is bounded by $1/k!$, and the second by $e - 1$, if $np < 1$. Show that if k is bounded, say $k \leq K$, the second term tends to zero as $n \to \infty$ and $p \to 0$ in such a way that np remains less than 1.

(b) Use these results to show that Eq. 7.20 is true in the sense that for every $\epsilon > 0$ there exists an N such that the magnitude of the difference between the two sides of Eq. 7.20 is less than ϵ for all k, provided $n \geq N$ and $np < 1$. *Hint:* Use the first term to bound the difference for all large values of k, then use the second term for the remaining values of k. (c) Show that the condition "$np < 1$" can be replaced by "np bounded."

*7.17   Show that

$$\frac{\binom{n}{k} p^k (1-p)^{n-k} - \dfrac{(np)^k}{k!} e^{-np}}{\dfrac{(np)^k}{k!} e^{-np}} = \frac{n!}{(n-k)! n^k} e^{np} (1-p)^{n-k} - 1.$$

Assume that k is small compared to n and note that

$$\frac{n!}{(n-k)! n^k} \doteq 1, \quad (1-p)^{n-k} \doteq (1-p)^n = [(1-p)^{1/p}]^{np}.$$

Thus show formally that Eq. 7.20 holds in the sense that the *relative* error between the two sides is small, if np stays bounded while $n \to \infty$ and k is small compared to n. *Hint:*

$$\lim_{h \to 0} (1-h)^{1/h} = e^{-1}.$$

*7.18   Calls arriving at a certain telephone exchange are found to obey approximately the following rules:

1. The number of calls arriving during any time interval is independent of the number arriving during any other nonoverlapping time interval.
2. The likelihood of a call arriving during any small time interval of length Δt is approximately proportional to Δt, say $\lambda \Delta t$.
3. The likelihood of more than one call arriving during any small interval of length Δt tends to zero as $\Delta t \to 0$.

(a) Let $P_n(t)$ be the likelihood that n calls arrive during some time interval of length t. Show that

$$P_n(t + \Delta t) = P_n(t) P_0(\Delta t) + P_{n-1}(t) P_1(\Delta t) + P_{n-2}(t) P_2(\Delta t)$$
$$+ \cdots + P_0(t) P_n(\Delta t). \quad (\psi)$$

Hint: If n calls come in during the interval of length $(t + \Delta t)$, how many came in during the first part of this interval?

(b) Discuss the assumption that

$$P_1(\Delta t) \doteq \lambda \Delta t$$

$$P_i(\Delta t) \doteq 0 \qquad (i > 1)$$

and show that these imply that

$$P_0(\Delta t) \doteq 1 - \lambda \Delta t.$$

(c) Deduce from step (b), and (ψ), that

$$\frac{dP_n}{dt} = -\lambda P_n + \lambda P_{n-1}. \qquad (\psi\psi)$$

(d) Verify that a set of solutions of ($\psi\psi$) is given by

$$P_{-1}(t) \equiv 0$$

$$P_n(t) = \frac{(\lambda t)^n}{n!} e^{-\lambda t} \qquad (n = 0, 1, 2, \ldots).$$

*7.19   Suppose that a very large number (infinitely many) of well-stirred reactors (see Exercise 5.30) are connected in series so that the fluid leaving one reactor instantly enters the next one, and that all of these reactors have the same mean residence time $\tau_1 = 1/\lambda$ (cf. Exercise 6.31). (a) If a molecule enters the ith ($i = 1, 2, 3, \ldots$) of these reactors at any time θ, let $q(j, \Delta t)$ ($j = 0, 1, 2, \ldots$) be the conditional probability that this molecule leaves the ith reactor (except when $j = 0$) during t to $(t + \Delta t)$, for any $t \geq \theta$ and $\Delta t > 0$, and is in the $(i + j)$th reactor at time $t + \Delta t$, given that it is in the ith reactor at time t. Assume as given (or show) that $q(j, \Delta t)$ is negligible for $j \geq 2$ in comparison to $\lambda \Delta t$. For small $\Delta t > 0$, show that

$$q(0, \Delta t) = \frac{[1 - F(t - \theta + \Delta t)]}{[1 - F(t - \theta)]} \doteq 1 - \lambda \Delta t,$$

$$q(1, \Delta t) + q(2, \Delta t) + \cdots = \frac{[F(t - \theta + \Delta t) - F(t - \theta)]}{[1 - F(t - \theta)]} \doteq \lambda \, \Delta t,$$

and therefore that

$$q(1, \Delta t) \doteq \lambda \Delta t.$$

(b) Let N_t be a random variable representing the number of reactors that a molecule passes through during any time interval of length t, so that if a molecule enters the first reactor at time $\theta = 0$ it is in the $(N_t + 1)$th reactor at time $\theta = t$. Let $p(k, t) = P(N_t = k)$, and show that

$$p(k, t + \Delta t) \doteq p(k, t)q(0, \Delta t) + p(k - 1, t)q(1, \Delta t).$$

(c) Conclude that N_t has the Poisson distribution given by

$$p(k, t) = \frac{(\lambda t)^k}{k!} e^{-\lambda t} \qquad (k = 0, 1, 2, \ldots).$$

CHAPTER **8** SPECIAL CONTINUOUS

DISTRIBUTIONS

IN THIS CHAPTER WE STUDY CERTAIN CONTINUOUS DISTRIBUTIONS THAT arise frequently. Actually they are all absolutely continuous, as will be seen.

8.1 The Rectangular Distribution

Let a and b be any two real numbers with $a < b$, and consider the function f defined by

$$f(x) = \begin{cases} \dfrac{1}{b-a} & (a \leq x \leq b) \\ 0 & \text{(otherwise)}. \end{cases} \tag{8.1}$$

Clearly $f(x) \geq 0$ for all x, and

$$\int_{-\infty}^{\infty} f(x)\, dx = 1.$$

Thus f may be viewed as the density function of a continuous random variable. A random variable with density function given by Eq. 8.1 is said to have the *rectangular distribution* on $[a, b]$ or to be *uniformly distributed* on $[a, b]$.

The computation of the mean, variance, and moment-generating function of this distribution is an easy exercise. The importance of the rectangular distribution arises from its simplicity, its obvious connection with the intuitive concept of equal likelihood, and its appearance in the probability transformation discussed at the end of Section 5.7.

8.2   The Normal Distribution

The normal or Gaussian distribution is one of the three principal distributions. It arises frequently in physical problems, and in fact there is a "mathematical reason" for this, as we shall see in Chapter 12. Also, the normal distribution has been taken as the basic distribution in statistics, a branch of mathematics based on probability.

If μ and σ are real numbers, with $\sigma > 0$, the density function of the normal distribution is

$$f(x) = \frac{1}{\sqrt{2\pi}\sigma} \exp\left[-\frac{1}{2}\left(\frac{x-\mu}{\sigma}\right)^2\right] \quad (-\infty < x < \infty). \quad (8.2)$$

(For typographical reasons, the common notation exp $[t]$ for e^t will sometimes be used.) Since the exponential function is nonnegative, f is clearly nonnegative. One way to check that

$$\int_{-\infty}^{\infty} f(x)\, dx$$

is unity is the following.

In the integral

$$\int_{-\infty}^{\infty} \frac{1}{\sqrt{2\pi}\sigma} \exp\left[-\frac{1}{2}\left(\frac{x-\mu}{\sigma}\right)^2\right] dx,$$

make the change of variable $t = (x - \mu)/\sigma$ to get the new form

$$\int_{-\infty}^{\infty} \frac{1}{\sqrt{2\pi}} \exp\left[-t^2/2\right] dt,$$

which by the evenness of the integrand is

$$\frac{2}{\sqrt{2\pi}} \int_{0}^{\infty} \exp\left[-t^2/2\right] dt.$$

This shows that it is enough to verify that

$$\int_{0}^{\infty} \exp\left[-t^2/2\right] dt = \sqrt{\frac{\pi}{2}}.$$

To this end we write

$$\left(\int_0^\infty \exp\left[-t^2/2\right] dt\right)^2 = \left(\int_0^\infty \exp\left[-x^2/2\right] dx\right)\left(\int_0^\infty \exp\left[-y^2/2\right] dy\right)$$

$$= \int_0^\infty \exp\left[-x^2/2\right] \left(\int_0^\infty \exp\left[-y^2/2\right] dy\right) dx$$

$$= \int_0^\infty \int_0^\infty \exp\left[-(x^2+y^2)/2\right] dy\, dx.$$

This last integral, however, may be viewed as the integral over the first quadrant of the function $\exp\left[-(x^2+y^2)/2\right]$. Changing to polar coordinates gives

$$\int_0^\infty \int_0^\infty \exp\left[-(x^2+y^2)/2\right] dy\, dx = \int_0^{\pi/2}\int_0^\infty \exp\left[-r^2/2\right] r\, dr\, d\theta$$

$$= \frac{\pi}{2}\left(-\exp\left[-r^2/2\right]\right)\Big|_0^\infty$$

$$= \frac{\pi}{2}.$$

Taking square roots completes the proof.

A random variable X with density function given by Eq. 8.2 is said to have the *normal distribution with mean μ and standard deviation σ, or with parameters (μ, σ)*. Our next task, of course, is to verify that the parameters μ and σ in Eq. 8.2 are indeed the mean and standard deviation of the distribution. To this end we compute the moment generating function M. Now

$$M(\theta) = E(e^{\theta X}) = \frac{1}{\sqrt{2\pi}\sigma}\int_{-\infty}^\infty \exp\left[\theta t\right] \exp\left[-\frac{1}{2}\left(\frac{t-\mu}{\sigma}\right)^2\right] dt$$

$$= \frac{1}{\sqrt{2\pi}\sigma}\int_{-\infty}^\infty \exp\left[\theta t - \frac{1}{2}\left(\frac{t-\mu}{\sigma}\right)^2\right] dt.$$

In this last integral we complete the square and write

$$M(\theta) = \frac{1}{\sqrt{2\pi}\sigma}\int_{-\infty}^\infty \exp\left[-\frac{1}{2}\left\{\frac{t}{\sigma} - \sigma\left(\theta + \frac{\mu}{\sigma^2}\right)\right\}^2 + \frac{1}{2}\sigma^2\left(\theta + \frac{\mu}{\sigma^2}\right)^2 - \frac{1}{2}\frac{\mu^2}{\sigma^2}\right] dt$$

$$= \exp\left[\mu\theta + \frac{1}{2}\sigma^2\theta^2\right] \cdot \frac{1}{\sqrt{2\pi}\sigma}\int_{-\infty}^\infty \exp\left[-\frac{1}{2}\left\{\frac{t}{\sigma} - \sigma\left(\theta + \frac{\mu}{\sigma^2}\right)\right\}^2\right] dt.$$

Changing the variable of integration here to

$$s = \frac{t}{\sigma} - \sigma\left(\theta + \frac{\mu}{\sigma^2}\right)$$

gives

$$M(\theta) = \exp\left[\mu\theta + \frac{1}{2}\sigma^2\theta^2\right] \cdot \frac{1}{\sqrt{2\pi}} \int_{-\infty}^{\infty} e^{-s^2/2}\, ds.$$

We have seen, however, that the value of the remaining integral is unity. Thus the moment generating function is given by

$$M(\theta) = \exp\left[\mu\theta + \tfrac{1}{2}\sigma^2\theta^2\right]. \tag{8.3}$$

It is an easy exercise to obtain the first two moments from this formula and check that μ is the mean of the distribution and σ is the standard deviation.

If X is a random variable with density function given by Eq. 8.2, its distribution function F is given by

$$F(x) = \int_{-\infty}^{x} \frac{1}{\sqrt{2\pi}\sigma} \exp\left[-\frac{1}{2}\left(\frac{t-\mu}{\sigma}\right)^2\right] dt, \tag{8.4}$$

and the probability that X takes a value in the interval $[a, b]$, a and b real numbers with $a \le b$, is

$$P(a \le X \le b) = \frac{1}{\sqrt{2\pi}\sigma} \int_{a}^{b} \exp\left[-\frac{1}{2}\left(\frac{t-\mu}{\sigma}\right)^2\right] dt. \tag{8.5}$$

Now, the integrals in Eqs. 8.4 and 8.5 cannot be evaluated in closed form. Tables are available, however, of the functions

$$\Phi_1(t) = \frac{1}{\sqrt{2\pi}} \int_{-\infty}^{t} e^{-s^2/2}\, ds \qquad (-\infty < t < \infty)$$

or

$$\Phi_2(t) = \frac{1}{\sqrt{2\pi}} \int_{0}^{t} e^{-s^2/2}\, ds \qquad (0 \le t < \infty).$$

Obviously,

$$\Phi_1(x) = \begin{cases} \dfrac{1}{2} + \Phi_2(x) & (x \ge 0) \\[2mm] \dfrac{1}{2} - \Phi_2(-x) & (x < 0). \end{cases}$$

To use whichever of these tables is available, in evaluating an integral such as Eq. 8.5, one makes the change of variables $s = (t - \mu)/\sigma$ to obtain

$$P(a \le X \le b) = \frac{1}{\sqrt{2\pi}} \int_{\frac{a-\mu}{\sigma}}^{\frac{b-\mu}{\sigma}} e^{-s^2/2} \, ds$$

$$= \Phi_1\left(\frac{b - \mu}{\sigma}\right) - \Phi_1\left(\frac{a - \mu}{\sigma}\right). \tag{8.6}$$

Example 8.1. A random variable X is normally distributed with mean 1 and standard deviation 2. What is the probability that $-5 \le X \le 3$? Here $a = -5$, $b = 3$, $\mu = 1$, $\sigma = 2$; so Eq. 8.6 becomes

$$P(-5 \le X \le 3) = \Phi_1\left(\frac{3 - 1}{2}\right) - \Phi_1\left(\frac{-5 - 1}{2}\right)$$

$$= \Phi_1(1) - \Phi_1(-3)$$

$$= \Phi_2(1) + \Phi_2(3).$$

From tables,

$$\Phi_2(1) = 0.3413,$$
$$\Phi_2(3) = 0.4987.$$

Thus

$$P(-5 \le X \le 3) = 0.8400.$$

8.3   The Gamma Distribution

A random variable is said to have the *gamma distribution with parameters α and β* $(\alpha > -1, \beta > 0)$ if its density function is

$$f(x) = \begin{cases} 0 & (x \le 0) \\ \dfrac{1}{\beta^{\alpha+1}\Gamma(\alpha + 1)} \, x^\alpha e^{-x/\beta} & (x > 0). \end{cases} \tag{8.7}$$

Here Γ denotes the gamma function, defined for positive arguments x by

$$\Gamma(x) = \int_0^\infty t^{x-1} e^{-t} \, dt. \tag{8.8}$$

By integrating by parts in Eq. 8.8 one can verify that

$$\Gamma(x + 1) = x\Gamma(x). \tag{8.9}$$

Furthermore, if $x = 1$ the integral in Eq. 8.8 is easily evaluated to give

$\Gamma(1) = 1$. This fact, and repeated use of Eq. 8.9, shows that for non-negative integers n

$$\Gamma(n + 1) = n!.$$

These are the only properties of the gamma function we shall need.

The integral in Eq. 8.8 can be evaluated analytically only for certain values of x. However, the function

$$\int_0^y t^{x-1} e^{-t} \, dt,$$

is available in tables and is called the *incomplete gamma function*. To see that these tables are sufficient for all dealings with the gamma distribution, notice that if X is a random variable with probability density function given by Eq. 8.7, and if $0 \le a < b$, then

$$P(a \le X \le b) = \int_a^b \frac{1}{\beta^{\alpha+1} \Gamma(\alpha + 1)} x^\alpha e^{-x/\beta} \, dx.$$

Now make the change of variable $t = x/\beta$ in this integral to get

$$P(a \le X \le b) = \int_{a/\beta}^{b/\beta} \frac{1}{\Gamma(\alpha + 1)} t^\alpha e^{-t} \, dt$$

$$= \frac{\int_0^{b/\beta} t^\alpha e^{-t} \, dt - \int_0^{a/\beta} t^\alpha e^{-t} \, dt}{\int_0^\infty t^\alpha e^{-t} \, dt},$$

where all three integrals in the last expression are incomplete gamma functions.

The gamma distribution is very useful because it is a relatively simple one, and because by varying its two parameters one can obtain a wide variety of distribution functions and therefore "fit" many experimentally determined curves. (This comment applies equally well to the normal distribution and to the beta distribution to be introduced in the next section.) In addition, the gamma distribution arises in physical problems.

Example 8.2. To see an example of this, suppose that the number of calls arriving at a telephone exchange during a time interval of length t is a random variable with the Poisson distribution*

$$g(k) = \frac{(\lambda t)^k}{k!} e^{-\lambda t} \qquad (k = 0, 1, 2, \ldots). \tag{8.10}$$

* See Exercise 7.17.

Suppose too that we wish to determine the *waiting time to the nth call*, that is the distribution of the random variable whose value is the length of time it takes for n calls to arrive. Denoting this random variable by X we have

$$P(X < 0) = 0 \tag{8.11}$$

$$P(0 \le X \le t) = \sum_{k=n}^{\infty} \frac{(\lambda t)^k}{k!} e^{-\lambda t}. \tag{8.12}$$

The first of these equations is obvious. The second simply says that the probability of waiting less than t minutes for n calls is the probability of n or more calls in t minutes.

Equations 8.11 and 8.12 give the distribution function F for X:

$$F(x) = \begin{cases} 0 & (x < 0) \\ \displaystyle\sum_{k=n}^{\infty} \frac{(\lambda x)^k}{k!} e^{-\lambda x} & (x \ge 0). \end{cases}$$

Differentiating and simplifying gives

$$F'(x) = f(x) = \begin{cases} 0 & (x < 0) \\ \dfrac{\lambda^n x^{n-1} e^{-\lambda x}}{\Gamma(n)} & (x \ge 0). \end{cases}$$

Thus we see that the waiting time to the nth call has the gamma distribution with parameters $(n - 1)$ and $1/\lambda$.

When $\alpha = 0$ the gamma distribution is frequently called the exponential distribution, since in that case the density function is simply $1/\beta \ e^{-x/\beta}$.

The moment generating function of the gamma distribution is

$$M(\theta) = \int_0^{\infty} \frac{1}{\beta^{\alpha+1}\Gamma(\alpha + 1)} x^\alpha \exp\left[-(x/\beta) + \theta x\right] dx.$$

Putting $t = (1/\beta - \theta)x$ gives, for $\theta < 1/\beta$,

$$\begin{aligned}
M(\theta) &= \int_0^{\infty} \frac{1}{\beta^{\alpha+1}\Gamma(\alpha + 1)} \frac{t^\alpha}{(1/\beta - \theta)^{\alpha+1}} e^{-t} \, dt \\
&= \left(\frac{1}{1 - \beta\theta}\right)^{\alpha+1} \frac{1}{\Gamma(\alpha + 1)} \int_0^{\infty} t^\alpha e^{-t} \, dt \\
&= \left(\frac{1}{1 - \beta\theta}\right)^{\alpha+1} \qquad\qquad (\theta < 1/\beta). \tag{8.13}
\end{aligned}$$

8.4 The Beta Distribution

If p and q are positive real numbers the beta function $\beta(p, q)$ is defined by

$$\beta(p, q) = \int_0^1 x^{p-1}(1 - x)^{q-1} \, dx.$$

A random variable is said to have the *beta distribution with parameters α and λ* $(\alpha, \lambda > -1)$ if its density function is

$$f(x) = \begin{cases} 0 & (x \leq 0 \text{ or } x \geq 1) \\ \dfrac{1}{\beta(\alpha + 1, \lambda + 1)} \, x^\alpha(1 - x)^\lambda & (0 < x < 1). \end{cases} \qquad (8.14)$$

The moments of this distribution are computed in the exercises. Notice that the beta distribution has a finite range of possible values, and that by appropriate choices of the parameters one can obtain a good assortment of distributions with this property. We defer an example to the exercises.

8.5 Other Distributions

Three continuous distributions are so important in statistics that we wish to mention them before concluding this chapter. In discussing these distributions we shall allude to the *independence of random variables*. This concept will be introduced in Chapter 9; for the moment the reader may take such allusions as intuitive statements. Later he will see that our statements can be proved by using the theory of derived distributions discussed in Sections 5.7, 9.4, and 10.6.

The χ^2 (read "chi square") *distribution with $2n$ degrees of freedom* has the density function

$$f(x) = \frac{x^{n-1}}{2^n \Gamma(n)} \, e^{-x/2} \qquad (0 \leq x < \infty);$$

this is what we have called the gamma distribution with parameters $(n - 1, 2)$. If $X_1, X_2, \ldots, X_{2n}$ are independent random variables, each having the normal distribution with mean zero and variance one, the random variable $X_1^2 + X_2^2 + \cdots + X_{2n}^2$ has the χ^2 distribution with $2n$ degrees of freedom.

If $X, X_1, X_2, \ldots, X_n$ are independent random variables, each with the unit normal distribution (i.e., with $\mu = 0$ and $\sigma = 1$), then the random variable

$$\frac{X}{\sqrt{\frac{1}{n}(X_1^2 + X_2^2 + \cdots + X_n^2)}}$$

has the *t distribution with n degrees of freedom*, with density function

$$f(x) = \frac{\Gamma\left(\frac{n+1}{2}\right)}{\Gamma\left(\frac{n}{2}\right)\sqrt{n\pi}}\left(1 + \frac{x^2}{n}\right)^{-(n+1)/2} \qquad (-\infty < x < \infty).$$

If $X_1, X_2, \ldots, X_m$ and $Y_1, Y_2, \ldots, Y_n$ are independent random variables, each with the unit normal distribution, then the random variable

$$\frac{n}{m}\frac{X_1^2 + X_2^2 + \cdots + X_m^2}{Y_1^2 + Y_2^2 + \cdots + Y_n^2}$$

has the *F distribution with (m, n) degrees of freedom*. The density function of this distribution is

$$f(x) = \frac{\Gamma\left(\frac{m+n}{2}\right)}{\Gamma\left(\frac{m}{2}\right)\Gamma\left(\frac{n}{2}\right)}\left(\frac{m}{n}\right)^{m/2} x^{(m/2)-1}\left(1 + \frac{m}{n}x\right)^{-(m+n)/2} \qquad (0 \le x < \infty).$$

An easy computation shows that if X has the F distribution with (m, n) degrees of freedom then the random variable

$$\frac{\left(\frac{m}{n}\right)X}{1 + \left(\frac{m}{n}\right)X}$$

has the beta distribution with parameters

$$\left(\frac{m}{2} - 1, \frac{n}{2} - 1\right).$$

8.6   Exercises

8.1   Streetcars depart on a certain route once every ten minutes. What is the average waiting time of a prospective passenger who arrives at his station at a random time?

8.2   Compute the mean, variance, and moment-generating function of the uniform distribution.

8.3   The errors in a certain length-measuring device are found to be normally distributed, with mean zero and standard deviation of one foot. What is the probability of a measurement error greater than three feet? Two feet? One foot?

8.4   (a) A random variable X is normally distributed with mean zero and standard deviation 1. Find a number y such that $P(|X| \geq y) = \frac{1}{2}$. (b) Find a function $C(\mu, \sigma)$ such that for a normally distributed random variable X with mean μ and standard deviation σ, $P(|X - \mu| \geq C) = \frac{1}{2}$.

8.5   The error in a certain angle-measuring device has been found to be normally distributed with mean one minute and σ of three minutes. What is the probability that a measurement is in error by more than three minutes? Repeat if one minute is subtracted from the measured value.

8.6   The lifetimes of two competing brands of vacuum tubes can be viewed as normally distributed random variables. Brand A has a mean life of 27 hours and a standard deviation of 5 hours, whereas brand B has $\mu = 30$, $\sigma = 2$. (a) Which brand should be chosen for use in an experimental aircraft with a flight time of 30 hours? (b) Same question for 34 hours. (c) What is the probability of a negative lifetime for each brand? (Notice that this can be interpreted as the probability that a tube is no good on delivery.)

*8.7   After a certain crushing process the nominal diameter D of rock particles is given approximately by $D = e^X$, where X has the normal distribution with parameters (μ_x, σ_x). (a) Derive the density function of D. (This is the so-called *lognormal* distribution.) (b) Express μ_x and σ_x in terms of the mean and standard deviation of D.

8.8   The length of telephone conversations has been found to have the exponential distribution with mean three minutes. What is the probability of a call lasting more than ten minutes?

8.9   A certain computer has been found to average one transistor failure per hour; failure of three or more transistors causes the computer to break down. Assuming that transistor failures have the Poisson distribution, what is the average trouble-free operating time?

8.10   (a) Show that if $\alpha > 0$ the gamma distribution has a mode equal to $\alpha\beta$. (b) Find the mean and variance of the gamma distribution.

8.11   The daily peak load in thousands of kva experienced at a certain electric power station, with a generating capacity of 25,000 kva, has been found to have the gamma distribution with parameters $\alpha = 1.5$, $\beta = 4.5$. What is the probability of an overload? *Hint:*

$$\int_0^{5.56} y^{1.5} e^{-v} \, dy \doteq 0.95 \, \Gamma(2.5).$$

8.12   (a) Sketch the density function of the beta distribution in the special cases $\alpha = \lambda = 0$; $\alpha = 0$, $\lambda = 1$; $\alpha = 1$, $\lambda = 0$. (b) Under what conditions does the beta distribution have a mode, and what is it? *Hint:* Beware of minima!

*8.13   (a) By writing

$$\Gamma(p) = \int_0^\infty x^{p-1} e^{-x} \, dx \text{ and } \Gamma(q) = \int_0^\infty y^{q-1} e^{-y} \, dy$$

and making the changes of variable $x = u^2$, $y = v^2$ before multiplying, show that

$$\Gamma(p)\Gamma(q) = 4 \int_0^\infty \int_0^\infty u^{2p-1} v^{2q-1} \exp\left[-(u^2 + v^2)\right] du \, dv.$$

(b) Introduce polar coordinates by setting $u = r \cos \theta$, $v = r \sin \theta$, in this result to get

$$\Gamma(p)\Gamma(q) = 4 \int_0^{\pi/2} \int_0^\infty r^{2p+2q-1} (\cos \theta)^{2p-1} (\sin \theta)^{2q-1} \exp\left[-r^2\right] dr \, d\theta$$

$$= \left[4 \int_0^{\pi/2} (\cos \theta)^{2p-1} (\sin \theta)^{2q-1} \, d\theta \right] \left[\int_0^\infty r^{2p+2q-1} \exp\left[-r^2\right] dr \right].$$

(c) In the first bracketed term, introduce the new variable of integration $x = \cos^2 \theta$, and in the second bracket put $\rho = r^2$, and thus show that

$$\frac{\Gamma(p)\Gamma(q)}{\Gamma(p+q)} = \beta(p, q).$$

8.14   (a) Show that the nth moment of the beta distribution is

$$\beta(n + \alpha + 1, \lambda + 1)/\beta(\alpha + 1, \lambda + 1).$$

(b) Use the result of Exercise 8.13 to rewrite the nth moment as

$$\mu'_n = \frac{(\alpha + 1)(\alpha + 2) \cdots (\alpha + n)}{(\alpha + \lambda + 2)(\alpha + \lambda + 3) \cdots (\alpha + \lambda + n + 1)}.$$

8.15   Experience has shown that a certain machining operation never takes more than ten minutes, and furthermore that the fraction of this time required has the beta distribution, with parameters varying from operator to operator. One employee has been found to average two minutes for this job, and the square root of his average squared time is four minutes. What are his parameters?

8.16 A second employee, on the job in Exercise 8.15, averages 6 minutes, but requires $6\frac{2}{3}$ minutes more frequently than any other time. What are his parameters?

8.17 (a) Show by differentiating each side that

$$\frac{1}{\sqrt{2\pi}} \exp\left[-\tfrac{1}{2}x^2\right] \frac{1}{x} = \frac{1}{\sqrt{2\pi}} \int_x^\infty \exp\left[-\tfrac{1}{2}t^2\right] \left[1 + \frac{1}{t^2}\right] dt + C$$

and

$$\frac{1}{\sqrt{2\pi}} \exp\left[-\tfrac{1}{2}x^2\right] \left[\frac{1}{x} - \frac{1}{x^3}\right] = \frac{1}{\sqrt{2\pi}} \int_x^\infty \exp\left[-\tfrac{1}{2}t^2\right] \left[1 - \frac{3}{t^4}\right] dt + D,$$

for $x > 0$. (b) By letting $x \to +\infty$, show that $C = D = 0$. (c) Show that

$$\int_x^\infty \exp\left[-\tfrac{1}{2}t^2\right] \left[1 - \frac{3}{t^4}\right] dt < \int_x^\infty \exp\left[-\tfrac{1}{2}t^2\right] dt < \int_x^\infty \exp\left[-\tfrac{1}{2}t^2\right] \left[1 + \frac{1}{t^2}\right] dt$$

and thus, by (a) and (b), that

$$\frac{1}{\sqrt{2\pi}} \exp\left[-\tfrac{1}{2}x^2\right] \left[\frac{1}{x} - \frac{1}{x^3}\right] < 1 - \Phi_1(x) < \frac{1}{\sqrt{2\pi}} \exp\left[-\tfrac{1}{2}x^2\right] \frac{1}{x}.$$

Thus show that for large values of x

$$1 - \Phi_1(x) \doteq \frac{1}{\sqrt{2\pi}} \exp\left[-\tfrac{1}{2}x^2\right] \frac{1}{x}$$

in the sense that the absolute value of the difference between the two sides is small, and is small compared to the left side.

8.18 The density function f of Exercise 6.36 can often be approximated by a normal or a general gamma density function with mean τ and standard deviation σ_T. For each of these, express (approximately) the quantity c'_e defined in Exercise 6.36(a) in terms of τ, σ_T, c_0, and k.

8.19 Refer to Exercise 7.19, and let S_n be the waiting time for a molecule to leave the nth reactor if it entered the first reactor at time zero; i.e., the residence time within the first n reactors. Let $\lambda = n/\tau$ (so that $\tau = n\tau_1$), and show that S_n has the gamma density function of Exercise 5.28(b).

CHAPTER 9 JOINT DISTRIBUTIONS

BOTH IN PRACTICE AND IN THEORY, IT IS FREQUENTLY NECESSARY TO consider the simultaneous behavior of several random variables associated with the same probability space. As will be seen in Chapters 10, 11, and 12, a very important general situation of this sort is that in which one is interested in a linear combination of random variables. In this chapter, we will therefore investigate briefly the simultaneous behavior of several random variables defined on the same sample space —i.e., joint probability distributions. Of course, this constitutes primarily extending the concepts and notation previously introduced in Chapters 5 and 6. Naturally, joint distributions can be described in terms of functions of several real variables, which are seen in calculus to be extensions of functions of a single variable.

9.1 The Distribution of Two Random Variables

In this section, we assume as given a probability space $(\Omega, \mathcal{S}, P)$, two random variables X and Y defined on the sample space Ω, and the distribution functions F_X and F_Y of X and Y, as described in Chapter 5.

The joint distribution of two random variables is a set function Q, which assigns in a certain way a probability to practically every subset of points in the usual (x, y) plane (two-dimensional Euclidean space). Although Q will not be used explicitly hereafter in this book, it is worthwhile to consider briefly its definition.

First, note that, for each ordered pair (x, y) of real numbers x and y, the set of all points ω in the sample space Ω for which the two conditions $X(\omega) \leq x$ and $Y(\omega) \leq y$ are satisfied forms an event (a member of $\mathcal{S}$), which will be denoted by $\{X \leq x, Y \leq y\}$; this event is the intersection of the two events $\{X \leq x\}$ and $\{Y \leq y\}$. In general, for practically every subset A of ordered pairs (x, y), the set of all points ω for which the ordered pair $[X(\omega), Y(\omega)]$ is in A is an event, which can be denoted by $\{\omega : [X(\omega), Y(\omega)] \text{ in } A\}$.

The *joint distribution* of X and Y is defined to be the set function Q defined by

$$Q(A) = P(\{\omega : [X(\omega), Y(\omega)] \text{ in } A\}) \qquad (9.1)$$

for practically every subset A of ordered pairs of real numbers. It can be shown that this set function is completely determined when its value is specified for every set of pairs (α, β) of real numbers of the form $\{(\alpha, \beta) : \alpha \leq x, \beta \leq y\}$; that is, when

$$Q(\{(\alpha, \beta) : \alpha \leq x, \beta \leq y\}) = P(\{\omega : X(\omega) \leq x, Y(\omega) \leq y\}) \qquad (9.2)$$

is assigned a numerical value for every (x, y). Thus, when a probability space $(\Omega, \mathcal{S}, P)$ and random variables X and Y are given, Q is completely determined by Eq. 9.2. On the other hand, when the left side of Eq. 9.2 is assigned appropriate values for all (x, y), a probability space $(\Omega, \mathcal{S}, P)$ and random variables X and Y on Ω can be constructed in many ways so that Eq. 9.2 is satisfied. As before, we will use the simpler but more ambiguous notation $P(X \leq x, Y \leq y)$ for both of the quantities in Eq. 9.2.

Given X and Y, the quantities in Eq. 9.2 actually depend only on the numerical values of x and y. Therefore, we can introduce the function F defined for all x and y by

$$F(x, y) = P(X \leq x, Y \leq y) \qquad (-\infty < x, y < \infty). \qquad (9.3)$$

This function uniquely determines the joint distribution of X and Y and is called their *joint distribution function*.

Since the events $\{X \leq x, Y \leq \infty\}$ and $\{X \leq x\}$ are identical, it is plausible (and can be proved) that

$$F(x, \infty) = P(X \leq x, Y \leq \infty) = P(X \leq x) = F_X(x)$$

and hence that

$$F_X(x) = F(x, \infty), \qquad F_Y(y) = F(\infty, y),$$
$$F(x, -\infty) = F(-\infty, y) = 0, \qquad F(\infty, \infty) = 1. \qquad (9.4)$$

Furthermore, F is monotonic nondecreasing and continuous on the right in each variable when the other one is fixed. If F is given, the probabilities of various events can be computed by using relations such as the following generalization of Eq. 5.5:

$$P(a_1 < X \le a_2, b_1 < Y \le b_2) = F(a_2, b_2) - F(a_2, b_1)$$
$$- F(a_1, b_2) + F(a_1, b_1), \quad (9.5)$$

which the reader is invited to prove.

The *joint probability function* g of X and Y is defined by

$$g(x, y) = P(X = x, Y = y) \quad (-\infty < x, y < \infty). \quad (9.6)$$

From Eq. 9.5, it is plausible that

$$g(x, y) = F(x, y) - \lim_{b \to y-} F(x, b) - \lim_{a \to x-} F(a, y) + \lim_{\substack{a \to x- \\ b \to y-}} F(a, b). \quad (9.7)$$

DISCRETE DISTRIBUTIONS

We define a *discrete joint distribution* to be a joint distribution whose joint probability function g has the following property: there are a countable (finite or countably infinite) number of values of x and a countable number of values of y, to be denoted by $\{x_i\}$ and $\{y_j\}$ for $i, j = 1, 2, 3, \ldots$, for which the (finite or infinite) double series

$$\sum_i \sum_j g(x_i, y_j)$$

has the sum 1, where the summation extends over all members of the sequences $\{x_i\}$ and $\{y_j\}$.

The numbers x_i and y_j can be called the possible values of X and Y. The numbers $g(x_i, y_j)$ are given by Eq. 9.6 and must satisfy the relations

$$g(x_i, y_j) \ge 0, \qquad \sum_i \sum_j g(x_i, y_j) = 1. \quad (9.8)$$

From Eqs. 9.3 and 9.6,

$$F(x, y) = \sum_{x_i \le x} \sum_{y_j \le y} g(x_i, y_j). \quad (9.9)$$

Since $\{X = x_i\}$ and $\{X = x_i, Y \le \infty\}$ are identical events, it is plausible that

$$g_X(x_i) = P(X = x_i) = \sum_j g(x_i, y_j) \quad (9.10)$$

for every fixed i and similarly that

$$g_Y(y_j) = P(Y = y_j) = \sum_i g(x_i, y_j) \qquad (9.11)$$

for every fixed j, where g_X and g_Y are the individual probability functions of X and Y. Of course, the sums in the above relations extend over all possible values of i or j.

Example 9.1. As in Example 5.1, let an ideal coin be tossed three times. Let X be the number of heads that occur on the first toss; then the possible values of X are 0 and 1, and $g_X(0) = g_X(1) = \frac{1}{2}$. Let Y be the total number of heads resulting from all three tosses; then the possible values of Y are 0, 1, 2, and 3, $g_Y(0) = g_Y(3) = \frac{1}{8}$, and

$$g_Y(1) = g_Y(2) = \frac{3}{8}.$$

On examining the eight equally likely ordered 3-tuples composing the usual sample space for this experiment, one finds that the ordered pair (X, Y) assumes each of the four values $(0, 0)$, $(0, 2)$, $(1, 1)$, $(1, 3)$ exactly once and each of the two values $(0, 1)$ and $(1, 2)$ exactly twice. Thus, $g(0, 0) = g(0, 2) = g(1, 1) = g(1, 3) = \frac{1}{8}$, and $g(0, 1) = g(1, 2) = \frac{1}{4}$. Table 9.1 presents the complete joint probability function of X and Y. The margins of the table contain the sums of the entries $g(x_i, y_j)$ by rows and by columns. The row totals yield $g_X(x_i)$ and illustrate Eq. 9.10, while the column totals yield $g_Y(y_j)$ and illustrate Eq. 9.11.

Table 9.1

$$g(x_i, y_j)$$

X \ Y	0	1	2	3	$g_X(x_i)$
0	$\frac{1}{8}$	$\frac{1}{4}$	$\frac{1}{8}$	0	$\frac{1}{2}$
1	0	$\frac{1}{8}$	$\frac{1}{4}$	$\frac{1}{8}$	$\frac{1}{2}$
$g_Y(y_j)$	$\frac{1}{8}$	$\frac{3}{8}$	$\frac{3}{8}$	$\frac{1}{8}$	1

In line with the fact that probability functions of single random variables are displayed in the margins of Table 9.1, distributions of single random variables are called *marginal distributions* when joint distributions are also under consideration. Thus, the functions F_X and F_Y of Eq. 9.4 are the *marginal distribution functions* of X and Y, and the functions g_X and g_Y of Eqs. 9.10 and 9.11 are *marginal probability functions*.

CONTINUOUS DISTRIBUTIONS

A joint distribution is called a *continuous joint distribution* if its distribution function is continuous at every pair of real values of its arguments. A joint distribution is called an *absolutely continuous joint distribution* if it is a continuous distribution and if also its distribution function F has the property that there is some nonnegative integrable function f, called the *joint density function*, such that

$$F(x, y) = \int_{-\infty}^{x} dx' \int_{-\infty}^{y} f(x', y') \, dy' \qquad (9.12)$$

for all x and y.

Differentiation of Eq. 9.12 shows that

$$f(x, y) = \frac{\partial^2}{\partial x \, \partial y} F(x, y). \qquad (9.13)$$

Since $F(\infty, \infty) = 1$, Eq. 9.12 also implies that

$$f(x, y) \geq 0, \qquad \int_{-\infty}^{\infty} \int_{-\infty}^{\infty} f(x, y) \, dx \, dy = 1. \qquad (9.14)$$

From Eqs. 9.4 and 9.12, we have

$$F_X(x) = F(x, \infty) = \int_{-\infty}^{x} dx' \int_{-\infty}^{\infty} f(x', y) \, dy; \qquad (9.15)$$

differentiation of this result implies that

$$f_X(x) = \int_{-\infty}^{\infty} f(x, y) \, dy. \qquad (9.16)$$

Similarly,

$$f_Y(y) = \int_{-\infty}^{\infty} f(x, y) \, dx. \qquad (9.17)$$

Note that Eqs. 9.16 and 9.17 are the present counterparts of Eqs. 9.10 and 9.11 and that they express the *marginal density functions* in terms of the joint density function. From Eqs. 9.15 and 9.16,

$$F_X(x) = \int_{-\infty}^{x} f_X(x')\, dx'$$

$$F_Y(y) = \int_{-\infty}^{y} f_Y(y')\, dy', \tag{9.18}$$

which shows that the marginal distributions are absolutely continuous when the joint distribution is absolutely continuous. Equations 9.5 and 9.12 show that

$$P(a_1 < X \le a_2, b_1 < Y \le b_2) = \int_{a_1}^{a_2} dx \int_{b_1}^{b_2} f(x, y)\, dy. \tag{9.19}$$

From Eq. 9.7, note finally that the probability function of every continuous joint distribution is identically zero and is therefore useless.

One often works exclusively with joint probability functions or joint density functions without ever knowing explicitly the corresponding joint distribution functions. For this purpose, note that any function g defined on a countable set of ordered pairs (x_i, y_j) of real numbers so that Eq. 9.8 is satisfied can serve as a joint probability function. Similarly, any integrable function f defined for all real values of x and y so that Eq. 9.14 is satisfied can serve as a joint density function.

Example 9.2.   Given the joint density function defined by

$$f(x, y) = \begin{cases} 8xy & (0 < x < 1, 0 < y < x) \\ 0 & \text{(otherwise)} \end{cases}$$

find the marginal density functions. Note that the two inequalities $0 < x < 1$ and $0 < y < x$ describe the interior of a triangle whose vertices are at the points $(0, 0)$, $(1, 0)$, and $(1, 1)$. From Eqs. 9.16 and 9.17, we have

$$f_X(x) = \begin{cases} \int_{0}^{x} 8xy\, dy = 4x^3 & (0 < x < 1) \\ 0 & \text{(otherwise)} \end{cases}$$

and

$$f_Y(y) = \begin{cases} \int_{y}^{1} 8xy\, dx = 4y(1 - y^2) & (0 < y < 1) \\ 0 & \text{(otherwise)} \end{cases}$$

For future use, note that $f(x, y) \ne f_X(x) f_Y(y)$.

Example 9.3.   Consider the joint distribution function defined by

$$F(x, y) = \begin{cases} 0 & (-\infty < x < 0 \text{ or } -\infty < y < 0) \\ (1 - e^{-\alpha x})y^2 & (0 \leq x < \infty, 0 \leq y \leq 1) \\ 1 - e^{-\alpha x} & (0 \leq x < \infty, 1 < y < \infty) \end{cases}$$

where α is a positive constant. From Eq. 9.4, note that

$$F_X(x) = \begin{cases} 0 & (-\infty < x < 0) \\ 1 - e^{-\alpha x} & (0 \leq x < \infty) \end{cases}$$

$$F_Y(y) = \begin{cases} 0 & (-\infty < y < 0) \\ y^2 & (0 \leq y \leq 1) \\ 1 & (1 < y < \infty) \end{cases}$$

By differentiating these relations we find that

$$f(x, y) = \begin{cases} 2\alpha y e^{-\alpha x} & (0 \leq x < \infty, 0 \leq y \leq 1) \\ 0 & (\text{otherwise}) \end{cases}$$

$$f_X(x) = \begin{cases} \alpha e^{-\alpha x} & (0 \leq x < \infty) \\ 0 & (-\infty < x < 0) \end{cases}$$

$$f_Y(y) = \begin{cases} 2y & (0 \leq y \leq 1) \\ 0 & (\text{otherwise}) \end{cases}$$

For future use, the reader is invited to verify that $F(x, y) = F_X(x)F_Y(y)$ and $f(x, y) = f_X(x)f_Y(y)$ for all values of x and y.

9.2   The Distribution of Several Random Variables

The concepts and notation introduced in the preceding section can be extended at once to the general case in which n random variables $X_1, X_2, \ldots, X_n$ are defined on the same sample space. Thus, the joint distribution of $X_1, X_2, \ldots, X_n$ is the set function Q defined by

$$Q(A) = P(\{\omega: [X_1(\omega), X_2(\omega), \ldots, X_n(\omega)] \text{ in } A\})$$

for practically every subset A of points in $(x_1, x_2, \ldots, x_n)$ space. This joint distribution is completely determined by its joint distribution function F, which is defined by

$$F(x_1, x_2, \ldots, x_n) = P(X_1 \leq x_1, X_2 \leq x_2, \ldots, X_n \leq x_n) \quad (9.20)$$

for all real numbers $x_1, x_2, \ldots, x_n$. Of course, Eq. 9.20 represents the probability that the n inequalities $X_1 \le x_1$, $X_2 \le x_2$, . . . , $X_n \le x_n$ are simultaneously satisfied. The function F satisfies natural extensions of equations such as 9.4 and 9.5. For example,

$$F_1(x_1) = F(x_1, \infty, \ldots, \infty),$$

where F_1 is the (marginal) distribution function of X_1.

The random variables $X_1, X_2, \ldots, X_n$ and their joint distribution are defined to be continuous if their joint distribution function is continuous at every point $(x_1, x_2, \ldots, x_n)$. They are said to be absolutely continuous if there is a nonnegative integrable function f, called their joint density function, such that

$$F(x_1, x_2, \ldots, x_n)$$
$$= \int_{-\infty}^{x_1} dx_1' \int_{-\infty}^{x_2} dx_2' \cdots \int_{-\infty}^{x_n} f(x_1', x_2', \ldots, x_n') \, dx_n' \quad (9.21)$$

for all real values of $x_1, x_2, \ldots, x_n$ and hence that

$$f(x_1, x_2, \ldots, x_n) = \frac{\partial^n}{\partial x_1 \, \partial x_2 \cdots \partial x_n} F(x_1, x_2, \ldots, x_n). \quad (9.22)$$

This joint density function satisfies the natural extensions of Eqs. 9.14 to 9.19. For example,

$$f_1(x_1)$$
$$= \int_{-\infty}^{\infty} \int_{-\infty}^{\infty} \cdots \int_{-\infty}^{\infty} f(x_1, x_2, \ldots, x_n) \, dx_2 \, dx_3 \cdots dx_n, \quad (9.23)$$

where f_1 is the (marginal) density function of X_1.

The discrete case can be developed as the natural extension of that presented in the preceding section. The more general cases will not be discussed.

9.3 Independent Random Variables

The random variables $X_1, X_2, \ldots, X_n$ (all defined on the same sample space) are defined to be *independent* if

$$P(X_1 \text{ in } A_1, X_2 \text{ in } A_2, \ldots, X_n \text{ in } A_n)$$
$$= P(X_1 \text{ in } A_1)P(X_2 \text{ in } A_2) \cdots P(X_n \text{ in } A_n) \quad (9.24)$$

for *practically every* n subsets $A_1, A_2, \ldots, A_n$ of real numbers. (Given $A_1, A_2, \ldots, A_n$, the reader should be able to show that the condition in Eq. 9.24 implies that the n events $\{\omega: X_i(\omega)$ in $A_i\}$ are mutually independent as defined in Section 4.2.)

It can be shown that Eq. 9.24 holds for practically all subsets A_i if and only if it holds for all subsets of real numbers having the special form $\{\alpha: \alpha \leq x_i\}$. Thus, *the random variables* $X_1, X_2, \ldots, X_n$ *are independent if and only if their joint distribution function* F *factors identically into the product of their individual marginal distribution functions* F_i; *i.e., if and only if*

$$F(x_1, x_2, \ldots, x_n) = F_1(x_1)F_2(x_2) \cdots F_n(x_n) \qquad (9.25)$$

for every set of real numbers $x_1, x_2, \ldots, x_n$. For example, two random variables having the (joint) distribution of Example 9.3 are independent, since $F(x, y) = F_X(x)F_Y(y)$ for all x and y.

For the absolutely continuous case, differentiation of both sides of Eq. 9.25 and use of Eq. 9.22 show that absolutely continuous random variables are independent if and only if their joint density function f factors identically into the product of their separate marginal density functions f_i; i.e., if and only if

$$f(x_1, x_2, \ldots, x_n) = f_1(x_1)f_2(x_2) \cdots f_n(x_n) \qquad (9.26)$$

for *every* set of real numbers $x_1, x_2, \ldots, x_n$. For example, this result shows that two random variables having the distribution of Example 9.3 are independent since $f(x, y) = f_X(x)f_Y(y)$ for all x and y. On the other hand, random variables with the distribution of Example 9.2 are not independent because $f(x, y) \neq f_X(x)f_Y(y)$. (See the exercises for additional information about independence of absolutely continuous random variables.)

For the discrete case, one can similarly show that discrete random variables are independent if and only if their joint probability function factors identically into the product of their separate marginal probability functions. For example, the random variables X and Y of Example 9.1 are not independent since it is obvious from Table 9.1 that $g(x_i, y_j) \neq g_X(x_i)g_Y(y_j)$.

Independent random variables have the following very important property: *Given any* n *random variables* $X_1, X_2, \ldots, X_n$ *and practically any* n *functions* $h_1, h_2, \ldots, h_n$ *of one real variable, let* $Y_1, Y_2, \ldots, Y_n$ *be the random variables defined by* $Y_i = h_i(X_i)$ *for* $i = 1, 2, \ldots, n$. *Then,* $Y_1, Y_2, \ldots, Y_n$ *are independent if* $X_1, X_2, \ldots, X_n$ *are independent.* To prove this assertion, let A_i for $i = 1, 2, \ldots, n$ be practically any subsets of real numbers, and let $h_i^{-1}(A_i)$ denote the set of real numbers α for which $h_i(\alpha)$ is in A_i; that is,

$$h_i^{-1}(A_i) = \{\alpha: h_i(\alpha) \text{ in } A_i\}.$$

Then, the event "Y_i is in A_i" occurs if and only if the event "X_i is in $h_i^{-1}(A_i)$" occurs. Therefore, Eq. 9.24 shows that

$$
\begin{aligned}
P(Y_1 \text{ in } A_1, &\, Y_2 \text{ in } A_2, \ldots, Y_n \text{ in } A_n) \\
&= P[X_1 \text{ in } h_1^{-1}(A_1), X_2 \text{ in } h_2^{-1}(A_2), \ldots, X_n \text{ in } h_n^{-1}(A_n)] \\
&= P[X_1 \text{ in } h_1^{-1}(A_1)]P[X_2 \text{ in } h_2^{-1}(A_2)] \cdots P[X_n \text{ in } h_n^{-1}(A_n)] \\
&= P(Y_1 \text{ in } A_1)P(Y_2 \text{ in } A_2) \cdots P(Y_n \text{ in } A_n).
\end{aligned}
$$

As will be seen, a common situation arises in which one is given several random variables, their individual distribution, probability, or density functions, and the postulate that the random variables are independent. In this case, the joint distribution, probability, or density function can be obtained by merely taking the product of all of the corresponding individual functions. This is particularly true when studying sequences of trials of an experiment. For example, when a die is tossed n times, the number of dots on the upturned face after the kth toss can be taken as a random variable X_k. The successive tosses (trials) are said to be independent if they are conducted in such a manner that the outcome of any one toss is not related in any way to the outcomes of the other tosses. Now, a little thought will convince one that the natural mathematical abstraction of this intuitive notion of independent trials is that $X_1, X_2, \ldots, X_n$ are independent random variables.

As an example of dependent (nonindependent) random variables, we remark that a Markov chain is the mathematical counterpart of a sequence of trials in which the outcome of the kth trial may depend on the outcome of the $(k - 1)$th trial but not on the outcomes of any other trials. If X_k is a random variable associated with the outcomes of the kth trial, then $X_1, X_2, \ldots, X_n$ are dependent.

9.4   Derived Distributions

Very often, one desires to find the distribution, density, or probability function of a random variable Y, which arises as a function $Y = h(X_1, X_2, \ldots, X_n)$ of n jointly distributed random variables

$X_1, X_2, \ldots, X_n$. An extremely important special case is that in which Y is the sum of these random variables. Of course, one approach to this problem is to evaluate first the distribution function of Y, which is given by

$$F_Y(y) = P[h(X_1, X_2, \ldots, X_n) \leq y] \tag{9.27}$$

for every real number y. If the joint distribution of $X_1, X_2, \ldots, X_n$ is absolutely continuous and has the density function f_X, Eq. 9.27 becomes

$$F_Y(y) = \underset{h(x_1, x_2, \ldots, x_n) \leq y}{\int\!\!\int \cdots \int} f_X(x_1, x_2, \ldots, x_n)\, dx_1\, dx_2 \cdots dx_n, \tag{9.28}$$

where the multiple integral extends over the region in $(x_1, x_2, \ldots, x_n)$ space for which $h(x_1, x_2, \ldots, x_n) \leq y$. Although this problem is an extension of that discussed in Section 5.7 and is conceptually clear, its explicit solution may require a complicated computation unless h is a sufficiently simple given function. (As indicated in Sections 6.5 and 10.6, integral transforms can also be used to solve such problems.)

Here we will consider only the simple but very important special case in which $Y = X_1 + X_2$, where the random variables X_1 and X_2 have an absolutely continuous joint distribution and the density function f_X. Then,

$$\begin{aligned} F_Y(y) &= P(X_1 + X_2 \leq y) \\ &= \underset{x_1 + x_2 \leq y}{\int\!\!\int} f_X(x_1, x_2)\, dx_1\, dx_2 \\ &= \int_{-\infty}^{\infty} dx_1 \int_{-\infty}^{y - x_1} f_X(x_1, x_2)\, dx_2 \\ &= \int_{-\infty}^{\infty} dx_1 \int_{-\infty}^{y} f_X(x_1, x_2' - x_1)\, dx_2'. \end{aligned} \tag{9.29}$$

Differentiation of the last equation in Eq. 9.29 gives the first of the two equations

$$f_Y(y) = \int_{-\infty}^{\infty} f_X(x_1, y - x_1)\, dx_1 = \int_{-\infty}^{\infty} f_X(y - x_2, x_2)\, dx_2, \tag{9.30}$$

which express the density function of $Y = X_1 + X_2$ in terms of an integral of the joint density function of X_1 and X_2. If X_1 and X_2 are independent,

$$f_Y(y) = \int_{-\infty}^{\infty} f_1(x_1) f_2(y - x_1)\, dx_1 = \int_{-\infty}^{\infty} f_1(y - x_2) f_2(x_2)\, dx_2, \tag{9.31}$$

where f_i is the density function of X_i. (The mathematical operation involved in Eq. 9.31 arises in many parts of mathematics and is called a *convolution;* we say that f_Y is the convolution of f_1 and f_2 and sometimes write $f_Y = f_1 * f_2$. Convolutions are discussed in Section 10.6.)

A second type of problem that often occurs can be stated as follows: Find the joint distribution, density, or probability function of the n random variables $Y_1, Y_2, \ldots, Y_n$ that arise as n functions

$$Y_i = h_i(X_1, X_2, \ldots, X_n)$$

of n jointly distributed random variables $X_1, X_2, \ldots, X_n$. In general, the solution of this type of problem requires advanced methods from the theory of transformation of independent variables, which will not be developed here. However, one important special case will be considered now.

If the functions h_i are sufficiently smooth and if the random variables X_i are jointly absolutely continuous with the density function f_X, then it can be shown that the random variables Y_i are jointly absolutely continuous with some density function f_Y. Let R_x be the region of $(x_1, x_2, \ldots, x_n)$ space in which $f_X(x_1, x_2, \ldots, x_n) > 0$. Let R_y be the region of $(y_1, y_2, \ldots, y_n)$ space composed of all points obtained from the variable transformation

$$y_1 = h_1(x_1, x_2, \ldots, x_n)$$
$$y_2 = h_2(x_1, x_2, \ldots, x_n)$$
$$\cdots \cdots \cdots \cdots \cdots \cdots \quad (9.32)$$
$$y_n = h_n(x_1, x_2, \ldots, x_n)$$

for all points $(x_1, x_2, \ldots, x_n)$ in R_x. Assume that there is a one-to-one correspondence between the points in R_x and those in R_y. Then it is plausible that we must have

$$\iint \cdots \int_{R_x} f_X(x_1, x_2, \ldots, x_n) \, dx_1 \, dx_2 \cdots dx_n$$
$$= \iint \cdots \int_{R_y} f_Y(y_1, y_2, \ldots, y_n) \, dy_1 \, dy_2 \cdots dy_n, \quad (9.33)$$

since each of these integrals must equal 1. Thus, given f_X, the problem of finding f_Y can be viewed as the problem of introducing in the integral on the left side of Eq. 9.33 the variable transformation 9.32. Now, let the latter have the inverse denoted by

$$x_1 = g_1(y_1, y_2, \ldots, y_n)$$

$$x_2 = g_2(y_1, y_2, \ldots, y_n)$$

$$\ldots \ldots \ldots \ldots \ldots \ldots$$

$$x_n = g_n(y_1, y_2, \ldots, y_n), \tag{9.34}$$

where the n functions g_i have continuous first partial derivatives at every point in R_y such that the Jacobian (determinant)

$$J(y_1, y_2, \ldots, y_n) = \frac{\partial(g_1, g_2, \ldots, g_n)}{\partial(y_1, y_2, \ldots, y_n)} = \begin{vmatrix} \dfrac{\partial g_1}{\partial y_1} & \dfrac{\partial g_1}{\partial y_2} & \cdots & \dfrac{\partial g_1}{\partial y_n} \\ \dfrac{\partial g_2}{\partial y_1} & \dfrac{\partial g_2}{\partial y_2} & \cdots & \dfrac{\partial g_2}{\partial y_n} \\ \cdots & \cdots & \cdots & \cdots \\ \dfrac{\partial g_n}{\partial y_1} & \dfrac{\partial g_n}{\partial y_2} & \cdots & \dfrac{\partial g_n}{\partial y_n} \end{vmatrix} \tag{9.35}$$

does not vanish at any point in R_y. Then, it is shown in advanced calculus that

$$f_Y(y_1, \ldots, y_n) = f_X[g_1(y_1, \ldots, y_n), g_2(y_1, \ldots, y_n),$$
$$\ldots, g_n(y_1, \ldots, y_n)] |J(y_1, \ldots, y_n)| \tag{9.36}$$

for every point in R_y, where $|J|$ denotes the magnitude of J. Also, $f_Y(y_1, \ldots, y_n) = 0$ for every point not in R_y. (Equation 9.36 is actually a generalization of Eq. 5.28.)

This second problem can often be used to solve the first problem stated above. Given a problem of the first type, a problem of the second type can usually be formulated (in many ways) by setting $Y_1 = Y$ and by introducing $(n-1)$ auxiliary random variables $Y_2, Y_3, \ldots, Y_n$. Then the density function f_Y of Eq. 9.28 is a one-dimensional marginal density function obtained from Eq. 9.36 by integrating it over the variables $y_2, y_3, \ldots, y_n$; that is,

$$f_Y(y)$$
$$= \int_{-\infty}^{\infty} \cdots \int_{-\infty}^{\infty} f_X[g_1(y, y_2, \ldots, y_n), \ldots, g_n(y, y_2, \ldots, y_n)]$$
$$|J(y, y_2, \ldots, y_n)| \, dy_2 \cdots dy_n. \tag{9.37}$$

9.5   Expectation

One can define and develop the Stieltjes integral with respect to functions of several variables by means of natural extensions of the treatment for functions of one variable. Although this will not be done here, it is expected that the reader will be satisfied that the results obtained hereafter are valid at least for absolutely continuous and discrete random variables. After the general Stieltjes integral is understood, one can see that our subsequent results are valid for general probability distributions.

Given the joint distribution function F_X of n random variables $X_1, X_2, \ldots, X_n$ and practically any function h of n real variables, the *expectation of the function h with respect to $X_1, X_2, \ldots, X_n$* is defined by

$$E_X[h(X_1, X_2, \ldots, X_n)]$$
$$= \int_{-\infty}^{\infty} \int_{-\infty}^{\infty} \cdots \int_{-\infty}^{\infty} h(x_1, x_2, \ldots, x_n)$$
$$dF_X(x_1, x_2, \ldots, x_n), \quad (9.38)$$

provided this integral is absolutely convergent. On the other hand, the expectation of the random variable $Y = h(X_1, X_2, \ldots, X_n)$ is given by

$$E(Y) = E[h(X_1, X_2, \ldots, X_n)] = \int_{-\infty}^{\infty} y \, dF_Y(y), \quad (9.39)$$

provided this integral is absolutely convergent, where F_Y is the distribution function of Y. A remarkable fact of importance in probability theory is the following generalization of Eq. 6.18: *For every n random variables $X_1, X_2, \ldots, X_n$ and practically every function h of n real variables,*

$$E[h(X_1, X_2, \ldots, X_n)] = E_X[h(X_1, X_2, \ldots, X_n)], \quad (9.40)$$

in the sense that if either of these expectations exists then so does the other, and the two are equal.

When the random variables X_i and Y are absolutely continuous and have the density functions f_X and f_Y, Eq. 9.40 takes the form

$$\int_{-\infty}^{\infty} y f_Y(y) \, dy = \int_{-\infty}^{\infty} \int_{-\infty}^{\infty} \cdots \int_{-\infty}^{\infty} h(x_1, x_2, \ldots, x_n)$$
$$f_X(x_1, x_2, \ldots, x_n) \, dx_1 \, dx_2 \cdots dx_n, \quad (9.41)$$

which involves only ordinary Riemann integrals. When all of the random variables are discrete, each side of Eq. 9.40 reduces to a summation of a finite or infinite (multiple) series.

Although a general proof of Eq. 9.40 cannot be given here, we consider two special cases. If X_1 and X_2 are jointly absolutely continuous and if $Y = X_1 + X_2$, then Eq. 9.30 shows that

$$\int_{-\infty}^{\infty} y f_Y(y)\, dy = \int_{-\infty}^{\infty} y\, dy \int_{-\infty}^{\infty} f_X(x_1, y - x_1)\, dx_1$$

$$= \int_{-\infty}^{\infty} \int_{-\infty}^{\infty} (x_1 + x_2) f_X(x_1, x_2)\, dx_1\, dx_2 \quad (9.42)$$

when the integrals are absolutely convergent, thus proving Eq. 9.41 and hence Eq. 9.40, for this case. If $X_1, X_2, \ldots, X_n$ are jointly absolutely continuous and if a problem of the second type considered in the preceding section can be formulated so that the density function f_Y of $Y = h(X_1, X_2, \ldots, X_n)$ has the form of Eq. 9.37, then

$$\int_{-\infty}^{\infty} y f_Y(y)\, dy$$

$$= \int_{-\infty}^{\infty} y\, dy \int_{-\infty}^{\infty} \cdots \int_{-\infty}^{\infty} f_X[g_1(y, y_2, \ldots, y_n),$$

$$\ldots, g_n(y, y_2, \ldots, y_n)] |J(y, y_2, \ldots, y_n)|\, dy_2 \cdots dy_n$$

$$= \int_{-\infty}^{\infty} \int_{-\infty}^{\infty} \cdots \int_{-\infty}^{\infty} h(x_1, x_2, \ldots, x_n)$$

$$f_X(x_1, x_2, \ldots, x_n)\, dx_1\, dx_2 \cdots dx_n, \quad (9.43)$$

which should at least make Eq. 9.41 plausible in this case.

It can be shown that the following generalization of Eqs. 6.19 and 9.40 is true: *If $X_1, X_2, \ldots, X_n$, and h are as in Eq. 9.40,*

$$Y = h(X_1, X_2, \ldots, X_n),$$

and H is practically any function of one real variable, then

$$E_Y[H(Y)] = E_X(H[h(X_1, X_2, \ldots, X_n)]), \quad (9.44)$$

if either of these expectations exists.

As in Section 6.3, we thus have two distinct concepts of expectation expressed in Eqs. 9.38 and 9.39. But these two expectations are practically always equal numerically and are therefore not distinguished hereafter.

The preceding material will now be illustrated by deriving several extremely important special results. First, note that substitution of $h(X_1, X_2, \ldots, X_n) = X_k$ for any fixed $k = 1, 2, \ldots,$ or n in Eqs.

9.38 through 9.40 shows that

$$E(X_k) = \int_{-\infty}^{\infty} \int_{-\infty}^{\infty} \cdots \int_{-\infty}^{\infty} x_k \, dF_X(x_1, x_2, \ldots, x_n), \quad (9.45)$$

which states the important fact that the expected value of each X_k can be computed from the joint distribution function without first finding its marginal distribution function. When the random variables X_i are jointly absolutely continuous, use of Eqs. 9.38 to 9.40 and 9.23 provides the following simple check of Eq. 9.45:

$$\begin{aligned}
E(X_1) &= \int_{-\infty}^{\infty} \int_{-\infty}^{\infty} \cdots \int_{-\infty}^{\infty} x_1 f_X(x_1, x_2, \ldots, x_n) \, dx_1 \, dx_2 \cdots dx_n \\
&= \int_{-\infty}^{\infty} x_1 \, dx_1 \int_{-\infty}^{\infty} \cdots \int_{-\infty}^{\infty} f_X(x_1, x_2, \ldots, x_n) \, dx_2 \cdots dx_n \\
&= \int_{-\infty}^{\infty} x_1 f_1(x_1) \, dx_1.
\end{aligned} \quad (9.46)$$

Since the right side of Eq. 9.42 can be written as the sum of two integrals, Eqs. 9.42 and 9.46 illustrate that

$$E(X_1 + X_2) = E(X_1) + E(X_2). \quad (9.47)$$

This *linearity property* is the most important property of the expectation operator.

The following result is a direct extension of Eq. 9.47 and also of Eq. 6.22: *If*

$$Y = c_0 + c_1 X_1 + c_2 X_2 + \cdots + c_n X_n,$$

where $c_0, c_1, c_2, \ldots, c_n$ *are any given constants and* $X_1, X_2, \ldots, X_n$ *are any given random variables with finite means, then*

$$E(Y) = c_0 + c_1 E(X_1) + c_2 E(X_2) + \cdots + c_n E(X_n). \quad (9.48)$$

To derive this relation, we use Eq. 9.45 and the fact that

$$\int_{-\infty}^{\infty} \int_{-\infty}^{\infty} \cdots \int_{-\infty}^{\infty} dF_X(x_1, x_2, \ldots, x_n) = 1$$

to see that

$$\begin{aligned}
E(Y) &= \int_{-\infty}^{\infty} \int_{-\infty}^{\infty} \cdots \int_{-\infty}^{\infty} \left(c_0 + \sum_{k=1}^{n} c_k x_k \right) dF_X(x_1, x_2, \ldots, x_n) \\
&= c_0 + \sum_{k=1}^{n} c_k \int_{-\infty}^{\infty} \int_{-\infty}^{\infty} \cdots \int_{-\infty}^{\infty} x_k \, dF_X(x_1, x_2, \ldots, x_n) \\
&= c_0 + \sum_{k=1}^{n} c_k E(X_k).
\end{aligned}$$

Next, *if* $X_1, X_2, \ldots, X_n$ *are independent random variables with finite means, then*

$$E(X_1 X_2 \cdots X_n) = E(X_1) E(X_2) \cdots E(X_n). \qquad (9.49)$$

To derive Eq. 9.49, we note that

$$E(X_1 X_2 \cdots X_n)$$
$$= \int_{-\infty}^{\infty} \int_{-\infty}^{\infty} \cdots \int_{-\infty}^{\infty} x_1 x_2 \cdots x_n \, dF_X(x_1, x_2, \ldots, x_n)$$
$$= \int_{-\infty}^{\infty} x_1 \, dF_1(x_1) \int_{-\infty}^{\infty} x_2 \, dF_2(x_2) \cdots \int_{-\infty}^{\infty} x_n \, dF_n(x_n)$$
$$= E(X_1) E(X_2) \cdots E(X_n),$$

where we have used the relation

$$dF_X(x_1, x_2, \ldots, x_n) = dF_1(x_1) \, dF_2(x_2) \cdots dF_n(x_n),$$

which holds for independent random variables. When the random variables are absolutely continuous so that $dF_k(x_k) = f_k(x_k) \, dx_k$, this relation appears obvious when reference is made to Eqs. 9.26 and 9.38 to 9.41. For the discrete case, one can see that the above computation is correct by replacing dF and dF_k by the probability functions g and g_k and by replacing each integral sign by a summation.

Note that Eq. 9.48 holds for *every* finite sequence of random variables having finite means, whereas Eq. 9.49 holds only for *independent* random variables.

Given any n independent random variables X_i and practically any n functions h_i of one real variable, recall that it was shown in Section 9.3 that the n random variables $Y_i = h_i(X_i)$ for $i = 1, 2, \ldots, n$ are independent. Thus, under these conditions, a direct corollary to Eq. 9.49 is the fact that

$$E[h_1(X_1) h_2(X_2) \cdots h_n(X_n)] = E[h_1(X_1)] E[h_2(X_2)] \cdots E[h_n(X_n)], \qquad (9.50)$$

provided every $h_i(X_i)$ has a finite mean.

As an important example of Eq. 9.50, we compute the moment-generating function of $Y = X_1 + X_2 + \cdots + X_n$. Thus Eqs. 9.40, 9.44, and 9.50 imply that

$$E(\exp[\theta Y]) = E(\exp[\theta(X_1 + X_2 + \cdots + X_n)])$$
$$= E(\exp[\theta X_1] \exp[\theta X_2] \cdots \exp[\theta X_n])$$
$$= E(\exp[\theta X_1]) E(\exp[\theta X_2]) \cdots E(\exp[\theta X_n]),$$

or

$$M_Y(\theta) = M_1(\theta) M_2(\theta) \cdots M_n(\theta) \qquad (9.51)$$

when X_1, X_2, . . . , X_n are independent, where M_Y and M_i are the moment-generating functions of Y and X_i. Equation 9.51 is extremely important in probability theory.

9.6 Covariance and Correlation

The *covariance* of (or between) two jointly distributed random variables X_1 and X_2 is defined to be the expectation of the cross product $(X_1 - \mu_1)(X_2 - \mu_2)$, where $\mu_i = E(X_i)$ for $i = 1$ and 2, and is often denoted by σ_{12} or by Cov (X_1, X_2). Thus,

$$\sigma_{12} = E[(X_1 - \mu_1)(X_2 - \mu_2)]$$
$$= E(X_1 X_2) - \mu_1 \mu_2, \qquad (9.52)$$

where the last equality follows from Eq. 9.48 after the cross product is expanded. The covariance generalizes the variance in the sense that it reduces to the variance when X_1 and X_2 are replaced by the same random variable. The importance of the covariance is due to its appearance in the basic formula for the variance of the sum of several random variables, which is presented in Section 10.4.

Two random variables, X_1 and X_2, which satisfy

$$E(X_1 X_2) = E(X_1)E(X_2), \qquad (9.53)$$

are said to be *uncorrelated*, for the reason indicated after Eq. 9.54. From Eq. 9.52, X_1 and X_2 satisfy Eq. 9.53 and therefore are uncorrelated if and only if their covariance is 0. Any two independent random variables are uncorrelated, since Eqs. 9.49 and 9.52 show that

$$\sigma_{12} = \mu_1 \mu_2 - \mu_1 \mu_2 = 0$$

when X_1 and X_2 are independent. But, as illustrated in Example 9.5, the converse of this statement is false; that is, two uncorrelated random variables are not necessarily independent.

The *coefficient of correlation* between X_1 and X_2 is a dimensionless quantity often denoted by ρ_{12} and defined by

$$\rho_{12} = \frac{\sigma_{12}}{\sigma_1 \sigma_2}, \qquad (9.54)$$

where σ_i is the standard deviation of X_i for $i = 1$ and 2. Of course, the coefficient of correlation between X_1 and X_2 is 0 if and only if X_1 and

X_2 are uncorrelated random variables. It can be shown (from one of the exercises) that ρ_{12} is always a number satisfying $-1 \le \rho_{12} \le 1$ and that $\rho_{12}^2 = 1$ if and only if X_1 or X_2 is an exact linear function of the other. The coefficient of correlation is widely used in the study of the interrelationships among dependent random variables.

Example 9.4. Compute the coefficient of correlation between the two random variables of Example 9.1. Let $X_1 = X$ and $X_2 = Y$. Then, one easily finds that $\mu_1 = \frac{1}{2}$, $\mu_2 = \frac{3}{2}$, $\sigma_1 = \frac{1}{2}$, $\sigma_2 = \sqrt{\frac{3}{2}}$,

$$E(X_1 X_2) = 0 + 1(\tfrac{1}{8}) + 2(\tfrac{1}{4}) + 3(\tfrac{1}{8}) = 1,$$

$\sigma_{12} = \frac{1}{4}$, and $\rho_{12} = 1/\sqrt{3} = 0.58$.

Example 9.5. Let X_1 and X_2 have the joint density function f defined by $f(x_1, x_2) = \frac{1}{2}$ inside the square with corners at the points $(1, 0)$, $(0, 1)$, $(-1, 0)$, and $(0, -1)$ in the (x_1, x_2) plane and otherwise $f(x_1, x_2) = 0$. Then, the marginal density functions are given by

$$f_i(x_i) = \begin{cases} 1 - |x_i| & (-1 < x_i < 1) \\ 0 & \text{(otherwise)} \end{cases}$$

for $i = 1, 2$. Clearly,

$$f(x_1, x_2) \ne f_1(x_1) f_2(x_2),$$

and thus X_1 and X_2 are not independent. But a short computation shows that

$$\mu_1 = \mu_2 = E(X_1 X_2) = \sigma_{12} = \rho_{12} = 0$$

and hence that X_1 and X_2 are uncorrelated.

9.7 Conditional Distributions

The concept of a conditional distribution is indispensable in the study of stochastic processes. This notion is basic in the mathematical treatment of jointly distributed random variables that are not independent and therefore are dependent. However, since conditional distributions are not used elsewhere in this book, only a brief introduction is given here.

Of course, the concept of a conditional distribution depends basically on the notion of conditional probability, which was discussed in Chapter 4. Recall that, given two events A and B on the same probability space, the conditional probability $P(A|B)$ of A given B is defined by

$$
\begin{aligned}
P(A|B) &= P(A \cap B)/P(B) \quad &&\text{if } P(B) > 0 \\
&= \text{undefined} \quad &&\text{if } P(B) = 0.
\end{aligned} \tag{9.55}
$$

First, let X and Y be jointly distributed discrete random variables as discussed in Section 9.1. Then, if $g_Y(y_j) > 0$ for a fixed y_j, Eqs. 9.6, 9.11, and 9.55 show that the conditional probability $g_{X|Y}(x_i|y_j)$ of the event $\{X = x_i\}$ given the event $\{Y = y_j\}$ is given by

$$
g_{X|Y}(x_i|y_j) = \frac{g(x_i, y_j)}{g_Y(y_j)} \text{ if } g_Y(y_j) > 0. \tag{9.56}
$$

Intuitively, Eq. 9.56 represents the probability that X assumes the value x_i when it is known that Y assumed the value y_j. For every fixed y_j such that $g_Y(y_j) > 0$, the function $g_{X|Y}$ has every property of an ordinary discrete probability function; for example,

$$
g_{X|Y}(x_i|y_j) \geq 0, \qquad \sum_i g_{X|Y}(x_i|y_j) = 1. \tag{9.57}
$$

This function $g_{X|Y}$ is called the *conditional probability function* of X given Y and represents the *conditional distribution* of X given Y. Of course, the conditional probability function $g_{Y|X}$ of Y given X is obtained in a similar way, and Eq. 9.56 shows that

$$
g(x_i, y_j) = g_{X|Y}(x_i|y_j)g_Y(y_j) = g_{Y|X}(y_j|x_i)g_X(x_i). \tag{9.58}
$$

When X and Y are *independent* random variables,

$$
g(x_i, y_j) = g_X(x_i)g_Y(y_j), \tag{9.59}
$$

and comparison of Eqs. 9.58 and 9.59 shows that

$$
\begin{aligned}
g_{X|Y}(x_i|y_j) &= g_X(x_i), \\
g_{Y|X}(y_j|x_i) &= g_Y(y_j).
\end{aligned} \tag{9.60}
$$

In general, the definition of a conditional distribution requires trickery. Suppose we are given an event A (such as, $\{X < x\}$) and a random variable Y, both defined on the same probability space. For every real number y, we wish to find the conditional probability $P(A|Y = y)$ of A given the event $\{Y = y\}$. But, for every continuous random variable Y, $P(Y = y) = 0$ for every real value of y. In general, $P(A|Y = y)$ therefore must be regarded as being undefined insofar as

Eq. 9.55 is concerned, and hence a new definition is needed. Although it seems natural to define

$$P(A|Y = y) = \lim_{h \to 0} P(A|y - h < Y < y + h) \qquad (9.61)$$

if the events $y - h < Y < y + h$ have positive probabilities for every $h > 0$, this is impossible because the limit usually does not exist.

In advanced probability theory, it is shown that there is a unique (practically everywhere) function $P(A|Y = y)$ of y that satisfies

$$P(A \cap \{Y \text{ in } B\}) = \int_B P(A|Y = y) \, dF_Y(y) \qquad (9.62)$$

for *practically every* (every Borel) set B of real numbers. This function is defined to be the *conditional probability of the event A given the random variable Y*. Of course, the left side of Eq. 9.62 is the probability of the intersection of the given event A and the event $\{Y \text{ in } B\}$ that Y assumes a value in B, and the integral extends over the set B. For example, if B is the set of all real numbers, Eq. 9.62 implies the useful formula

$$P(A) = \int_{-\infty}^{\infty} P(A|Y = y) \, dF_Y(y). \qquad (9.63)$$

It can be shown that the function $P(A|Y = y)$ defined by Eq. 9.62 satisfies a relation similar to 9.61 in spirit but different in detail. When X and Y are discrete and A is the event $\{X = x_i\}$, it can also be shown that $P(A|Y = y)$ takes the form of Eq. 9.56 at $y = y_j$.

Given two random variables X and Y, the *conditional distribution function* of X given Y, denoted by $F_{X|Y}$, is naturally defined by

$$F_{X|Y}(x|y) = P(X \le x|Y = y) \qquad (9.64)$$

for every pair of real numbers x and y. By setting $A = \{X \le x\}$ and $B = \{\alpha : \alpha \le y\}$ in Eq. 9.62, we find that

$$P(X \le x, Y \le y) = \int_{-\infty}^{y} P(X \le x|Y = y') \, dF_Y(y')$$

and hence that the joint distribution function F of X and Y can be expressed in terms of $F_{X|Y}$ by means of the important formula

$$F(x, y) = \int_{-\infty}^{y} F_{X|Y}(x|y') \, dF_Y(y') \qquad (9.65)$$

for all x and y.

Next, consider the special case in which X and Y have an absolutely continuous joint distribution. Then, the *conditional density function* of X given Y, denoted by $f_{X|Y}$, is given by

$$f_{X|Y}(x|y) = \frac{\partial}{\partial x} F_{X|Y}(x|y). \tag{9.66}$$

If we replace $dF_Y(y')$ by $f_Y(y') \, dy'$ in Eq. 9.65 and differentiate the result, we find that

$$\frac{\partial}{\partial y} F(x, y) = F_{X|Y}(x|y)f_Y(y).$$

Differentiation of this equation with respect to x shows that

$$f(x, y) = f_{X|Y}(x|y)f_Y(y) \tag{9.67}$$

and hence that

$$f_{X|Y}(x|y) = \frac{f(x, y)}{f_Y(y)} \text{ if } f_Y(y) > 0. \tag{9.68}$$

For every fixed y such that $f_Y(y) > 0$, the function $f_{X|Y}$ has every property of an ordinary probability density function; for example,

$$f_{X|Y}(x|y) \geq 0,$$
$$\int_{-\infty}^{\infty} f_{X|Y}(x|y) \, dx = 1. \tag{9.69}$$

When X and Y are independent so that

$$f(x, y) = f_X(x)f_Y(y), \tag{9.70}$$

Eqs. 9.67 and 9.70 indicate that

$$f_{X|Y}(x|y) = f_X(x),$$
$$f_{Y|X}(y|x) = f_Y(y). \tag{9.71}$$

Of course, all of the foregoing notions can be extended to several random variables, but this will not be done here.

Example 9.6. For the discrete random variables of Example 9.1, $g_{Y|X}(y_j|x_i)$ is given in the following tabulation:

y_j	0	1	2	3
$g_{Y|X}(y_j|0)$	$\frac{1}{4}$	$\frac{1}{2}$	$\frac{1}{4}$	0
$g_{Y|X}(y_j|1)$	0	$\frac{1}{4}$	$\frac{1}{2}$	$\frac{1}{4}$

Example 9.7. For the absolutely continuous random variables of

Example 9.2, we find from Eq. 9.68 that

$$f_{X|Y}(x|y) = 2x/(1 - y^2) \qquad (0 < y < 1, y < x < 1)$$
$$f_{Y|X}(y|x) = 2x^{-2}y \qquad (0 < x < 1, 0 < y < x).$$

Otherwise, these functions are defined to be zero. These functions can be used to compute various conditional probabilities; for example,

$$P(0.7 < X < 0.8|Y = \tfrac{1}{2}) = \int_{0.7}^{0.8} f_{X|Y}(x|\tfrac{1}{2})\, dx = 0.20.$$

9.8   Exercises

9.1   Two unbiased coins and an unbiased die are tossed simultaneously and independently. Let X be the number of heads showing on the two coins and Y be the number of spots on the upturned face of the die. (a) Describe a probability space for this experiment. (b) Find the joint probability function of X and Y and their marginal probability functions, without using Eqs. 9.10 and 9.11. (c) Verify the validity of Eqs. 9.10 and 9.11 in this case. (d) What is the probability of each of the events $\{X = 1, 2 \le Y < 5\}$ and $\{X > 0, Y \le 4\}$?

9.2   Two balls are drawn, without replacement, from an urn containing one white, two red, and two black balls. Let X and Y be the number of white and the number of red balls drawn. Describe a sample space, and find the joint and marginal probability functions of X and Y.

9.3   The discrete random variables X and Y have the joint probability function

$$g(x, y) = \frac{\lambda^x e^{-\lambda} p^y q^{x-y}}{y!(x-y)!} \qquad (y = 0, 1, \ldots, x; x = 0, 1, 2, \ldots),$$

where λ, p, and q are constants with $\lambda > 0$, $0 < p < 1$, and $q = 1 - p$. Find the marginal probability functions of X and Y.

9.4   Let X and Y have the joint density function

$$f(x, y) = xe^{-x^2/2}e^{-y} \qquad (0 < x < \infty, 0 < y < \infty).$$

(a) Find the joint distribution function and the marginal density functions of X and Y. (b) Compute the probability of each of the events $\{X > 2, Y \ge 1\}$ and $\{Y + X^2 \le 2\}$.

9.5   The joint density function of X_1 and X_2 has the form

$$f(x_1, x_2) = cx_1(x_1 - x_2) \qquad (0 < x_1 < 2, -x_1 < x_2 < x_1).$$

Evaluate the constant c, and find the marginal density functions of X_1 and X_2.

9.6 Let (L, W) be the coordinates of a point chosen at random inside the rectangle $\{0 < L < 3, 0 < W < 2\}$. (a) If $X = L$ and $Y = LW$, so that Y is the area of a rectangle of length L and width W, evaluate separately the joint and marginal distribution functions of X and Y. (b) Use differentiation to find the joint and marginal density functions of X and Y, and verify the validity of Eqs. 9.16 and 9.17 in this case. (c) Use Eq. 9.5 and also 9.19 to compute the probability of the event $\{1 < X \leq 2, 2 \leq Y < 5\}$.

9.7 The random variables X and Y have a *joint normal distribution* if their joint density function has the form

$$f(x, y) = \frac{1}{2\pi\sigma_1\sigma_2 \sqrt{1 - \rho^2}} \exp[-Q/2] \qquad (-\infty < x, y < \infty),$$

where $\quad Q = \dfrac{1}{1 - \rho^2}\left[\dfrac{(x - \mu_1)^2}{\sigma_1^2} - \dfrac{2\rho(x - \mu_1)(y - \mu_2)}{\sigma_1\sigma_2} + \dfrac{(y - \mu_2)^2}{\sigma_2^2}\right]$

and $\mu_1, \mu_2, \sigma_1, \sigma_2$, and ρ are real constants with $\sigma_1 > 0, \sigma_2 > 0$, and $-1 < \rho < 1$. Find the marginal distributions of X and Y, and verify that f is a joint density function. *Hint:* Complete square in exponent.

9.8 If ten balanced dice are tossed independently, let X_k be the number of dots appearing on the kth die, for $k = 1, 2, \ldots, 10$. Use Eq. 9.24 to compute the probability that, simultaneously, $2 < X_2 \leq 3, X_5 = 1, 3$, or $6, 0 \leq X_7 < 3, 1 < X_{10} \leq 5$, while the other X_k's may assume any values.

*9.9 Suppose the joint density function f of two random variables X and Y satisfies $f(x, y) > 0$ inside some region R bounded by a closed curve (which does not intersect itself) in the (x, y) plane and $f(x, y) = 0$ for all points (x, y) outside of R. Show that X and Y are independent if and only if (a) $f(x, y)$ factors (in R) identically into the product of any pure function of x times any pure function of y in the form $f(x, y) = g_1(x)g_2(y)$, and (b) R is a rectangle of the form $a_1 \leq x \leq a_2, b_1 \leq y \leq b_2$ for some constants a_1, a_2, b_1, and b_2, which may be $\pm \infty$.

9.10 As parts 1, 2, $\ldots$, 6, state, with your reasons, whether the random variables X and Y of Exercises 9.1, 9.2, $\ldots$, 9.6 are independent.

9.11 If X and Y have the normal distribution of Exercise 9.7, show that X and Y are independent if and only if $\rho = 0$.

*9.12 Suppose the daily maximum temperature during September in Atlanta can be viewed as a random variable T with the distribution function

$$F(t) = \begin{cases} \exp[-b(a - t)^c] & (-\infty < t \leq a) \\ 1 & (a < t < \infty), \end{cases}$$

where $a, b > 0$, and $c > 0$ are constants. (a) If we assume (as a first approximation) that the maximum temperatures on successive days are statistically independent, find the distribution and density functions G and g for the maximum temperature T_m during September. (b) Show that $\sigma_m = \sigma_t(30)^{-1/c}$, where σ_t and σ_m are the standard deviations of T and T_m. *Hint*: $G(t) = [F(t)]^{30}$. (When c is close to 3.5, the above function F is a sufficiently good approximation to the normal distribution function, for some purposes.)

9.13   If X_1 and X_2 are independent random variables with the density functions

$$f_i(x_i) = 3a_i x_i^2 \exp(-a_i x_i^3) \qquad (0 < x_i < \infty, i = 1, 2),$$

where a_1 and a_2 are positive constants, evaluate $P(X_1 > X_2)$.

***9.14**   Suppose we make seven independent observations of a random variable having a density function f. What is the probability of the event E that each of the last two observations is larger than all of the first five observations?   *Hint*: Substitute $u = F(x_5)$ in

$$P(E) = \int_{-\infty}^{\infty} \frac{5!}{4!1!} \left[\int_{-\infty}^{x_5} f(x)\, dx \right]^4 f(x_5) \left[\int_{x_5}^{\infty} f(x)\, dx \right]^2 dx_5.$$

(A result such as this is called *nonparametric*, because it does not depend on the form of f.)

9.15   Let X_1 and X_2 be independent and have exponential distributions, so that

$$f_1(x_1) = ae^{-ax_1}$$

and

$$f_2(x_2) = be^{-bx_2}$$

for $0 < x_1, x_2 < \infty$, where $a > 0$ and $b > 0$. Derive the density function of the sum $Y = X_1 + X_2$.

9.16   Derive the density function of the quotient of two independent, normally distributed random variables, with parameters $(0, 1)$.

9.17   If X and Y have the joint distribution of Exercise 9.2, find the probability function of (a) $Z = Y - X$, (b) $Z = XY$.

9.18   Let X_1 and X_2 be independent and have the same exponential density function $e^{-x}(0 < x < \infty)$.   (a) Use Eqs. 9.36 and 9.37 to derive the joint and marginal density functions of $U = X_1 + X_2$ and $V = X_1/X_2$. (b) Use Eqs. 9.27 and 9.31 to derive the density functions of U and V. (c) Are U and V independent?

9.19   (a) If X_1 and X_2 have the distribution of Exercise 9.5, derive the density function of $Y = X_1|X_2|$. (b) Use Eqs. 9.38 and also 9.39 to find $E(Y)$. and thus verify Eq. 9.40 in this case. (c) Compute $E(X_1)$ and $E(|X_2|)$, and show that $E(X_1|X_2|) \neq E(X_1)E(|X_2|)$.

9.20   If X_1, X_2, and Y have the distributions of Exercise 9.15, separately compute their means, and verify Eq. 9.47 in this case.

9.21   If X and Y have the joint distribution of Exercises 9.2 and 9.17, find the mean of (a) $Z = Y - X$ and (b) $Z = XY$. (c) Is $E(XY) = E(X)E(Y)$? Why?

9.22   In Exercise 9.6, let $Z = W$ be a random variable, and compute the mean of $Y = XZ$. Is $E(Y) = E(X)E(Z)$? Why?

9.23   Let a biased coin, with probability p of heads, be tossed independently n times, and let X_k be the number (0 or 1) of heads appearing at the kth toss. Evaluate $E(X_1 + X_2 + \cdots + X_n)$ and $E(X_1 X_2 \cdots X_n)$.

*9.24   The *joint moment-generating function* (if it exists) of two random variables X and Y is defined by $M(\theta_1, \theta_2) = E[\exp{(\theta_1 X + \theta_2 Y)}]$. Evaluate $M(\theta_1, \theta_2)$ for the normal distribution of Exercise 9.7.

9.25   Compute the covariance and the coefficient of correlation of the two random variables defined in: (a) Example 9.2, (b) Example 9.3, (c) Exercise 9.2, (d) Exercise 9.5, (e) Exercise 9.6.

9.26   (a) If X and Y have the normal distribution of Exercise 9.7, find their coefficient of correlation. (b) Show that X and Y are independent if and only if they are uncorrelated if and only if $\rho = 0$.

*9.27   Let X_1 and X_2 be any two jointly distributed random variables which have finite, positive variances. (a) If a and b are any real constants, deduce that

$$[E(X_1 - a)(X_2 - b)]^2 \le [E(X_1 - a)^2][E(X_2 - b)^2],$$

which is a form of *Schwarz's inequality*. (b) Use this to show that $-1 \le \rho_{12} \le 1$. (c) Also, deduce that $\rho_{12}^2 = 1$ if and only if there is a constant c ($\ne 0$) such that $c(X_1 - \mu_1) - (X_2 - \mu_2) = 0$ (with probability one) and that then $\rho_{12} = c/|c|$. *Hint:* For every real s, define $h(s) = E[s(X_1 - a) - (X_2 - b)]^2$. Note that $h(s) \ge 0$ for all s and that the quadratic equation $h(s) = 0$ has either no real solutions or one solution.

9.28   If X and Y have the joint distribution of: (a) Exercise 9.2, (b) Exercise 9.3, (c) Exercise 9.6, find the conditional probability or density function of Y given X.

9.29   If X and Y have the joint normal distribution of Exercise 9.7, find (a) the conditional density function, (b) the mean

$$m_Y(x) = \int_{-\infty}^{\infty} y f_{Y|X}(y|x)\, dy,$$

and (c) the variance $\sigma_Y^2(x)$ of the conditional distribution of Y given X. (The function m_Y is usually called the *conditional expectation of Y given X* and represents the so-called *regression for the mean of Y on X*, and σ_Y^2 is the *conditional variance of Y given X*.)

9.30   Compute the conditional mean and variance of each conditional distribution of Exercise 9.28.

*9.31   (a) Prove that a nonnegative absolutely continuous random variable X has an exponential distribution if and only if its density and distribution functions f and F satisfy $f(x + y) = f(x)[1 - F(y)]$ for all $x \geq 0$ and $y \geq 0$. *Hint* for if part: Differentiate, and set $x = 0$. (b) Show that $P(X > x + y | X > y) = P(X > x)$, and discuss what this relation implies about a telephone conversation whose length has an exponential distribution. (c) Formulate and prove a similar result for the geometric distribution.

9.32   Let the independent random variables X and χ^2 have, respectively, the normal distribution with parameters $(0, 1)$ and the chi-square distribution with n degrees of freedom (see Section 8.5). (a) Show that the new random variable $R = \sqrt{\chi^2/n}$ has the so-called *root-mean-square distribution* with n degrees of freedom, whose density function is

$$f_R(r) = \frac{2(n/2)^{n/2}}{\Gamma(n/2)} \, r^{n-1} e^{-nr^2/2} \qquad (0 < r < \infty).$$

(b) Show that $T = X/R$ has the t distribution presented in Section 8.5. *Hint:* First view R as fixed at r, and use Eq. 5.28 to find from f_X the conditional density function $f_{T|R}$. Use the substitution $u = (r\sqrt{n + t^2})/\sqrt{2}$ to integrate $f_{T|R}(t|r)f_R(r)$ over all r.

9.33   Let the independent random variables χ_m^2 and χ_n^2 have chi-square distributions with m and n degrees of freedom, as described in Section 8.5. (a) Show that $Y_n = \chi_n^2/n$ has the so-called *mean-square distribution* with n degrees of freedom, whose density function is

$$f_{Y_n}(y_n) = \frac{(n/2)^{n/2}}{\Gamma(n/2)} \, y_n^{(n/2)-1} e^{-ny_n/2} \qquad (0 < y_n < \infty).$$

(b) Show that $X = Y_m/Y_n$ has the F distribution discussed in Section 8.5. *Hint:* As in Exercise 9.32, find the conditional density function of X given Y_n, and use the substitution $u = y_n(mx + n)/2$ to integrate the joint density function of X and Y_n over all y_n.

APPLICATIONS IN ENGINEERING

*9.34   Show that the joint density function of the random variables X and Y of Exercise 6.32 is given by

$$g(x, y) = \tau^{-1} f(x + y) \qquad (x \geq 0, y \geq 0),$$

where f is the density function of T, and verify that g is a joint density function, which has the marginal density functions g_X and g_Y of Exercise 6.32. *Hint:* Show that

$$g(x, y) \, \Delta x \, \Delta y = g(x + \theta, y - \theta) \, \Delta x \, \Delta y$$

for $0 < \theta < y$ and therefore that $g(x, y) = h(x + y)$ for some function h which can be found by setting

$$g_X(x) = \int_0^\infty h(x + y) \, dy.$$

9.35   In Exercise 9.34, let $f(t) = At^{b-1} \exp(-at^b)$ for $0 \le t < \infty$, where $a > 0$ and $b > 0$ are constants. Find A, τ, $g(x, y)$, $g_X(x)$, and $g_Y(y)$.

9.36   If $f(t) = \tau^{-1} \exp[-t/\tau]$ for $0 \le t < \infty$, are X and Y of Exercise 9.34 independent? Why? (cf. Exercises 5.30, 6.34, and 9.31.)

9.37   Let $F(t) = 0$ for $t < \tau$ and $F(t) = 1$ for $t \ge \tau$. (a) Find the marginal density functions of X and Y described in Exercises 6.32 and 9.34. (b) Are X and Y independent? Why? (cf. Exercises 6.35 and 9.40.)

9.38   In Exercise 9.34, express the density function of $Z = X + Y$ in terms of the density function f of T. Explain why $Z \ne T$, even though the residence time of a *single* molecule is the sum of its age and its future lifetime.

9.39   If X has a finite variance, use integration by parts and results of Exercise 6.33 to show that the coefficient of correlation of X and Y of Exercise 9.34 is given by

$$\rho_{XY} = 1 - \frac{E(X^2)}{2\sigma_X^2} = 1 - \frac{E(T^3)}{6\tau\sigma_X^2}.$$

9.40   For the residence-time distribution of (a) Exercise 9.36, (b) Exercise 9.37, use the result of Exercise 9.39 to compute ρ_{XY}. (c) What do the answers to part (b) and Exercises 6.32 and 9.27(c) imply about X and Y in that case?

9.41   If f is the gamma density function with mean τ and standard deviation σ_T, express and sketch ρ_{XY} of Exercise 9.39 as a function of $\tau/\sigma_T \ge 0$. Relate this result with those of Exercise 9.40.

*9.42   Let $f(t) = (a/b)(1 - t/b)^{a-1}$ for $0 < t < b$, where $b = \tau(a + 1)$, $a > 0$, and $\tau > 0$ are constants. (a) Use the distribution function to show that this distribution approaches that of Exercise 9.36 as $a \to \infty$ and that of Exercise 9.37 as $a \to 0$. (b) Express and sketch ρ_{XY} of Exercise 9.39 as a function of $\tau/\sigma_T \ge 1$, where τ and σ_T are the mean and standard deviation of f. (c) Find the conditional density function $g_{X|Y}(x|y)$ of X given Y. (d) Evaluate the conditional expectation and the conditional variance of X given Y; i.e.,

$$m(y) = \int_{-\infty}^\infty x g_{X|Y}(x|y) \, dx$$

and

$$\sigma_X^2(y) = \int_{-\infty}^\infty [x - m(y)]^2 g_{X|Y}(x|y) \, dx.$$

(cf. Exercises 9.29 and 9.30.)

*9.43   As indicated in Exercise 6.36, for a specified residence-time distribution, there must usually be some mixing of molecules which have different ages. But the residence-time distribution only partially determines the
amount of this mixing and therefore the flow pattern. Danckwerts and
Zwietering (see the bibliography) used a numerical quantity J, called the
"degree of segregation," as a measure of such mixing. For a given function f,
they showed that J can have any value between a maximum of 1 and a
nonnegative minimum, to be denoted by J_m, and that these limits correspond
respectively to the limits c'_e and c''_e of c_e described in Exercises 6.36 and 6.37.
The maximum value of J corresponds to "complete segregation," for which
the mixing required by the specified residence-time distribution occurs as
late as possible; that is, at the reactor exit. The minimum value of J occurs
when there is "maximum mixedness," in which entering molecules are instan-
taneously mixed, and thereafter remain mixed, with those molecules in the
reactor that will leave mixed together. If $m(y)$ is the conditional mean of X
given $Y = y$, cf. Exercise 9.42 (d), then J_m can be written as

$$J_m = E[m(Y) - \mu_X]^2/\text{Var}(X).$$

(a) For the function f given in Exercise 9.42, express and sketch J_m as a
function of $\tau/\sigma_T \geq 1$. (b) Discuss how the results of part (a) and Exercises
9.40, 9.41, and 9.42 are related. (In general, $J_m \neq \rho_{XY}^2$.)

*9.44   Refer to Exercises 9.42 and 9.43, and let $\sigma_m^2 = E[m(Y) - \mu_X]^2$.
Let h be any function for which $E[h(Y)] = \mu_X$, let

$$\rho_{Xh}^2 = (\text{Cov}[X, h(Y)])^2/\text{Var}(X)\,\text{Var}[h(Y)],$$

and let $Q_h = 1 - (1 - \sigma_m^2/\sigma_X^2)\rho_{Xh}^2$. Use the results of Exercise 9.27 to show
that, for all such functions h, the maximum value assumed by Q_h is the
maximum value, 1, of J and that the minimum value assumed by Q_h is the
minimum value, J_m, of J. Discuss.

CHAPTER 10   SUMS OF RANDOM

VARIABLES

IN THIS CHAPTER, OUR CENTRAL PURPOSE IS TO INVESTIGATE CERTAIN useful properties of sums of several given random variables. It is shown in Section 10.1 that a binomially distributed random variable is the sum of certain other random variables and in Section 10.5 that a linear combination of several independent normally distributed random variables has a normal distribution. Sections 10.2 and 10.3 contain generalizations of the material in Section 10.1 and of the binomial distribution. Formulas for the mean and variance of a linear combination of any given random variables are presented in Section 10.4. Finally, integral transforms are used in Section 10.6 to study the probability distributions of sums of independent random variables.

10.1   Independent Bernoulli Trials

As will become apparent, certain mathematical models of basic importance in probability theory are those that have evolved from considerations of a sequence of trials of an experiment whose outcomes have been classified in two categories, usually called "success" and "failure" and denoted by the letters S and F. The model for a single trial of such an experiment is called a *Bernoulli trial*. For one Bernoulli trial, the sample space is usually taken to be $\Omega = \{S, F\}$, the set of two letters S and F; and probabilities are assigned to the four subsets of Ω in terms of two given nonnegative numbers p and q, such that

$$P(\{F\}) = q, \qquad P(\{S\}) = p, \qquad p + q = 1. \qquad (10.1)$$

159

Actually, every Bernoulli trial is conceptually equivalent to the model for tossing a biased coin once, for which p is the probability of a "head" and q is the probability of a "tail."

Now let X be the discrete random variable on Ω defined by

$$X(F) = 0, \qquad X(S) = 1. \tag{10.2}$$

Intuitively, X assumes the value 1 (or 0) when a success (or failure) occurs. The probability distribution of X is called the *Bernoulli distribution* with parameter p and has the probability function given by

$$g(0) = q, \qquad g(1) = p \qquad (p \geq 0, q \geq 0, p + q = 1). \tag{10.3}$$

Given an experiment of the above type, recall that there was constructed in Section 7.1 a certain probability space $(\Omega_n, \mathcal{S}_n, P_n)$ as a model for a sequence of n independent repeated trials of the given experiment. This sample space Ω_n is composed of the 2^n ordered n-tuples of the form $(\omega_{n1}, \omega_{n2}, \ldots, \omega_{nn})$, where ω_{nk} for $k = 1, 2, \ldots, n$ denotes any one of the elements in Ω; that is, $\omega_{nk} = S$ or F. Thus, each elementary event (member of Ω_n) represents a sequence of possible outcomes of n successive trials of the given experiment. Also, recall from Section 7.1 that P_n is defined by assigning to each elementary event containing k S's and $(n - k)$ F's the probability $p^k q^{n-k}$. This model is often called n *independent repeated Bernoulli trials*.

In order to prove a useful theorem and also to exhibit a family of independent random variables, we will now introduce a certain random variable X_k for each $k = 1, 2, \ldots, n$. X_k assumes the value 1 (or 0) when, in intuitive terms, the outcome of the kth trial is success (or failure). These X_k are n random variables defined simultaneously on the same sample space Ω_n. To be precise, for each $k = 1, 2, \ldots, n$, let X_k denote the random variable on Ω_n which takes the value 1 when $\omega_{nk} = S$ and the value 0 when $\omega_{nk} = F$, where ω_{nk} denotes the kth element of an ordered n-tuple in Ω_n. In terms of the events A_k and their complements A_k^c introduced in Section 7.1, X_k can be described by

$$X_k(A_k) = 1, \qquad X_k(A_k^c) = 0. \tag{10.4}$$

Since it was shown in Section 7.1 that $P_n(A_k) = p$ and $P_n(A_k^c) = q$, it follows from Eq. 10.4 that every one of the random variables X_k has the probability function given in Eq. 10.3 and therefore has a Bernoulli distribution with parameter p.

For n independent repeated Bernoulli trials, it was also indicated in

Section 7.1 that any n events with distinct subscripts among the $2n$ events A_k and A_k^c for $k = 1, 2, \ldots, n$ are independent. An easy direct consequence of this and Eq. 10.4 is that the value assumed by any one of the random variables X_k is not related in any manner to the values assumed by the remaining ones. This agrees with the intuitive notion that when a coin is tossed independently n times, the outcome of any toss should not be related to the outcomes of the other tosses. In terms of the discussion in Section 9.3, the X_k are thus independent random variables.

Next, we introduce the *sum* S_n of the n random variables X_k; i.e., we let

$$S_n = X_1 + X_2 + \cdots + X_n. \tag{10.5}$$

This sum is a function whose domain is the sample space Ω_n and is therefore a random variable on Ω_n, since each of the X_k's has this property. Thus, the random variable S_n is the sum of n independent Bernoulli-distributed random variables, which have the same parameter p. Intuitively, S_n gives the number of successes during n independent repeated trials and is therefore identical to the random variable S_n shown in Section 7.1 to have the binomial distribution with parameters (n, p).

We have thus obtained the following result: *The sum of n independent random variables having Bernoulli distributions with a common parameter p has the binomial distribution with parameters (n, p).* This is the simplest of several *addition theorems* for independent random variables, which are extremely useful in probability theory.

For a final remark, suppose one is interested in the number of heads obtained when one tosses, once, each of n different biased coins. An appropriate model for such an experiment is a simple generalization of the above model, which is obtained by removing the requirement that the X_k's have the same parameter p. Thus given any $2n$ nonnegative numbers p_k and q_k such that $p_k + q_k = 1$ for $k = 1, 2, \ldots, n$, the probability P_n can be redefined (by the reader) so that X_k has the probability function given by

$$\begin{aligned} g_k(0) &= P_n(X_k = 0) = q_k, \\ g_k(1) &= P_n(X_k = 1) = p_k. \end{aligned} \tag{10.6}$$

In this case, S_n is still the sum of n independent Bernoulli-distributed random variables but does not generally have a binomial distribution; some properties of its distribution are given in Sections 10.4 and 10.6.

10.2   Generalized Independent Bernoulli Trials

It is instructive (but not explicitly useful elsewhere in this book except in some exercises) to consider briefly how the material in Section 10.1 can be generalized in certain directions. As a first step, we consider the analogs for a sequence of n independent tosses of a biased die. For a single toss, the six possible outcomes are denoted here by $E_1, E_2, \ldots, E_6$, with E_i the outcome that i dots appeared on the upturned face. Thus, we can set $\Omega = \{E_1, E_2, \ldots, E_6\}$ and can assign probabilities to the subsets of Ω by choosing six nonnegative numbers $p_1, p_2, \ldots, p_6$ for which $p_1 + p_2 + \cdots + p_6 = 1$ and by setting $P(\{E_i\}) = p_i$. (Of course, each p_i should be chosen in some way so that it approximates the relative frequency of the appearance of i dots.) The sample space Ω_n can be defined as the set of 6^n ordered n-tuples in which each element is $E_1, E_2, \ldots,$ or E_6. The set function P_n can be defined by assigning to each elementary event (ordered n-tuple) containing n_1 E_1's, n_2 E_2's, $\ldots,$ and n_6 E_6's the probability $p_1^{n_1} p_2^{n_2} \cdots p_6^{n_6}$, for every set of nonnegative integers $n_1, n_2, \ldots, n_6$ for which $n_1 + n_2 + \cdots + n_6 = n$. (See the exercises for a proof, using Eq. 10.7, that the sum of these probabilities is indeed 1.) This model reduces to that of the preceding section if one replaces the subscript 6 by 2 and then sets $p_1 = p$, $p_2 = q$, $n_1 = k$, and $n_2 = n - k$.

Given any probability space, one can of course construct and analyze many different families, or collections, of random variables. However, both theoretical and applied considerations usually dictate particular interest in certain specific families of random variables. In the present case, for example, one is often interested in the family of n independent random variables $X_1, X_2, \ldots, X_n$ defined on Ω_n so that each X_k represents the number of dots appearing at the kth toss. Then, for example, the sum S_n in Eq. 10.5 represents the total number of dots that appear during all n tosses, and the random variable S_n/n represents the arithmetic average number of dots per toss. The reader should be able to use various results presented in later sections to find the properties of such random variables.

In the following discussion a certain generalization of the binomial distribution will be derived, because it is important and also because it illustrates a family of *dependent* (not independent) random variables. For each $i = 1, 2, \ldots, 6$, let the discrete random variable Y_i have as possible values the numbers of times the symbol E_i can appear in an ordered n-tuple in Ω_n. Thus the possible values of Y_i are 0, 1, . . . , n. Intuitively, Y_i represents the number of times exactly i dots appear when the die is tossed n times. Since some number of dots must appear on each toss, the relation $Y_1 + Y_2 + \cdots + Y_6 = n$ must hold, so that the Y_i's are very much related and hence $Y_1, Y_2, \ldots, Y_6$ is a family of dependent random variables.

Now, given n and six nonnegative numbers $n_1, n_2, \ldots, n_6$, for which $n_1 + n_2 + \cdots + n_6 = n$, consider the probability, to be denoted by $g_n(n_1, n_2, \ldots, n_6)$, that the six relations $Y_1 = n_1$, $Y_2 = n_2, \ldots, Y_6 = n_6$ are simultaneously satisfied. In other words, we desire the probability of the compound event composed of all n-tuples in Ω_n which contain exactly $n_1\, E_1$'s, $n_2\, E_2$'s, . . . , and $n_6\, E_6$'s. The number of n-tuples in this compound event is simply the number of permutations of n objects in which n_i of the objects are alike $(i = 1, 2, \ldots, 6)$ and is thus $n!/n_1!n_2! \cdots n_6!$. Since every elementary event of interest here has the same probability $p_1^{n_1}p_2^{n_2} \cdots p_6^{n_6}$, we thus find that

$$g_n(n_1, n_2, \ldots, n_6) = \frac{n!}{n_1!n_2! \cdots n_6!} p_1^{n_1}p_2^{n_2} \cdots p_6^{n_6} \quad (10.7)$$

for every set of nonnegative integers $n_1, n_2, \ldots, n_6$ for which $n_1 + n_2 + \cdots + n_6 = n$.

As described in Chapter 9, we say that the random variables $Y_1, Y_2, \ldots, Y_6$ have the *joint distribution* which has the *joint probability function* given in Eq. 10.7. This joint distribution is a generalization of the binomial distribution and is a special multinomial distribution. The joint probability function for the *general multinomial distribution* has the form of Eq. 10.7 with the subscript 6 replaced by an arbitrary positive integer m, so that g_n becomes a function of m discrete variables.

With the subscript 6 replaced by an arbitrary positive integer m in the above discussion, it should now be clear how the material in Section 10.1 can be extended to obtain a mathematical model for a sequence of n independent trials of an experiment whose outcomes have been classified in m different categories. More difficult but valid extensions are those in which each idealized trial may have a countably infinite or even an uncountably infinite number of possible outcomes.

For example, it is often expedient to idealize an experiment so that each trial has as its possible outcomes the set of all real numbers. Then the sample space Ω_n is simply all of ordinary n-dimensional Euclidean space, S_n is of course a very complicated collection of subsets of Ω_n, and P_n must be defined in some way in accordance with the particular situation of interest. For example, one might (but does not have to) think of such a probability space for the n normally distributed random variables considered in Section 10.5.

In order to indicate just how far this process of generalization can be pushed, we finally mention some other extensions of the above models, which involve ideas of basic importance in the general theories of probability and stochastic processes. First observe that one is very often interested in the behavior as n varies (usually as $n \to \infty$) of some statistical property of the outcomes of n trials of some experiment, such as the sum in Eq. 10.5. In such cases, it is mathematically desirable to have a *fixed* probability space (Ω, S, P) which does not depend on n, as do those probability spaces previously considered in this chapter. For this purpose, one useful sample space Ω can be obtained (roughly speaking) by letting $n \to \infty$ in the appropriate one of those models indicated previously. Then Ω is a collection of *infinite sequences* instead of ordered n-tuples. But, since an infinite sequence can be viewed as a function whose domain is the set of all positive integers, we can say that such a sample space is a set of functions of a particular type. Now, it is a simple matter, at least intuitively, to consider the possibility of more general sample spaces, which are collections of functions of more general types. For example, one can consider as a sample space the collection of all real-valued functions of one variable t which are continuous at every real value of t. The construction and profitable use of probability spaces and families of random variables on such complicated sample spaces can be accomplished by using advanced mathematical methods, which obviously cannot be pursued here.

10.3   Stochastic Processes

We pause here to point out that the material of Chapters 10, 11, and 12 actually constitutes a discussion of some properties of certain simple stochastic processes and that most of it can be extended for more general stochastic processes.

Although any finite family of random variables (such as those families considered previously in this chapter) is sometimes called a *finite stochastic process*, the name "stochastic process" is generally reserved for a family containing an *infinite* number of random variables. More precisely, a *stochastic process* is a family of random variables (on any given probability space) that contains one random variable X_t for every element t in some given infinite set T of real numbers or of more general objects, such that every finite collection of the form $X_{t_1}, X_{t_2}, \ldots, X_{t_m}$ has a joint distribution. Furthermore, the set of all these joint distributions must be *consistent* in the sense that the joint distribution of any finite set of random variables, say

$$Y = (X_{t_1}, X_{t_2}, \ldots, X_{t_m}),$$

must be identical with the marginal joint distribution of this set Y obtained from the joint distribution of any finite set of random variables containing the set Y as a subset.

For example, if T is the set of all positive integers, the stochastic process is an infinite sequence $X_1, X_2, X_3, \ldots$ of random variables. In Chapters 11 and 12, we will be interested primarily in the probabilistic behavior as $n \to \infty$ of the sum S_n of the first n random variables in such a sequence.

The name stochastic process usually also connotes that the parameter t represents "time," so that one has a random variable X_t associated with each time in some set of times. For example, the models of Sections 10.1 and 10.2 can be interpreted in this way if we imagine that one trial is performed at the end of each one-minute period of time, so that the kth trial occurs at time k minutes. Thus, the theory of stochastic processes may be called the dynamic part of statistical theory, because it is concerned with the time-dependent behavior of random processes.

For a simple but important intuitive example of a stochastic process, consider very small particles immersed in a gas or liquid, such as smoke particles suspended in air. In 1827, the English botanist Robert Brown first observed with a microscope the phenomenon, now known as Brownian motion, that such particles exhibit ceaseless irregular motion. Let the random variable S_t denote the displacement after t minutes of a particle in Brownian motion from its starting point. Einstein showed in 1905 that S_t has a normal distribution with mean 0, variance $2Dt$, and hence the density function

$$f(x) = \left(\frac{1}{4\pi Dt}\right)^{1/2} \exp\left[-x^2/4Dt\right],$$

where D is a diffusion coefficient which depends on the absolute temperature and the friction coefficient of the surrounding medium. In this case, there is clearly a random variable S_t for every nonnegative real number t.

Finally, recall from the exercises of Chapter 7 the derivation of the Poisson probability function by means of a certain system of differential equations. We remark that generalizations of this derivation lead naturally to a class of stochastic processes known as Markov processes. For an excellent introductory account of this, the reader is referred to the last chapter of Feller's book listed in the bibliography.

10.4   Mean and Variance of a Linear Function

Let $X_1, X_2, \ldots, X_n$ be any n given random variables. (Here and subsequently, every such reference to several random variables is to contain implicitly the assumption that all of the random variables are associated with the same probability space and therefore have a joint distribution. Although any abstract probability space is adequate for this general purpose, it is sometimes very helpful to think of one of those probability spaces indicated in Sections 10.1 and 10.2.) If $c_0, c_1, c_2, \ldots, c_n$ are any given real-valued constants such that at least one of $c_1, c_2, \ldots, c_n$ is not zero, we consider in this section the mean and variance of the new random variable Y defined by

$$Y = c_0 + c_1X_1 + c_2X_2 + \cdots + c_nX_n. \tag{10.8}$$

In Section 9.5, it was shown that *the mean of Y can be expressed in terms of the means of the X_k's in the form*

$$E(Y) = c_0 + c_1E(X_1) + c_2E(X_2) + \cdots + c_nE(X_n), \tag{10.9}$$

if every X_k has a finite mean. That this relation is plausible for discrete random variables can be seen by viewing the mean as a weighted arithmetic average of the type indicated in Section 6.2.

In general, the variance of Y involves the *covariance* σ_{ij} of each pair of random variables X_i and X_j. Although a detailed treatment of the covariance is given in Section 9.6, it is necessary to have here only its basic mathematical properties. First, it can be expressed in terms of the means μ_i and μ_j of X_i and X_j as

$$\sigma_{ij} = E[(X_i - \mu_i)(X_j - \mu_j)] = E(X_iX_j) - \mu_i\mu_j, \qquad (10.10)$$

where the last equality follows from Eq. 10.9 after the product $(X_i - \mu_i)(X_j - \mu_j)$ is expanded. If X_i and X_j have finite variances, then they necessarily have a finite covariance and also finite means. If $i = j$ so that X_i and X_j are the same random variable, Eq. 10.10 reduces to the variance $\sigma_i^2 = \sigma_{ii}$ of X_i. Finally, for any two *independent* (or merely uncorrelated) random variables X_i and X_j, $E(X_iX_j) = \mu_i\mu_j$, and thus $\sigma_{ij} = 0$.

The variance of the random variable Y in Eq. 10.8 is given by

$$\sigma^2 = \sum_{i=1}^{n} \sum_{j=1}^{n} c_ic_j\sigma_{ij}, \qquad (10.11)$$

if every random variable X_k has a finite variance. To derive this formula, note that Eqs. 10.8 and 10.9 imply that

$$Y - \mu = \sum_{k=1}^{n} c_k(X_k - \mu_k),$$

where $\mu = E(Y)$ and $\mu_k = E(X_k)$. This and Eqs. 10.9 and 10.10 show that

$$\begin{aligned}
\sigma^2 &= E[(Y - \mu)^2] \\
&= E\left[\sum_{i=1}^{n} \sum_{j=1}^{n} c_ic_j(X_i - \mu_i)(X_j - \mu_j) \right] \\
&= \sum_{i=1}^{n} \sum_{j=1}^{n} c_ic_jE[(X_i - \mu_i)(X_j - \mu_j)] \\
&= \sum_{i=1}^{n} \sum_{j=1}^{n} c_ic_j\sigma_{ij},
\end{aligned}$$

which is the desired result.

When $X_1, X_2, \ldots, X_n$ are independent (or merely uncorrelated) random variables, Eq. 10.11 reduces to the important formula

$$\sigma^2 = \sum_{k=1}^{n} c_k^2\sigma_k^2, \qquad (10.12)$$

since then $\sigma_{ij} = 0$ for all $i, j = 1, 2, \ldots, n$ with $i \neq j$ and $\sigma_{ii} = \sigma_i^2$.

Example 10.1. Consider a sequence of n independent random variables X_k having Bernoulli distributions of the form of Eq. 10.6, which are not necessarily identical. Then each X_k has the mean

$$\mu_k = (0)q_k + (1)p_k = p_k$$

and the variance

$$\sigma_k^2 = E(X_k^2) - \mu_k^2 = (0)q_k + (1)p_k - p_k^2 = p_k q_k.$$

With $c_0 = 0$ and $c_k = 1$ for $k = 1, 2, \ldots, n$, Eqs. 10.9 and 10.12 now show that the sum S_n of these n random variables has the mean μ and the variance σ^2 given by

$$\mu = \sum_{k=1}^{n} p_k \text{ and } \sigma^2 = \sum_{k=1}^{n} p_k q_k.$$

If the n X_k's are identically distributed so that $p_k = p$ and $q_k = q$ for $k = 1, 2, \ldots, n$, then these formulas reduce to $\mu = np$ and $\sigma^2 = npq$. Since S_n has a binomial distribution with parameters (n, p) in this case, we have just proved that the mean and variance of a binomial distribution are np and npq. Of course, these results agree with those obtained in Section 7.1 from the moment-generating function.

10.5 Linear Function of Normal Random Variables

As discussed in Sections 5.7 and 9.4, a general problem that frequently arises can be stated as follows: Given that a new random variable Y is defined in terms of a function of one or several other random variables, derive the distribution of Y. The addition theorem derived in Section 10.1 provides a simple example. Such problems often amount basically to variable transformations and can be solved by using any one of several different mathematical procedures. In this section, we will use a general elementary method to solve one such problem and thus to prove a very important theorem, which will be useful in Chapter 12. A shorter, more elegant derivation of this result is given as an example in Section 10.6.

The following theorem will be proved: *Let the random variables $X_1, X_2, \ldots, X_n$ appearing in Eq. 10.8 be independent and have normal distributions with respective parameters $(\mu_1, \sigma_1), (\mu_2, \sigma_2), \ldots,$*

(μ_n, σ_n). *Then the random variable Y of Eq. 10.8 has a normal distribution whose mean μ and variance σ^2 are given by*

$$\mu = c_0 + c_1\mu_1 + c_2\mu_2 + \cdots + c_n\mu_n$$
$$\sigma^2 = c_1^2\sigma_1^2 + c_2^2\sigma_2^2 + \cdots + c_n^2\sigma_n^2. \tag{10.13}$$

To prove this theorem, it is sufficient to consider the following two special cases: (A) $Y = a + bX$, where a and $b \neq 0$ are real constants and X has a normal distribution, and (B) $Z = X + Y$, where X and Y have normal distributions. It is left as an exercise for the reader to show that the theorem follows from these two results at once by induction. (Actually, Eq. 10.13 also follows immediately from Eqs. 10.9 and 10.12.)

PROOF FOR CASE (A)

Let

$$f(x) = \frac{1}{\sqrt{2\pi}\sigma} \exp\left[-(x - \mu)^2/2\sigma^2\right] \qquad (-\infty < x < \infty).$$

Then, for $b > 0$, the distribution function of $Y = a + bX$ is given by

$$G(y) = P(Y \leq y) = P(a + bX \leq y)$$
$$= P\left(X \leq \frac{y - a}{b}\right) = \int_{-\infty}^{(y-a)/b} f(x)\, dx \qquad (-\infty < y < \infty),$$

and the corresponding density function is

$$g(y) = \frac{d}{dy} G(y) = \frac{1}{b} f\left(\frac{y - a}{b}\right) \qquad (b > 0).$$

For $b < 0$, $b = -|b|$,

$$G(y) = P(a - |b|X \leq y) = P\left(X \geq \frac{y - a}{b}\right)$$
$$= \int_{(y-a)/b}^{\infty} f(x)\, dx = 1 - \int_{-\infty}^{(y-a)/b} f(x)\, dx \qquad (-\infty < y < \infty),$$

and

$$g(y) = -\frac{1}{b} f\left(\frac{y - a}{b}\right) = \frac{1}{|b|} f\left(\frac{y - a}{b}\right) \qquad (b < 0).$$

Thus, for $b \neq 0$, we can multiply $f(x)$ by $1/|b|$ and replace x by

$(y - a)/b$ to find that Y has the density function

$$g(y) = \frac{1}{\sqrt{2\pi}(|b|\sigma)} \exp\left[-[y - (a + b\mu)]^2/2b^2\sigma^2\right] \qquad (-\infty < y < \infty),$$

which is the density function of a normal distribution with mean $a + b\mu$ and variance $b^2\sigma^2$.

PROOF FOR CASE (B)

As described in Sections 9.1 through 9.3, two independent continuous random variables X and Y with density functions f_1 and f_2 have a joint distribution with the joint density function f given by $f(x, y) = f_1(x)f_2(y)$, so that the total probability 1 is (intuitively speaking) smeared over a region of the (x, y) plane instead of over a single axis of real numbers. In the present case, $f(x, y)$ is the product of two normal density functions, so that

$$f(x, y) = \frac{1}{2\pi\sigma_1\sigma_2} \exp\left[-\frac{(x - \mu_1)^2}{2\sigma_1^2} - \frac{(y - \mu_2)^2}{2\sigma_2^2}\right],$$

for $-\infty < x, y < \infty$.

For every fixed z, the value of the distribution function $G(z)$ of the random variable $Z = X + Y$ is simply the probability that $X + Y \leq z$ and can be obtained by integrating $f(x, y)$ over that part of the (x, y) plane for which $x + y \leq z$; thus,

$$G(z) = \int_{-\infty}^{\infty} f_1(x) \, dx \int_{-\infty}^{z-x} f_2(y) \, dy.$$

Differentiation of this relation gives the density function

$$g(z) = \int_{-\infty}^{\infty} f_1(x)f_2(z - x) \, dx \qquad (-\infty < z < \infty).$$

To show that g is the density function of a normal distribution, first note that

$$f_1(x)f_2(z - x) = \frac{1}{2\pi\sigma_1\sigma_2} e^{-Q},$$

where

$$Q = \frac{(x - \mu_1)^2}{2\sigma_1^2} + \frac{(z - x - \mu_2)^2}{2\sigma_2^2}.$$

Now, complete the square on x to find that

$$Q = \frac{\sigma_1^2 + \sigma_2^2}{2\sigma_1^2\sigma_2^2} \left(x - \frac{\sigma_2^2\mu_1 + \sigma_1^2 z - \sigma_1^2\mu_2}{\sigma_1^2 + \sigma_2^2} \right)^2 + \frac{(z - \mu_1 - \mu_2)^2}{2(\sigma_1^2 + \sigma_2^2)}.$$

Next, let

$$\mu = \mu_1 + \mu_2,$$

$$\sigma^2 = \sigma_1^2 + \sigma_2^2,$$

$$u = x - \frac{\sigma_2^2\mu_1 + \sigma_1^2 z - \sigma_1^2\mu_2}{\sigma_1^2 + \sigma_2^2}.$$

Then,

$$g(z) = \frac{1}{2\pi\sigma_1\sigma_2} \int_{-\infty}^{\infty} e^{-Q} \, dx$$

$$= \frac{1}{2\pi\sigma_1\sigma_2} \exp\left[-(z-\mu)^2/2\sigma^2\right] \int_{-\infty}^{\infty} \exp\left[-\sigma^2 u^2/2\sigma_1^2\sigma_2^2\right] du.$$

Letting $v = \sigma u/\sigma_1\sigma_2$ and $du = \sigma_1\sigma_2 \, dv/\sigma$ in this shows that

$$g(z) = \frac{1}{2\pi\sigma} \exp\left[-(z-\mu)^2/2\sigma^2\right] \int_{-\infty}^{\infty} e^{-v^2/2} \, dv$$

$$= \frac{1}{\sqrt{2\pi}\,\sigma} \exp\left[-(z-\mu)^2/2\sigma^2\right] \qquad (-\infty < z < \infty),$$

since we know from Section 8.2 that

$$\frac{1}{\sqrt{2\pi}} \int_{-\infty}^{\infty} e^{-v^2/2} \, dv = 1.$$

Thus $Z = X + Y$ has the density function of a normal distribution with mean $\mu = \mu_1 + \mu_2$ and variance $\sigma^2 = \sigma_1^2 + \sigma_2^2$.

10.6   Convolutions

In Section 9.4, Eq. 9.31, it was shown that the density function of the sum Y of two *independent* absolutely continuous random variables X_1 and X_2 with density functions f_1 and f_2 is given by

$$f_Y(y) = \int_{-\infty}^{\infty} f_1(y - x) f_2(x) \, dx \qquad (10.14)$$

for all real values of y.

An analogous relation can easily be derived for the sum of two *independent* discrete random variables X_1 and X_2 which have only nonnegative integers for possible values. Thus, for $i = 1$ and 2 and $k = 0, 1, 2, \ldots$, let $g_i(k) = P(X_i = k)$, where $g_i(k)$ may have the value 0 at any number of values of k so long as it is a probability function. The event $\{X_1 = j, X_2 = k\}$ then has the probability $g_1(j)g_2(k)$, since X_1 and X_2 are independent. The event $\{X_1 + X_2 = r\}$ is the union of the $r + 1$ mutually exclusive events

$$\{X_1 = r, X_2 = 0\}, \{X_1 = r - 1, X_2 = 1\}, \ldots , \{X_1 = 0, X_2 = r\}.$$

Therefore, the probability function g_Y of $Y = X_1 + X_2$ is given by

$$g_Y(r) = g_1(r)g_2(0) + g_1(r - 1)g_2(1) + \cdots + g_1(0)g_2(r)$$

$$= \sum_{k=0}^{r} g_1(r - k)g_2(k) \tag{10.15}$$

for $r = 0, 1, 2, \ldots$.

If F_1 and F_2 are the distribution functions of X_1 and X_2, it easily follows from Eqs. 10.14 and 10.15 that the distribution function F_Y of $Y = X_1 + X_2$ for either of these special cases is given by

$$F_Y(y) = \int_{-\infty}^{\infty} F_1(y - x) \, dF_2(x) \qquad (-\infty < y < \infty). \tag{10.16}$$

Furthermore, it can be shown that the distribution function of the sum of *any* two *independent* random variables is given by Eq. 10.16.

The mathematical operation leading to the left side of Eq. 10.14, 10.15, or 10.16 from the two functions appearing in the right side occurs frequently in mathematics. This operation is called a *convolution* (or composition, or faltung) and is often denoted by $*$. Thus, the above three equations may be written as $f_Y = f_1 * f_2$, $g_Y = g_1 * g_2$, and $F_Y = F_1 * F_2$. We also say, for example, that F_Y is the convolution of F_1 and F_2.

Of course, Eq. 10.16 can be used repeatedly to find the convolution F_Y of the distribution functions $F_1, F_2, \ldots , F_n$ of n independent random variables X_k. This convolution F_Y is the distribution function of the sum Y of the n X_k's and may be written as

$$F_Y = F_1 * F_2 * \cdots * F_n. \tag{10.17}$$

Instead of explicitly performing the $(n - 1)$ integrations indicated in Eq. 10.17, one can often compute a convolution much more efficiently by using moment-generating functions, characteristic functions, or discrete generating functions. For this purpose, recall that it was shown in Section 9.5, Eq. 9.51, that the moment-generating function

M_Y of the sum $Y = X_1 + X_2 + \cdots + X_n$ of n independent random variables is given by

$$M_Y(\theta) = M_1(\theta)M_2(\theta) \cdots M_n(\theta) \qquad (10.18)$$

when the moment-generating functions M_k of all the random variables X_k exist. If the random variables X_k are also identically distributed so that $M_k(\theta) = M_X(\theta)$ for $k = 1, 2, \ldots, n$, Eq. 10.18 reduces to the important special case

$$M_Y(\theta) = M_X^n(\theta). \qquad (10.19)$$

When M_Y can be evaluated from either of these relations, one can usually use the properties of moment-generating functions discussed in Section 6.5 to find various properties of the sum Y.

Note that Eq. 10.18 is a symbolic statement of the following theorem: *The moment-generating function of the sum of several independent random variables is equal to the product of their separate moment-generating functions, if all the random variables have moment-generating functions.* Of course, this theorem remains true if "moment-generating" is replaced by "characteristic" or by "discrete generating."

Example 10.2. Use moment-generating functions to derive the theorem of Section 10.5. First, recall that the moment-generating function of a normally distributed random variable X_k with mean μ_k and variance σ_k^2 is

$$M_k(\theta) = \exp\left(\mu_k\theta + \frac{\sigma_k^2\theta^2}{2}\right).$$

Now, note that the moment-generating functions of $c_0 + c_1X_1$ and c_kX_k are

$$E[\exp(c_0\theta + c_1\theta X_1)] = \exp(c_0\theta)M_1(c_1\theta)$$

and

$$E[\exp(c_k\theta X_k)] = M_k(c_k\theta).$$

Since $c_0 + c_1X_1, c_2X_2, \ldots, c_nX_n$ are n independent random variables, a direct application of Eq. 10.18 shows that

$$M_Y(\theta) = \exp(c_0\theta)M_1(c_1\theta)M_2(c_2\theta) \cdots M_n(c_n\theta)$$

$$= \exp(c_0\theta)\prod_{k=1}^{n}\exp\left(c_k\mu_k\theta + \frac{c_k^2\sigma_k^2\theta^2}{2}\right)$$

$$= \exp\left(\mu\theta + \frac{\sigma^2\theta^2}{2}\right)$$

where μ and σ^2 are given in Eq. 10.13. Therefore, Y has a normal distribution with mean μ and variance σ^2.

Example 10.3.   Consider the sum S_n of n independent random variables X_k having Bernoulli distributions of the form of Eq. 10.6 that are not necessarily identical. Then the moment-generating function of each X_k is $M_k(\theta) = q_k + p_k e^\theta$, and Eq. 10.18 therefore shows that the moment-generating function M_n^* of S_n is given by

$$M_n^*(\theta) = \prod_{k=1}^n (q_k + p_k e^\theta). \tag{10.20}$$

But, since also

$$M_n^*(\theta) = \sum_{j=0}^n g_n(j) e^{j\theta}, \tag{10.21}$$

where $g_n(j) = P(S_n = j)$ is the probability function of S_n, one can find $g_n(j)$ as the coefficient of $e^{j\theta}$ when Eq. 10.20 is expanded in the form of Eq. 10.21. Thus, for $n = 2$, $g_2(0) = q_1 q_2$, $g_2(1) = q_1 p_2 + p_1 q_2$, and $g_2(2) = p_1 p_2$, which can easily be checked directly. Using the methods of Section 6.5, one can of course find from Eq. 10.20 all moments of S_n. Finally, if the n X_k's are identically distributed so that $M_k(\theta) = q + p e^\theta$, Eq. 10.19 or 10.20 shows that

$$M_n^*(\theta) = (q + p e^\theta)^n,$$

thus proving once more that the sum of n independent random variables having a common Bernoulli distribution has a binomial distribution.

10.7   Exercises

10.1   In terms of independent repeated Bernoulli trials, discuss: (a) Exercise 7.1(a), (b) Exercise 7.1(b), (c) Exercise 7.2, and (d) Exercise 7.3.

10.2   In Experiment 1.1, let success occur if the number on the upper horizontal face is 5, 10, 15, or 20, and let failure occur if any other number appears. Use the procedure of Section 10.1 to find the probability of k successes in n independent trials.

10.3   Suppose each of m people independently and simultaneously tosses a coin, which has probability p_1 of heads, where $m \geq 3$.   (a) What is the probability p of an "odd man"; i.e., that either exactly one head or exactly one tail will result? (b) What is this probability when $m = 5$ and all the coins are "fair," with $p_1 = \frac{1}{2}$? (Recall the game of "odd man out.")

10.4 The *negative binomial distribution* with parameters (r, p), for $r > 0$, $0 \le p \le 1$, and $q = 1 - p$, has the probability function

$$g(x) = \binom{r + x - 1}{x} p^r q^x \qquad (x = 0, 1, 2, \ldots),$$

where, by definition,

$$\binom{r + x - 1}{x} = \frac{1}{x!} (r + x - 1)(r + x - 2) \cdots (r + 1)(r).$$

(a) Show that

$$\binom{r + x - 1}{x} = (-1)^x \binom{-r}{x}$$

and then use the binomial theorem to show that g is indeed a probability function. (b) Find the moment-generating function of this distribution.

10.5 In an unlimited sequence of independent repeated Bernoulli trials, let the random variable S_r denote the number of failures encountered before the rth success, where r is any positive integer. Use a simple combinatorial argument to show that S_r has the distribution of Exercise 10.4. (When r is a positive integer, this distribution is often called the *Pascal distribution*. For $r = 1$ it reduces to the *geometric distribution*.)

10.6 Consider an unlimited sequence of independent trials of the experiment of Exercise 10.3. (a) If $p_1 = \frac{1}{2}$ and $m = 5$, what is the probability that at least three trials are required to get an "odd man"? What is the average number of trials required? (b) With the same p_1 and m, describe the distribution of S_r, if $S_r + r$ is the number of the trial at which the rth appearance of "odd man" occurs. (c) Show that S_r can be written as $S_r = X_1 + X_2 + \cdots + X_r$, where the X_k's are independent and have the same geometric distribution.

10.7 If a balanced die is tossed independently n times, what is the joint probability function of the random variables $Y_1, Y_2, \ldots, Y_6$ defined in Section 10.2? What is the probability that $(Y_1, Y_2, \ldots, Y_6)$ takes the value $(0, 2, 0, 1, 2, 0)$?

10.8 Suppose that the weather in a certain locale is classified for each day as good, fair, or bad, and that these occur with the respective relative frequencies $\frac{1}{4}$, $\frac{1}{2}$, and $\frac{1}{4}$. If weather conditions for successive days were statistically independent, what would be the likelihood of one good, four fair, and two bad days during a week?

10.9 Show that the sum, Σ^*, of Eq. 10.7 over all nonnegative $n_1, n_2, \ldots, n_6$ for which $n_1 + n_2 + \cdots + n_6 = n$ is 1. *Hint:*

$$\Sigma^* g_n(n_1, n_2, \ldots, n_6) = (p_1 + p_2 + \cdots + p_6)^n.$$

10.10 As described in Section 10.3, the displacement after t minutes of a particle in Brownian motion has (approximately) the normal density function

$$f(t, x) = (4\pi Dt)^{-1/2} \exp(-x^2/4Dt) \qquad (-\infty < x < \infty, t > 0).$$

Show that this function satisfies the partial differential equation

$$\frac{\partial f}{\partial t} = D \frac{\partial^2 f}{\partial x^2},$$

which is basic in the theories of heat conduction and diffusion.

10.11   Use Eqs. 10.9 and 10.11 to find the mean and standard deviation of the number of successes in ten independent trials of the experiment described in Exercise 10.2.

10.12   If X and Y have the distribution of Example 9.1, compute the mean and variance of $Z = -5 + 2X - 4Y$.

10.13   A certain factory produces bolts, whose individual weight can be viewed as a random variable with mean 2 ounces and standard deviation 0.03 ounce. What is the average and standard deviation of the weight of 100 such bolts?

10.14   (a) If S_r has the Pascal distribution of Exercise 10.5, use the representation of S_r as a sum, illustrated in Exercise 10.6(c), to find the mean and variance of S_r. (b) Find the mean and variance of the negative binomial distribution of Exercise 10.4 from its moment-generating function.

10.15   (a) Carbon resistors as delivered by the manufacturer have a "nominal" value, e.g., 100 ohms. The actual resistance of such a resistor is $(100 + X)$ ohms, where X can be viewed as a random variable with zero mean. In so-called "silver tolerance" resistors the standard deviation of X is 5 percent of the nominal value (e.g., 5 ohms in the case of a 100-ohm resistor), whereas in "gold tolerance" resistors the standard deviation is 1 percent of the nominal value. Are n 100-ohm silver-tolerance resistors, in series, as good as a single $100n$-ohm gold-tolerance resistor? (b) Discuss other situations of this type; e.g., measuring long distances with short rulers, or large volumes of liquid with small graduates.

10.16   Let X, Y, and Z be independent random variables whose respective standard deviations are 12, 5, and 9. Find numerical values for the covariance and the coefficient of correlation of the two random variables $U = X + Y$ and $V = X - Z$.

*10.17   In Example 10.1, let $p = (p_1 + p_2 + \cdots + p_n)/n$ be the average probability of success, and show that $\text{Var}(S_n) = np - \Sigma p_k^2$. For fixed p and n, deduce (by calculus) that, among all permissible values of $p_1, p_2, \ldots, p_n$ such that $\Sigma p_k = np$, $\text{Var}(S_n)$ assumes its *maximum* value when $p_1 = p_2 = \cdots = p_n = p$. Explain how this suggests the following conclusion: For a fixed average quality p of n independent machines or workers, the output will be least uniform when all the machines or workers are equal. Can you apply this more generally—for example, to education or politics?

*10.18   From an urn containing m red and n white balls, k balls are selected at random, one at a time and without replacement, where $0 < k \leq (m + n)$. For $j = 1, 2, \ldots , k$, let X_j be a random variable that assumes the values 1 or 0 according to whether the jth ball selected is or is not red. (a) Show that $P(X_j = 1) = m/(m + n)$ and therefore that

$$E(X_j) = \frac{m}{m + n}, \qquad \text{Var } (X_j) = \frac{mn}{(m + n)^2}.$$

(b) If $i \neq j$, show that

$$E(X_i X_j) = \frac{m(m - 1)}{(m + n)(m + n - 1)},$$

$$\text{Cov } (X_i, X_j) = \frac{-mn}{(m + n)^2(m + n - 1)}.$$

(c) If $S_k = X_1 + X_2 + \cdots + X_k$, deduce that

$$E(S_k) = \frac{km}{m + n},$$

$$\text{Var } (S_k) = \frac{kmn}{(m + n)^2} \left(1 - \frac{k - 1}{m + n - 1} \right).$$

(d) Relate these results to the mean and variance of the hypergeometric distribution.

10.19   If X_1 and X_2 have independent normal distributions with means 6 and 8 and variances 20 and 4, respectively, what is the distribution of $Y = 3 + X_1 - 2X_2$? Evaluate $P(Y > -1)$.

10.20   Suppose the weight of the bolts of Exercise 10.13 has a normal distribution. If Y is the weight of 100 bolts, estimate the probability that $|Y - 200| < 0.6$.

10.21   Many stochastic processes can be specified in terms of simple functional equations which contain some random variables. For example, consider the differential equation and initial condition

$$\frac{dX}{dt} = AX + B, \qquad X(0) = X_0,$$

in which A, B, and X_0 are given independent random variables. (a) For any fixed values of A, B, and X_0, show that

$$X(t) = X_0 e^{tA} + BA^{-1}(e^{tA} - 1).$$

(b) If B and X_0 have finite means and if A has a moment-generating function M, show that

$$E[X(t)] = E(X_0)M(t) + E(B) \int_0^t M(\theta) \, d\theta.$$

(c) If also $B = 0$ and X_0 has a finite variance, show that

$$\text{Var}\ [X(t)] = E(X_0^2)M(2t) - E^2(X_0)M^2(t).$$

10.22   (a) In Exercise 10.21 let $B = 0$, $E(X_0) = 1$, and A have a gamma distribution with parameters $(1, 1)$. For $0 \leq t < 1$, compare graphically $E[X(t)]$ and the integral of the problem: $dx/dt = 2x$, $x(0) = 1$, obtained from Exercise 10.21 by replacing A and X_0 by their means 2 and 1. (b) Repeat part (a) for $0 \leq t < \infty$ when A has a normal distribution with $\mu = -1$ and $\sigma = 1$ and therefore $dx/dt = -x$, $x(0) = 1$.

*10.23   If $X(t)$ is specified by

$$\frac{d^2X}{dt^2} - AX = B,$$

$$X(0) = X_0, \quad \frac{d}{dt}X(0) = X_0',$$

in which A, B, X_0, and X_0' are independent random variables which have finite means, show that

$$X(t) = X_0 \cosh (t \sqrt{A}) + (X_0'/\sqrt{A}) \sinh (t \sqrt{A})$$
$$+ (B/A)[\cosh (t \sqrt{A}) - 1]$$

and therefore that, if A also has a moment-generating function,

$$E[X(t)] = \sum_{n=0}^{\infty} E(A^n) \left[E(X_0) \frac{t^{2n}}{(2n)!} + E(X_0') \frac{t^{2n+1}}{(2n+1)!} + E(B) \frac{t^{2n+2}}{(2n+2)!} \right].$$

10.24   Use *(a) direct methods—e.g., Eq. 10.14 or 10.15—and (b) moment-generating functions to derive the addition theorems stated below. Let T_k for $k = 1, 2, \ldots , n$ be n independent random variables, and let $X_n = T_1 + T_2 + \cdots + T_n$. Then:
   (1) If each T_k has the Bernoulli distribution with parameter p, X_n has the binomial distribution with parameters (n, p).
   (2) If each T_k has the geometric distribution with parameter p, X_n has the Pascal distribution with parameters (n, p). (See Exercise 10.5.)
   (3) If each T_k has the exponential distribution with parameter μ (and density function $\mu^{-1}e^{-t/\mu}$), X_n has the gamma distribution with parameters $(n - 1, \mu)$.

10.25   Use *(a) direct methods—e.g., Eq. 10.14 or 10.15—and (b) moment-generating functions to derive the addition theorems stated below. Let X_k for $k = 1, 2, \ldots , m$ be m independent random variables, and let $S_m = X_1 + X_2 + \cdots + X_m$. Then:
   (1) If X_k has the binomial distribution with parameters (n_k, p) (so that the X_k's may have different n_k's but the same p), S_m has the binomial distribution with parameters (n, p), where $n = n_1 + n_2 + \cdots + n_m$.
   (2) If X_k has the negative binomial distribution with parameters (n_k, p),

S_m has the negative binomial distribution with parameters (n, p), where $n = n_1 + n_2 + \cdots + n_m$. (See Exercise 10.4.)

(3) If X_k has the Poisson distribution with parameter λ_k, S_m has the Poisson distribution with parameter $\lambda = \lambda_1 + \lambda_2 + \cdots + \lambda_m$.

(4) If X_k has the normal distribution with parameters (μ_k, σ_k), S_m has the normal distribution with parameters (μ, σ), where $\mu = \mu_1 + \mu_2 + \cdots + \mu_m$ and $\sigma^2 = \sigma_1^2 + \sigma_2^2 + \cdots + \sigma_m^2$.

(5) If X_k has the gamma distribution with parameters (α_k, β), S_m has the gamma distribution with parameters (α, β), where $\alpha = \alpha_1 + \alpha_2 + \cdots + \alpha_m + (m - 1)$.

10.26 (a) If X has the normal distribution with parameters $(0, 1)$, use Eq. 5.31 to show that $Y = X^2$ has the gamma distribution with parameters $(-\frac{1}{2}, 2)$, which is also the chi-square distribution with one degree of freedom. (See Section 8.5.) (b) If each of the independent random variables X_1, X_2, $\ldots$, X_n has the normal distribution with parameters $(0, 1)$, use part (5) of Exercise 10.25 to show that $X_1^2 + X_2^2 + \cdots + X_n^2$ has the chi-square distribution with n degrees of freedom. (c) State an addition theorem for independent random variables with chi-square distributions.

*10.27 Let X_1 and X_2 have the joint normal distribution of Exercise 9.7, and let $U = a_0 + a_1 X_1 + a_2 X_2$ and $V = b_0 + b_1 X_1 + b_2 X_2$, where the a_i's and b_i's are given constants. (a) Express the means, variances, and covariance of U and V in terms of those of X_1 and X_2. (b) If $a_1 b_2 - a_2 b_1 \neq 0$, show that U and V have a joint normal distribution, and therefore that each of them has a normal distribution. (c) By induction, conclude that a linear combination of correlated normally distributed random variables has a normal distribution.

10.28 In one method of measuring a residence-time distribution, as described in Exercise 5.27, a relatively small quantity of some "tracer" molecules is injected into the feed stream during a short period of time. Let T_1 and T_2 be the times at which a tracer molecule enters and leaves the reactor, so that the residence time of this molecule is $T = T_2 - T_1$. Suppose one has experimentally measured the density functions f_i of T_i, for $i = 1$ and 2, and can therefore compute the means μ_i and standard deviations σ_i. Assuming that T_1 and T are independent, find parameters α and β, as functions of μ_i and σ_i, such that the distribution of T can be approximated by a gamma distribution with parameters α and β.

10.29 Let T_k be the residence time of a molecule in the kth well-stirred reactor of Exercises 7.19 and 8.19. Use Eq. 10.19 to show that $S_n = T_1 + T_2 + \cdots + T_n$ has the density function of Exercise 5.28(b).

10.30 If the residence time of the kth $(k = 1, 2, \ldots, n)$ of n reactors connected in series (as in Exercise 7.19) has a gamma distribution with parameters (α_k, β), what is the distribution of the residence time in all n reactors?

THE LAW OF LARGE NUMBERS AFFORDS A PHILOSOPHICAL JUSTIFICATION for all attempts to estimate a probability experimentally. It justifies the relative frequency theory of probability and therefore constitutes part of the foundation of statistics. Moreover, it contains the fundamental meaning of the expected value of a random variable. In this chapter, we will study some special cases of this law and will briefly discuss its various implications, particularly in terms of experimental measurements. First, we will study an important inequality.

11.1 The Chebyshev Inequality

We have previously pointed out that a small variance indicates that large deviations from the mean are improbable. A more precise form of this statement is the Chebyshev (1821–1894, sometimes spelled Tchebichev, Tchebysheff, etc.) inequality, which is an exceedingly useful theoretical tool because of its complete universality.

Theorem 11.1. If X is a random variable with mean μ and finite variance σ^2, then

$$P(|X - \mu| > \epsilon) \leq \frac{\sigma^2}{\epsilon^2} \qquad (11.1)$$

for every $\epsilon > 0$.

To prove Eq. 11.1, note that $|x - \mu| \geq \epsilon$ when $x \leq \mu - \epsilon$ or $x \geq \mu + \epsilon$. This, the definition of variance, and the facts that

$$\int_{\mu-\epsilon}^{\mu+\epsilon} (x - \mu)^2 \, dF(x) \geq 0 \text{ and } P(X = \mu - \epsilon) \geq 0$$

imply that

$$\sigma^2 = \int_{-\infty}^{\infty} (x - \mu)^2 \, dF(x)$$

$$\geq \int_{-\infty}^{\mu - \epsilon} (x - \mu)^2 \, dF(x) + \int_{\mu + \epsilon}^{\infty} (x - \mu)^2 \, dF(x)$$

$$\geq \epsilon^2 \left[\int_{-\infty}^{\mu - \epsilon} dF(x) + \int_{\mu + \epsilon}^{\infty} dF(x) \right]$$

$$= \epsilon^2 [F(\mu - \epsilon) + 1 - F(\mu + \epsilon)]$$

$$= \epsilon^2 [P(X \leq \mu - \epsilon) + P(X > \mu + \epsilon)]$$

$$\geq \epsilon^2 P(|X - \mu| > \epsilon),$$

which proves the theorem.

If we let $\epsilon = h\sigma$ for $h > 0$, Chebyshev's inequality is easily rewritten as

$$P(|X - \mu| > h\sigma) \leq \frac{1}{h^2} \text{ or } P(|X - \mu| \leq h\sigma) \geq 1 - \frac{1}{h^2}. \quad (11.2)$$

This shows that the probability is never more than $1/h^2$ that X assumes a value outside the closed interval from $\mu - h\sigma$ to $\mu + h\sigma$. Alternatively, the probability is at least 0.9375 that X will assume a value within four standard deviations of its mean, and the probability is at least 0.99 that an observed value of X will lie within ten standard deviations of the mean. This interpretation shows that the variance is a measure of the spread, or dispersion, of a probability distribution.

Chebyshev's inequality does not provide a practical method of estimating probabilities, since the right side of the first relation in Eq. 11.2 is usually much larger than the left side. In fact, no new information is obtained from it when $h \leq 1$ since then $1/h^2 \geq 1$. The reader is referred to the exercises for some examples of the relative sizes of the right and left sides of Eq. 11.2 and also for examples that illustrate that the bound $1/h^2$ cannot be improved in general. Of course, better bounds can be obtained if one introduces various explicit restrictions on the distribution of X.

11.2 The Weak Law of Large Numbers

In 1837, Poisson published the first general formulation of a certain scientific law, which is now known as the empirical law of large numbers because it applies to the outcomes of a large number of trials of an experiment. For a modern discussion of a mathematical version of this law, we assume that a probability space $(\Omega, \mathcal{S}, P)$ and an infinite sequence $X_1, X_2, X_3, \ldots$ of random variables on Ω are given. (It is often convenient, but not necessary, to think of a model of the type indicated in Section 10.2.) We introduce the new random variables S_n and $\bar{X}_n$ for $n = 1, 2, 3, \ldots$ defined by

$$S_n = X_1 + X_2 + \cdots + X_n \tag{11.3}$$

and

$$\bar{X}_n = \frac{1}{n} S_n = \frac{1}{n} (X_1 + X_2 + \cdots + X_n). \tag{11.4}$$

Clearly, S_n is the sum of the first n random variables X_k, and $\bar{X}_n$ is the arithmetic average of these random variables. Also, we recall from Section 10.4 that the mean m_n and variance s_n^2 of S_n are given by

$$m_n = \sum_{k=1}^{n} \mu_k \quad \text{and} \quad s_n^2 = \sum_{j=1}^{n} \sum_{k=1}^{n} \sigma_{jk}, \tag{11.5}$$

where μ_k and $\sigma_{kk} = \sigma_k^2$ are the mean and variance of X_k and σ_{jk} is the covariance of X_j and X_k. Furthermore, $E(\bar{X}_n) = m_n/n$, and

$$\text{Var}(\bar{X}_n) = s_n^2/n^2.$$

First, we consider the special case in which $X_1, X_2, X_3, \ldots$ are *independent, identically distributed random variables*, as are those Bernoulli-distributed random variables first introduced in Section 10.1. In this case, all of the random variables X_k have exactly the same distribution and hence the same mean $\mu = \mu_k$ and the same variance $\sigma^2 = \sigma_k^2$. Thus, $m_n = n\mu$, and $E(\bar{X}_n) = \mu$. Also, since $X_1, X_2, \ldots, X_n$ are independent, $\sigma_{jk} = 0$ for $j \neq k$, $s_n^2 = n\sigma^2$, and $\text{Var}(\bar{X}_n) = \sigma^2/n$. For this situation, the following version of the weak law of large numbers holds:

Theorem 11.2. If $X_1, X_2, X_3, \ldots$ are independent, identically distributed random variables and if $\mu = E(X_k)$ exists, then for every $\epsilon > 0$

$$\lim_{n \to \infty} P(|\bar{X}_n - \mu| > \epsilon) = 0. \tag{11.6}$$

In this generality, the theorem was first published by Khintchine in 1929. For a general proof see Exercise 11.15. It will be proved now only under the additional assumption that the X_k's have a finite variance σ^2. Then, we can replace X, μ, and σ^2 in the Chebyshev inequality

(Eq. 11.1) by $\bar{X}_n$, $\mu = E(\bar{X}_n)$, and $\sigma^2/n = \text{Var}\,(\bar{X}_n)$ to find that

$$P(|\bar{X}_n - \mu| > \epsilon) \leq \sigma^2/n\epsilon^2.$$

Since σ and ϵ are positive constants, the last quantity in this relation approaches zero as $n \to \infty$, which proves the desired result.

In words, this theorem asserts that if n is a very large integer, the probability is very close to zero that the random variable $\bar{X}_n$ will differ from the common expected value μ of the X_k's by more than any arbitrarily prescribed small difference ϵ. Alternatively, when n is a given large integer, the probability is very close to 1 that $\bar{X}_n$ is very close to μ.

RELATIVE FREQUENCIES

Theorem 11.2 contains a mathematical counterpart of the following intuitive notion of probability: If the outcome A occurs n_A times during n identical trials of an experiment and if n is large enough, then the relative frequency n_A/n should be close to the probability p of A. To make this vague notion precise, we translate "identical trials" as "independent repeated Bernoulli trials" with probability p for success. As in Section 10.1, we therefore let X_k equal 1 or 0 according to whether the outcome of the kth trial is A or is not A, $p = P(X_k = 1)$, and $q = P(X_k = 0) = 1 - p$. Then $\bar{X}_n$ is a random variable, which represents the relative frequency of A, $\mu = E(X_k) = E(\bar{X}_n) = p$, and Eq. 11.6 becomes

$$\lim_{n \to \infty} P(|\bar{X}_n - p| > \epsilon) = 0. \tag{11.7}$$

This result is known as the *Bernoulli law of large numbers*, since it was first found by Jacob Bernoulli. It was published posthumously in 1713 and is the first-published limit theorem of probability theory. (As shown in the exercises, a direct proof of Eq. 11.7 can be based on a simple analysis of the binomial probability function.)

Intuitively, Eq. 11.7 states that when n is a sufficiently large and fixed integer, the relative frequency n_A/n is very likely to be close to p. But it does not say that $\bar{X}_n$ is bound to stay near p if n is increased nor that $\bar{X}_n$ should become stabilized near p as n increases. As seen in Section 11.4, the strong law of large numbers justifies such statements.

It should be noted that Eq. 11.7 does not imply that the actual number n_A of occurrences of an outcome A is close to the expected number np of occurrences of A. For example, if $n_A = np + \sqrt{n}$, then n_A deviates from np by $\sqrt{n}$, which is large when n is large, while

$$\lim_{n \to \infty} \frac{n_A}{n} = \lim_{n \to \infty} \frac{np + \sqrt{n}}{n} = p.$$

There naturally arises the question of how many trials should be made in order to obtain a "good" estimate of p. To answer this question one must compute n so that with a given high probability α, an observed value of $\bar{X}_n$ will be within a specified distance ϵ from p, for any possible value of p. Given α and ϵ, the problem is therefore to find n so that

$$P(|\bar{X}_n - p| \leq \epsilon) \geq \alpha \text{ for all } p \text{ in } 0 \leq p \leq 1. \qquad (11.8)$$

A crude lower bound on n can be obtained from Chebyshev's inequality, since Var $(\bar{X}_n) = pq/n \leq 1/4n$ for all p in $0 \leq p \leq 1$ and Eq. 11.1 imply that

$$P(|\bar{X}_n - p| \leq \epsilon) \geq 1 - \frac{1}{4n\epsilon^2} \text{ for all } p \text{ in } 0 \leq p \leq 1. \qquad (11.9)$$

It follows from Eq. 11.9 that Eq. 11.8 is satisfied if

$$n \geq \frac{1}{4\epsilon^2(1 - \alpha)}. \qquad (11.10)$$

For example, $n \geq 2000$ when $\epsilon = 0.05$ and $\alpha = 0.95$. Usually, a much smaller lower bound on n than that of Eq. 11.10 can be found by using the normal approximation to the binomial distribution, which is discussed in Section 12.2.

GENERALIZATION

Theorem 11.2 is a special case of the general weak law of large numbers, which appears in numerous forms in the theory of probability. In general, we say that *the sequence $\{X_k\}$ of random variables with finite means obeys the weak law of large numbers if for every $\epsilon > 0$*

$$\lim_{n \to \infty} P\left(\frac{|S_n - m_n|}{n} > \epsilon\right) = 0, \qquad (11.11)$$

where S_n and m_n are given in Eqs. 11.3 and 11.5. Note that the X_k's are not required to be independent or identically distributed or to have finite variances.

Another special case of the weak law is the following direct consequence of Chebyshev's inequality: *the sequence* $\{X_k\}$ *of random variables obeys the weak law of large numbers if the variance* s_n^2 *of* S_n *is finite for all n and* $s_n/n \to 0$ *as* $n \to \infty$. For a proof, note that

$$P\left(\frac{|S_n - m_n|}{n} > \epsilon\right) \leq \frac{1}{\epsilon^2}\left(\frac{s_n}{n}\right)^2, \tag{11.12}$$

which tends to 0 as n tends to ∞.

11.3   Experimental Measurements

Here let us start with the universal problem of accurately estimating from experimental data the numerical value of some unknown quantity under specified conditions. In engineering and experimental sciences, the first step is to perform several times an experiment designed to measure the unknown number. Insofar as possible, the several trials of the experiment are often conducted so that: (A) all of the trials are made under *identical* conditions—i.e., all relevant quantities (independent variables), such as mass, temperature, pressure, etc., except the one being measured (the dependent variable), have the same values during all of the trials; and (B) the several trials are *independent* in the sense that the outcome of any trial is not influenced in any manner by the outcomes of the other trials. Since these conditions usually cannot be accurately satisfied in practice and because there are often inherent random processes involved, the values obtained are seldom identical and in fact usually exhibit many properties of randomness. For these reasons, it is appropriate to abstract a probabilistic model for this procedure in the hope of attaining a better understanding of it.

One can always imagine (or construct, if desirable) some probability space $(\Omega, \mathcal{S}, P)$ as a model for the whole experimental procedure of making n trials of the basic experiment. (The type of model indicated in Section 10.2 is often useful.) The quantity to be measured can be viewed as a random variable X on Ω which has a fixed but unknown probability distribution. Furthermore, for $k = 1, 2, \ldots, n$, the possible numerical-valued outcomes of the kth trial can be viewed as the possible values that a random variable X_k on Ω can assume. The experimental condition (A) can be abstracted in the form: The n random variables $X_1, X_2, \ldots, X_n$ are *identically distributed*, and each of them has the same distribution as X. Finally, condition (B) can be abstracted in the form: $X_1, X_2, \ldots, X_n$ are *independent* random variables. Thus, we obtain the model of n independent, identically distributed random variables.

When one makes n trials of the experiment, one obtains n *numbers* $x_1, x_2, \ldots, x_n$. Depending on the viewpoint, these numbers constitute either one sample from the joint distribution of the n random variables $X_1, X_2, \ldots, X_n$ or n samples from the distribution of X since each of the X_k's has the same distribution as X. Now our problem is to estimate the properties, particularly the mean μ and variance σ^2, of the unknown quantity X from these n numbers.

ESTIMATE OF THE MEAN

The commonly used natural estimate of the mean μ is the arithmetic average

$$\bar{x}_n = \frac{1}{n}(x_1 + x_2 + \cdots + x_n). \tag{11.13}$$

Clearly, $\bar{x}_n$ is only one observation of the random variable

$$\bar{X}_n = \frac{1}{n}(X_1 + X_2 + \cdots + X_n). \tag{11.14}$$

However, since the mean and variance of $\bar{X}_n$ are μ and σ^2/n (where μ and σ are unknown constants) and σ^2/n is very small when n is sufficiently large, it seems very likely that when n is large and fixed, $\bar{x}_n$ will be very near the unknown fixed value μ and will therefore be a good estimate of μ. This is precisely the notion that is formalized in Theorem 11.2. Because of Eq. 11.12, condition (B) is not generally necessary for the conclusion that $\bar{x}_n$ will very likely be near μ when n is large. But if condition (A) is not satisfied, then the X_k's are not identically distributed, and if their means are different then $\bar{x}_n$ merely estimates $(1/n)$ $(\mu_1 + \mu_2 + \cdots + \mu_n)$.

Also, it seems plausible that if n is increased, the magnitude of the difference between $\bar{x}_n$ and μ will become and *remain* small so that $\bar{x}_n$

will become stabilized near μ; i.e., that

$$\lim_{n \to \infty} \bar{X}_n = \mu. \tag{11.15}$$

Intuitively, this cannot be true for *every* conceivable sequence of trials. But it can be shown (under mild restrictions) that this relation is true with probability one; i.e., that

$$P(\lim_{n \to \infty} \bar{X}_n = \mu) = 1, \tag{11.16}$$

so that the cases where Eq. 11.15 does not hold form a negligible exception. Thus, we have a brief view of the strong law of large numbers, which is discussed in the next section.

An argument similar to that used to obtain Eq. 11.10 gives a crude lower bound (in terms of the unknown constant σ) for how large n must be in order to obtain a "good" estimate of μ. Thus, given α and ϵ, the relation

$$P(|\bar{X}_n - \mu| \leq \epsilon) \geq \alpha \tag{11.17}$$

will be satisfied if

$$n \geq \sigma^2 / (1 - \alpha)\epsilon^2. \tag{11.18}$$

Thus, a lower bound on n can be estimated if σ can be estimated by any means. For some scientific measurements, σ is small so that a small value (e.g., 3 or 4) of n can be used. On the other extreme, σ is large for some statistical quantities, and n may have to be a large number, say in the hundreds. Of course, when σ can be estimated, much smaller estimated lower bounds on n can usually be obtained by using other methods, such as the central limit theorem.

ESTIMATE OF THE VARIANCE

In statistics, the quantity $\bar{x}_n$ is known as an *unbiased* estimate of the mean μ since $E(\bar{X}_n) = \mu$. Similarly, we will show here that

$$s_n^2 = \frac{1}{n-1} \sum_{k=1}^{n} (x_k - \bar{x}_n)^2 \qquad (n > 1) \tag{11.19}$$

is an unbiased estimate of the variance σ^2 of X, when the X_k's are independent and identically distributed. Thus, we wish to show that the expected value of the random variable

$$Y_n^2 = \frac{1}{n-1} \sum_{k=1}^{n} (X_k - \bar{X}_n)^2 \tag{11.20}$$

is σ^2. First, note that

$$\sum_{k=1}^{n} (X_k - \bar{X}_n)^2 = \sum_{k=1}^{n} [(X_k - \mu) - (\bar{X}_n - \mu)]^2$$

$$= \sum_{k=1}^{n} [(X_k - \mu)^2 - 2(X_k - \mu)(\bar{X}_n - \mu) + (\bar{X}_n - \mu)^2]$$

$$= \sum_{k=1}^{n} (X_k - \mu)^2 - n(\bar{X}_n - \mu)^2,$$

since $\sum_{k=1}^{n} (X_k - \mu)(\bar{X}_n - \mu) = n(\bar{X}_n - \mu)^2.$

Therefore,

$$E(Y_n^2) = \frac{1}{n-1} \left(\sum_{k=1}^{n} E[(X_k - \mu)^2] - nE[(\bar{X}_n - \mu)^2] \right)$$

$$= \frac{1}{n-1} [n\sigma^2 - n(\sigma^2/n)] = \sigma^2, \tag{11.21}$$

where we have used the facts that Var $(X_k) = \sigma^2$ and Var $(\bar{X}_n) = \sigma^2/n$. Note that the estimate $s_n = (s_n^2)^{1/2}$ of the standard deviation σ will generally be biased because

$$E(Y_n) \neq [E(Y_n^2)]^{1/2}.$$

The weak law of large numbers justifies the statement that the one observation s_n^2 of the random variable Y_n^2 will very likely be very close to σ^2 when n is large enough. To see this, we first write Y_n^2 in the form

$$Y_n^2 = \frac{1}{n} (Z_1 + Z_2 + \cdots + Z_n),$$

where $Z_k = \frac{n}{n-1} (X_k - \bar{X}_n)^2.$

While the Z_k's are obviously dependent random variables, it follows from Eq. 11.12 that

$$\lim_{n \to \infty} P(|Y_n^2 - \sigma^2| > \epsilon) = 0 \tag{11.22}$$

at least when

$$\frac{1}{n^2} \operatorname{Var}(nY_n^2) = \operatorname{Var}(Y_n^2) \to 0 \text{ as } n \to \infty.$$

Now it can be shown by means of fairly complicated algebra that

$$\operatorname{Var}(Y_n^2) = \frac{1}{n}\left[\mu_4 - \frac{(n-3)\sigma^4}{n-1}\right], \tag{11.23}$$

where $\mu_4 = E[(X - \mu)^4]$. Thus, Eq. 11.22 will hold when the fourth central moment μ_4 of X is finite.

The property of being unbiased is by no means as desirable a property of an estimate as its name suggests. It is merely one of several properties (including consistency, relative efficiency, and sufficiency) that a good statistical estimate should possess. Frequently, all of these properties cannot be simultaneously satisfied and questions of unbiasedness are often outweighed by other considerations. Thus, even though s_n^2 is the correct unbiased estimate of the variance σ^2, other statistical principles lead some people to use the estimate given by

$$\hat{s}_n^2 = \frac{1}{n} \sum_{k=1}^n (x_k - \bar{x}_n)^2. \tag{11.24}$$

Since $\hat{s}_n^2 = \dfrac{n-1}{n} s_n^2$, $\hat{s}_n^2$ is clearly a biased estimate; nevertheless, $\hat{s}_n$ and s_n are approximately equal for large n. The interested reader is referred to any good book on statistics for information about such questions.

11.4   The Strong Law of Large Numbers

The strong law is more important than the weak law of large numbers, because, as indicated previously, it (instead of the weak law) contains the mathematical counterpart of the intuitive notion that successive relative frequencies should become stabilized near the probability of an event. However, a thorough discussion requires more elaborate methods than we wish to develop in this book; therefore, no proofs and only a brief discussion are given here. We remark that the first general formulation of the strong law was made by Cantelli (1917), after Borel and Hausdorff had treated certain special cases.

As described in Section 11.2, a sequence $\{X_k\}$ of random variables
with finite means obeys the weak law of large numbers if for every
$\epsilon > 0$

$$\lim_{n \to \infty} P\left(\frac{|S_n - m_n|}{n} > \epsilon\right) = 0, \qquad (11.11)$$

where S_n and m_n are given in Eqs. 11.3 and 11.5. Under the same
circumstances, we say that *a sequence $\{X_k\}$ of random variables with
finite means obeys the strong law of large numbers if for every $\epsilon > 0$*

$$\lim_{n \to \infty} P\left(\max_{j \geq n} \frac{|S_j - m_j|}{j} > \epsilon\right) = 0, \qquad (11.25)$$

where $\max_{j \geq n} Y_j$ denotes the largest value in the infinite sequence
$Y_n, Y_{n+1}, Y_{n+2}, \ldots$.

The condition of Eq. 11.25 is much stronger than that of Eq. 11.11,
in the sense that 11.11 is always satisfied when 11.25 is satisfied,
whereas the converse statement is false. With

$$Y_j = \frac{|S_j - m_j|}{j} \qquad (j = 1, 2, 3, \ldots),$$

Eq. 11.11 says that for each fixed large integer n it is very unlikely
that Y_n will be larger than any arbitrarily prescribed small number
$\epsilon > 0$. For every large integer n, Eq. 11.25 says that it is very unlikely
that any one of the random variables $Y_n, Y_{n+1}, Y_{n+2}, \ldots$ will be
larger than any arbitrarily prescribed ϵ or, alternatively, that it is very
likely that all of the relations $Y_n \leq \epsilon, Y_{n+1} \leq \epsilon, Y_{n+2} \leq \epsilon, \ldots$ will be
simultaneously satisfied. This means roughly that with an over-
whelming probability Y_n becomes and remains small as n increases.

For a rough but useful analogy, let $\{a_n\}$ be an infinite sequence of
real numbers. Then, the weak law is analogous to the statement that
$a_n \to 0$ as $n \to \infty$, whereas the strong law is analogous to the statement
that

$$\sum_{j=n}^{\infty} a_j \to 0$$

as $n \to \infty$. To see this, let $a_n = P(Y_n > \epsilon)$, and note that the event

$$\{\max_{j \geq n} Y_j > \epsilon\}$$

occurs if and only if any one of the events $\{Y_j > \epsilon\}$ for $j = n, n + 1,$

$n + 2, \ldots$ occurs, so that

$$P(\max_{j \geq n} Y_j > \epsilon) = P\left(\bigcup_{j=n}^{\infty} \{Y_j > \epsilon\}\right)$$

$$\leq \sum_{j=n}^{\infty} P(Y_j > \epsilon)$$

$$= \sum_{j=n}^{\infty} a_j. \qquad (11.26)$$

The example $a_n = 1/n$ shows that $a_n \to 0$ can hold while

$$\sum_{j=n}^{\infty} a_j \to 0$$

does not hold.

It can be shown that the condition in Eq. 11.25 can be reformulated as

$$P\left(\lim_{n \to \infty} \frac{S_n - m_n}{n} = 0\right) = 1, \qquad (11.27)$$

so that those cases for which the relation

$$\lim_{n \to \infty} \frac{S_n - m_n}{n} = 0 \qquad (11.28)$$

does not hold form a negligible exception. For the special case of a sequence of identically distributed random variables, Eqs. 11.27 and 11.28 reduce to Eqs. 11.16 and 11.15.

It can be shown that *a sequence of independent random variables X_k with finite variances σ_k^2 obeys the strong law of large numbers if the series*

$$\sum_{k=1}^{\infty} \sigma_k^2/k^2 \qquad (11.29)$$

converges. For example, this condition is satisfied when $\sigma_k^2 = \sigma^2$ is independent of k, since then

$$\sum_{k=1}^{\infty} \sigma^2/k^2 = \sigma^2\pi^2/6.$$

Furthermore, the above result can be used to show that *every sequence of independent, identically distributed random variables having a common finite mean obeys the strong law of large numbers.*

11.5   Exercises

11.1   If X has a (a) rectangular, (b) exponential, (c) normal distribution, evaluate and sketch $P(|X - \mu| > h\sigma)$ as a function of $h > 0$. On the same graph, sketch the upper bound h^{-2} of Chebyshev's inequality.

11.2   Let X have the probability function $g(-1) = g(1) = \frac{1}{2}$. For $h > 0$, sketch $P(|X| > h)$ and the upper bound h^{-2} provided by Chebyshev's inequality.

11.3   (a) If every X_k of Theorem 11.2 has a normal distribution with mean 0 and variance 1, compute exact values of $P(|\bar{X}_n| > \epsilon)$ for $\epsilon = \frac{1}{2}$ and $n = 4, 9, 16, 36$, and also for $\epsilon = \frac{1}{16}$ and $n = 100, 225, 400, 900$. (b) Compute the corresponding upper bounds provided by Chebyshev's inequality.

11.4   Estimate the minimum number of times that a fair coin must be tossed independently so that the probability will be at least 0.95 that the observed relative frequency of heads will be between 0.4 and 0.6. (cf. Exercise 12.7.)

11.5   An experimental measurement $\bar{X}_n$ of the unknown relative frequency p of an event (e.g., of "redheads" in a large city) is to be obtained. If it is known that (a) $0 < p < 1$, (b) $0 < p < 0.2$, estimate the number of independent observations required so that the probability will be at least 0.98 that $\bar{X}_n$ will differ from p by at most 0.05. (cf. Exercise 12.7.)

11.6   If every X_k has the same Cauchy distribution, does the sequence $\{X_k\}$ obey the (weak) law of large numbers? Why?

11.7   Let Y have a rectangular distribution on the interval 0 to 2π. For $k = 1, 2, 3, \ldots$, let $X_k = \sin kY$. For $n = 1, 2, 3, \ldots$, let $S_n = X_1 + X_2 + \cdots + X_n$. (a) Find μ_k, σ_k, σ_{jk}, m_n, and s_n. Are X_j and X_k independent? Uncorrelated? (b) Is Eq. 11.11 satisfied in this case? Why?

11.8   The following values resulted from six independent measurements of a certain quantity X: 11, 9, 13, 11, 10, 12. Obtain unbiased estimates for the mean and variance of X.

11.9   Estimate the required number of observations of a random quantity X, if the probability is to be at least 0.95 that the sample average $\bar{X}_n$ will not differ from the true mean μ by more than (a) 25 percent, (b) 10 percent, (c) 5 percent of the standard deviation σ of X. (cf. Exercise 12.7.)

11.10   From Eqs. 11.13 and 11.19, deduce that

$$s_n^2 = \frac{1}{n-1} \left(\sum_{k=1}^{n} x_k^2 - n\bar{x}_n^2 \right)$$

$$= \frac{1}{n-1} \left[\sum_{k=1}^{n} x_k^2 - \frac{1}{n} \left(\sum_{k=1}^{n} x_k \right)^2 \right].$$

11.11   When 100 independent observations x_k of a random quantity X are obtained, it is found that $\Sigma x_k = 500$ and $\Sigma x_k^2 = 4975$. Find estimates for the mean and standard deviation of X.

11.12   Derive Eq. 11.23.

THEORETICAL EXERCISES

11.13   Use the binomial probability function to prove the Bernoulli law of large numbers (Eq. 11.7). *Hint:* Given n, ϵ, and p, with $0 < \epsilon < p$ and $0 < p < 1$, let s be the largest integer smaller than $n(p - \epsilon)$. Let

$$g(n, k) = \binom{n}{k} p^k q^{n-k},$$

and show that, for $k \leq s$,

$$\frac{g(n, k - 1)}{g(n, k)} = \frac{kq}{(n - k + 1)p} \leq \frac{sq}{(n - s + 1)p},$$

$$\frac{g(n, s - j)}{g(n, s)} \leq \left(\frac{sq}{(n - s + 1)p}\right)^j \qquad (j = 0, 1, \ldots, s),$$

$$P[S_n < n(p - \epsilon)] < g(n, s) \frac{(n - s + 1)p}{(n + 1)p - s}.$$

Use a similar computation for $P[S_n > n(p + \epsilon)]$.

*11.14   Assume the result derived in Exercise 10.27 that the sum S_n of n correlated normally distributed random variables X_k has a normal distribution, with mean and variance given by Eq. 11.5. For simplicity, assume that $\sigma_k = \sigma$ does not depend on k. (a) If

$$a_n = \frac{2}{n(n - 1)} \sum_{k=2}^{n} \sum_{j=1}^{k-1} \sigma_{jk},$$

show that $s_n^2 = n\sigma^2 + (n^2 - n)a_n$. (b) If $\sigma_{jk} = \sigma_{12}$ does not depend on k or $j \neq k$, show that $a_n = \sigma_{12}$ and that $\sigma_{12} \geq 0$ must then hold, since $s_n^2/n^2 \geq 0$ for all n. (c) Use the result of Exercise 8.17 to show that, for every $\epsilon > 0$,

$$P(|S_n - m_n| > \epsilon n) \begin{cases} = 2[1 - \Phi_1(\epsilon n/s_n)] \\[2mm] < \dfrac{2s_n}{\sqrt{2\pi}\,\epsilon n} \exp\left(-\dfrac{\epsilon n^2}{2s_n^2}\right) \\[2mm] > \dfrac{2s_n}{\sqrt{2\pi}\,\epsilon n} \left(1 - \dfrac{s_n^2}{\epsilon^2 n^2}\right) \exp\left(-\dfrac{\epsilon n^2}{2s_n^2}\right). \end{cases}$$

(d) If $a_n = \sigma_{12} = 0$, or if $a_n \to 0$ as $n \to \infty$, verify the validity of Eq. 11.11 in this case. (e) If $a_n = \sigma_{12} \neq 0$, or if $a_n \to a \neq 0$ as $n \to \infty$, show that there is an $\epsilon > 0$ for which $\lim P(|S_n - m_n| > \epsilon n) > 0$, so that the sequence $\{X_k\}$ does not obey the law of large numbers.

*11.15   *Proof of Theorem 11.2.* The weak law of large numbers for independent, identically distributed random variables X_k, which do not necessarily
have a finite variance but have a finite mean $\mu = E(X_k)$, is to be proved here
by the *method of truncation* (which is an important standard tool in probability theory). For fixed $\epsilon > 0$ and each $n = 1, 2, 3, \ldots$, define two new
collections of independent, identically distributed random variables by

$$U_k = X_k, \; V_k = 0 \quad \text{if } |X_k| \leq \epsilon n,$$

$$U_k = 0, \quad V_k = X_k \text{ if } |X_k| > \epsilon n,$$

for $k = 1, 2, \ldots, n$. (a) Let $\mu'_n = E(U_k)$, and show that $|\mu'_n - \mu| < \delta$ for
arbitrary $\delta > 0$ and all sufficiently large n. (b) Note that $E(|X_k|) = a$ is
finite, and infer that $\text{Var}(U_k) \leq \epsilon a n$. (c) Use Chebyshev's inequality to
deduce that

$$P(|\bar{U}_n - \mu'_n| > \delta) \leq \epsilon a \delta^{-2},$$

where of course $\bar{U}_n = (U_1 + U_2 + \cdots + U_n)/n$. (d) From (a) and (c),
conclude that

$$P(|\bar{U}_n - \mu| > 2\delta) \leq \epsilon a \delta^{-2}.$$

(e) Show that $P(V_k \neq 0) \leq \epsilon n^{-1}$ for all sufficiently large n. (f) Use (e) to
deduce that

$$P(\bar{V}_n \neq 0) \leq P(V_1 \neq 0 \text{ or } V_2 \neq 0 \text{ or } \ldots \text{ or } V_n \neq 0) \leq \epsilon.$$

(g) Show that

$$P(|\bar{X}_n - \mu| > 2\delta) \leq P(|\bar{U}_n - \mu| > 2\delta) + P(\bar{V}_n \neq 0).$$

(h) From (d), (f), and (g) conclude that, for all sufficiently large n,

$$P(|\bar{X}_n - \mu| > 2\delta) \leq \epsilon + \epsilon a \delta^{-2}.$$

Since δ and then ϵ can be chosen arbitrarily small, this proves the desired
result.

CHAPTER 12 THE CENTRAL LIMIT

THEOREM

THE CENTRAL LIMIT THEOREM IS ONE OF THE MOST REMARKABLE theorems in the whole of mathematics and is perhaps the most important theorem in all of probability and statistics from both the theoretical and applied points of view. It asserts that, under certain mild restrictions, the sum of a large number of independent random variables has approximately a normal distribution, regardless of what distributions the summands have. The remarkable feature of this theorem is that it places virtually no restrictions on the forms of the distributions of the individual random variables. Therefore, it provides a practical method for computing approximate values of probabilities associated with sums of arbitrarily distributed independent random variables. In this chapter, we will discuss briefly some special cases of this theorem but will only indicate proofs for very special cases, since proofs require advanced mathematical methods.

12.1   Discussion of the Central Limit Theorem

The simplest form of the central limit theorem was first formulated by de Moivre during the early part of the eighteenth century. Since then, many mathematicians, including Gauss, Laplace, Chebyshev, Markov, Lyapunov, Lindeberg, Feller, and Lévy, investigated conditions under which the central limit theorem holds for sequences of independent random variables. In fact the major problem of probability theory prior to 1935 was the determination of the exact conditions for the validity of this theorem. During more recent years, extensive

work has been devoted to the extension of the central limit theorem to
the case of dependent random variables.

We will first consider an almost trivial special case of the modern
central limit theorem. From Section 10.5 recall that the sum S_n of n
independent, normally distributed random variables $X_1, X_2, \ldots, X_n$
has a normal distribution whose mean m_n and variance s_n^2 are given by

$$m_n = \sum_{k=1}^{n} \mu_k \text{ and } s_n^2 = \sum_{k=1}^{n} \sigma_k^2, \qquad (12.1)$$

where μ_k and σ_k^2 are the mean and variance of X_k. Similarly, note that
the standardized random variable

$$\frac{1}{s_n}(S_n - m_n) = \frac{1}{s_n}(X_1 - \mu_1) + \cdots + \frac{1}{s_n}(X_n - \mu_n) \quad (12.2)$$

has the unit normal distribution (with mean 0 and variance 1). This
statement remains true when n varies; and, in particular, we trivially
find that for every fixed real value of z,

$$\lim_{n \to \infty} P\left(\frac{1}{s_n}(S_n - m_n) \le z\right) = \Phi(z), \qquad (12.3)$$

where Φ is the distribution function of the unit normal distribution;
that is,

$$\Phi(z) = \frac{1}{\sqrt{2\pi}} \int_{-\infty}^{z} e^{-t^2/2}\, dt. \qquad (12.4)$$

Equation 12.3 is an exceedingly special case of the central limit theorem.

In general, we assume as given a probability space $(\Omega, \mathfrak{S}, P)$ and an
infinite sequence $X_1, X_2, X_3, \ldots$ of random variables on Ω, which
have finite means and variances. As usual, we let S_n denote the sum of
the first n X_k's and let m_n and s_n^2 denote the mean and variance of S_n.
Of course, when the X_k's are not independent, s_n^2 is not correctly given
by Eq. 12.1 but by 11.5. However, the standardized random variable
of Eq. 12.2 always has mean 0 and variance 1, for every positive
integer n. Now, we say that *the sequence $\{X_k\}$ obeys the central limit
theorem if relation 12.3 is satisfied for every fixed real value of z;* i.e., if
the distribution of $\frac{1}{s_n}(S_n - m_n)$ approaches the unit normal distribution as $n \to \infty$. Of course, in order to say that a given sequence $\{X_k\}$
obeys the central limit theorem, one must show mathematically that
Eq. 12.3 is satisfied.

An important special case of this general situation is that in which the X_k's are independent and identically distributed, as described in Sections 11.2 and 11.3. For this case, the following theorem was first published by Lindeberg in 1922:

Theorem 12.1.   If $X_1, X_2, X_3, \ldots$ are independent, identically distributed random variables and if $\mu = E(X_k)$ and $\sigma^2 = \text{Var } (X_k)$ exist, then for every fixed real z

$$\lim_{n \to \infty} P\left(\frac{S_n - n\mu}{\sigma \sqrt{n}} \leq z\right) = \Phi(z). \tag{12.5}$$

After noting that $m_n = n\mu$ and $s_n^2 = n\sigma^2$ in this case, one sees that Eq. 12.5 has the form of Eq. 12.3. Under the additional restriction that the X_k's have a moment-generating function, the proof of Theorem 12.1 will be indicated in Section 12.3.

The computational importance of Theorem 12.1 lies in the fact that, for sufficiently large n, it asserts that

$$P(S_n \leq z\sigma \sqrt{n} + n\mu) \doteq \Phi(z), \tag{12.6}$$

where $\doteq$ denotes "approximately equal to." From this, we can express approximately the distribution function F_n of S_n in terms of the unit normal distribution function as

$$F_n(y) = P(S_n \leq y) \doteq \Phi\left(\frac{y - n\mu}{\sigma \sqrt{n}}\right), \tag{12.7}$$

where $y = z\sigma \sqrt{n} + n\mu$.

There remains the question about how large n must be so that Eq. 12.7 will give a "good" approximation. Although this question has been extensively investigated mathematically, the answer is of course not simple and depends on how precise an approximation is required. As shown at the beginning of this section, Eq. 12.7 will provide an exact value when the X_k's are normally distributed. Otherwise, the rate of approach to a normal distribution depends on how closely the common distribution of the X_k's resembles a normal distribution. When nothing is known about this common distribution, a useful rule of thumb is that a value of n greater than 25 is usually adequate.

Example 12.1.   Suppose cans of fruit are packed independently so that the net weight per can is a random variable with mean 8 ounces and variance 0.5 ounces². A carton of 48 cans would then have a net average weight of $48(8) = 384$ ounces and a variance of

$$48(0.5) = 24 \text{ ounces}^2.$$

By Theorem 12.1, the net weight of a carton would have approximately a normal distribution with mean 384 and variance 24. Now, one can compute approximately the probabilities of various events; for example,

P(carton weight > 24.5 pounds)

$$= 1 - P(\text{carton weight} \le 24.5 \text{ pounds})$$
$$\doteq 1 - \Phi\left(\frac{392 - 384}{\sqrt{24}}\right) \doteq 0.051.$$

Example 12.2. Sometimes, one initially knows (approximately) the standard deviation σ of a random variable but does not know the mean. For this situation, consider the problem of deciding how large n must be in order to get a good estimate of the unknown mean μ by the procedure described in Section 11.3. Assuming σ is finite, Theorem 12.1 implies that the random variable $\bar{X}_n$ of Eq. 11.14 has approximately a normal distribution for sufficiently large n. In fact, with $S_n = n\bar{X}_n$, we find from Eq. 12.5 that, for every fixed real z and for all sufficiently large n,

$$P(\bar{X}_n - \mu \le z\sigma/\sqrt{n}) \doteq \Phi(z).$$

To see that this relation provides another indication of the validity of the weak law of large numbers, first note from it that

$$P(|\bar{X}_n - \mu| > z\sigma/\sqrt{n}) \doteq 2[1 - \Phi(z)] \tag{12.8}$$

for every fixed $z > 0$ and for all large n. Since $\Phi(z) \to 1$ as $z \to \infty$, the right side of Eq. 12.8 and $z\sigma/\sqrt{n}$ can both be made as small as one desires by first assigning to z a sufficiently large fixed value and by then choosing n large enough. From Eq. 12.8 we can also estimate the rate of convergence for the weak law of large numbers as n increases. For example,

$$P(|\bar{X}_{25} - \mu| > \sigma/5) \doteq 2[1 - \Phi(1)] \doteq 0.317,$$
$$P(|\bar{X}_{100} - \mu| > \sigma/5) \doteq 2[1 - \Phi(2)] \doteq 0.046.$$

Finally, it is noteworthy (and should be easily proved by the reader) that the relation $P(|\bar{X}_n - \mu| \le \epsilon) \ge \alpha$ for given ϵ and α will be satisfied approximately if $n \geq (z\sigma/\epsilon)^2$ where z is the solution of the equation $2\Phi(z) - 1 = \alpha$, which can be found by using tables of the normal distribution.

Example 12.2 illustrates the fact that the central limit theorem often contains the weak law of large numbers as a special case and is a mathematically stronger result. However, it is true that some sequences of random variables obey the weak law of large numbers but do not obey the central limit theorem, and conversely.

Various other sufficient conditions for a sequence of independent random variables to obey the central limit theorem have been discovered. Although these will not be discussed here, necessary and sufficient conditions will be stated briefly. Suppose that $\{X_k\}$ is an infinite sequence of independent random variables and that X_k has a finite mean μ_k and a finite variance σ_k^2 (not necessarily the same) for every k. Also, for each real number $\epsilon > 0$ and each positive integer n, introduce the "truncated" random variables Y_k defined for

$$k = 1, 2, \ldots, n$$

by

$$
\begin{aligned}
Y_k &= X_k - \mu_k & \text{if} \quad |X_k - \mu_k| \leq \epsilon s_n, \\
Y_k &= 0 & \text{if} \quad |X_k - \mu_k| > \epsilon s_n,
\end{aligned}
\tag{12.9}
$$

where s_n is defined in Eq. 12.1. Note that Y_k depends on both ϵ and n and that, when ϵs_n is large enough, the variances of X_k and Y_k are both at least approximately equal to

$$E(Y_k^2) = \int_{\mu_k - \epsilon s_n}^{\mu_k + \epsilon s_n} (x - \mu_k)^2 \, dF_k(x),$$

where F_k is the distribution function of X_k. Now, *the sequence* $\{X_k\}$ *of independent random variables obeys the central limit theorem and*

$$\lim_{n \to \infty} \max_{k \leq n} \left(\frac{\sigma_k}{s_n} \right) = 0$$

if and only if, for every $\epsilon > 0$,

$$\frac{1}{s_n^2} \sum_{k=1}^{n} E(Y_k^2) \to 1 \ as \ n \to \infty.
\tag{12.10}$$

Lindeberg and Feller first published, respectively, in 1922 and 1935 the "if" and the "only if" parts of this theorem.

For one application of this theorem, we remark that it implies the following noteworthy result: *Every uniformly bounded sequence* $\{X_k\}$ *of independent random variables for which* $s_n \to \infty$ *obeys the central limit theorem.* To see this, we must show that Eq. 12.10 is satisfied for every $\epsilon > 0$. That $\{X_k\}$ is a uniformly bounded sequence means that there is some constant A such that $|X_k| < A$ for every k. Given this A and any $\epsilon > 0$, we can choose a large integer N so that $s_n > 2A/\epsilon$ for every $n \geq N$, because $s_n \to \infty$ as $n \to \infty$. Since then

$$|X_k - \mu_k| \leq 2A < \epsilon s_n$$

and hence $Y_k = X_k - \mu_k$ for every $n \geq N$, the left side of Eq. 12.10 is identically equal to 1 for every $n \geq N$, which proves the desired result. Here, the basic requirement that $s_n \to \infty$ is equivalent to the condition that the infinite series

$$\sum_{k=1}^{\infty} \sigma_k^2$$

does not converge—i.e., that the variances σ_k^2 do not decrease too rapidly as $k \to \infty$.

12.2   Normal Approximation of the Binomial Distribution

In Section 10.1, we saw that a binomially distributed random variable with parameters (n, p) can be viewed as the sum S_n of n independent, identically distributed random variables X_k for which

$$P(X_k = 1) = p \text{ and } P(X_k = 0) = q = 1 - p.$$

With $\mu = p$ and $\sigma^2 = pq$, Theorem 12.1 thus clearly implies that the standardized binomial distribution approaches a normal distribution as $n \to \infty$ with p fixed. More accurately, we have

$$\lim_{n \to \infty} P\left(\frac{S_n - np}{\sqrt{npq}} \leq z\right) = \Phi(z) \tag{12.11}$$

for every fixed real z and hence for large n

$$F_n(y) = P(S_n \leq y) \doteq \Phi\left(\frac{y - np}{\sqrt{npq}}\right). \tag{12.12}$$

More explicitly, Eq. 12.12 asserts that, for large n,

$$\sum_{k \leq y} \binom{n}{k} p^k q^{n-k} \doteq \frac{1}{\sqrt{2\pi}} \int_{-\infty}^{z} e^{-t^2/2}\, dt, \qquad (12.13)$$

where

$$z = \frac{y - np}{\sqrt{npq}}.$$

This result is generally known as the de Moivre–Laplace limit theorem, since it was first stated by de Moivre about 1730 for the case $p = \frac{1}{2}$ and was first proved for arbitrary values of p by Laplace about 1812. In many introductory texts, this theorem is proved by an elementary argument based on Stirling's formula,

$$n! \sim \sqrt{2\pi}\, n^{n+1/2} e^{-n},$$

which is indicated in the exercises. Nevertheless, since a binomial distribution has a moment-generating function, the proof indicated in Section 12.3 contains as a special case a proof of the de Moivre–Laplace theorem.

The function on the left side of Eq. 12.12 is a step function having jumps only at the nonnegative integers smaller than n, whereas the function on the right side is continuous and increases monotonically as y (or z) increases from $-\infty$ to $+\infty$. But for n large enough, these two functions take approximately the same values at each argument, with the graph of the continuous function generally passing through the middle of the steps of the step function.

Generally, Eq. 12.12 may be used to approximate the probability that S_n takes a value equal to or smaller than some integer, say, n_2. However, a better approximation is obtained by noting that

$$F_n(n_2) = P(S_n \leq n_2) = P(S_n \leq n_2 + \tfrac{1}{2})$$
$$\doteq \Phi\left(\frac{n_2 + \tfrac{1}{2} - np}{\sqrt{npq}}\right). \qquad (12.14)$$

This so-called "continuity correction" (addition of $\frac{1}{2}$ to n_2) helps adjust for the fact that a step function is being approximated by a continuous function. This correction is most helpful when n is small and is clearly negligible when $1/2\sqrt{npq}$ is negligible. Of course, if n_1 and n_2 are two integers such that $0 \leq n_1 \leq n_2 \leq n$, we find that

$$P(n_1 \leq S_n \leq n_2) \doteq \Phi\left(\frac{n_2 + \tfrac{1}{2} - np}{\sqrt{npq}}\right) - \Phi\left(\frac{n_1 - \tfrac{1}{2} - np}{\sqrt{npq}}\right). \qquad (12.15)$$

On setting $n_1 = n_2 = k$ in Eq. 12.15, one finds the following approximation for the binomial probability function:

$$\binom{n}{k} p^k q^{n-k} \doteq \frac{1}{\sqrt{2\pi}} \int_{(k-np-\frac{1}{2})/(\sqrt{npq})}^{(k-np+\frac{1}{2})/(\sqrt{npq})} \exp\left[-t^2/2\right] dt. \quad (12.16)$$

A second such formula,

$$\binom{n}{k} p^k q^{n-k} \doteq \frac{1}{\sqrt{2\pi npq}} \exp\left[-(k-np)^2/2npq\right], \quad (12.17)$$

can be made plausible by noting that the summand in the left side of Eq. 12.13 should be approximately equal to the derivative with respect to y of the right side of Eq. 12.13, with $y = k$. Relation 12.17 can be derived directly by use of Stirling's formula, as shown in Exercise 12.17.

These approximations are very useful because they provide easy alternatives to the laborious computations necessary to evaluate exactly binomial probabilities. Of course, there arises the question of how good these approximations are. This question has been investigated extensively but does not have a simple answer. When $p = q = \frac{1}{2}$, the binomial distribution is symmetrical about its mean and resembles the normal distribution more than when $p \neq q$. In view of remarks made in Section 12.1, we therefore should expect these approximations will be best for fixed n when $p = q = \frac{1}{2}$ and that they will get progressively worse as p moves closer to 0 or 1. This is indeed what happens. Thus the best approximations are obtained when n is large and p is close to $\frac{1}{2}$. As a rule of thumb, satisfactory approximations are usually obtained by using the normal approximation when $np > 5$ and $nq > 5$. For a more detailed discussion of this question as well as for several relevant references, the reader is referred to page 245 in the book by Parzen listed in the bibliography.

Finally, we will merely indicate the existence of certain other general relations among binomial, Poisson, and normal distributions. (Also see Exercises 12.18 and 12.19.) Recall from Section 7.4 that, when n is large and p is small (say, $p < .1$), the binomial probability function can be approximated by the Poisson probability function in the form

$$\binom{n}{k} p^k q^{n-k} \doteq \frac{(np)^k}{k!} e^{-np}. \quad (12.18)$$

When np is small enough, Eq. 12.18 gives a better approximation than

12.16 or 12.17. On the other hand, when p is small and n is very large so that np is large enough, the four quantities in Eqs. 12.16 through 12.18 are approximately equal. This makes plausible the following useful fact: when $\lambda(= np \doteq npq)$ is large enough,

$$\frac{\lambda^k e^{-\lambda}}{k!} \doteq \frac{1}{\sqrt{2\pi\lambda}} \exp\left[-(k-\lambda)^2/2\lambda\right], \tag{12.19}$$

i.e., the Poisson and normal distributions approximate each other.

Example 12.3. When $n = 4$ and $p = \frac{1}{2}$, we obtain from Eq. 12.14 the exact and approximate values given in the following table:

k	0	1	2	3	4
$F_4(k)$	0.0625	0.3125	0.6875	0.9375	1.0000
Normal Approximation	0.0668	0.3085	0.6915	0.9332	0.9938

Without the continuity correction, the last row would be 0.0228, 0.1587, 0.5000, 0.8413, 0.9773.

Example 12.4. When a biased coin with probability $p = \frac{1}{3}$ of heads on a single toss is tossed independently 180 times, what is the probability that the total number X of heads satisfies $50 \leq X \leq 70$? Let $n_1 = 50$, $n_2 = 70$, $n = 180$, $p = \frac{1}{3}$, and $q = \frac{2}{3}$ in Eq. 12.15 to find that

$$P(50 \leq X \leq 70) \doteq \Phi\left(\frac{10.5}{\sqrt{40}}\right) - \Phi\left(-\frac{10.5}{\sqrt{40}}\right) \doteq 0.903.$$

The reader may find it worthwhile to contemplate evaluation of the exact probability, which has the form

$$P(50 \leq X \leq 70) = \sum_{k=50}^{70} \binom{180}{k} \left(\tfrac{1}{3}\right)^k \left(\tfrac{2}{3}\right)^{180-k}$$

12.3　On Proving the Central Limit Theorem

Here, we indicate a proof of Theorem 12.1 under the additional assumption that the common distribution of the random variables X_k has a moment-generating function.

In addition to the properties of moment-generating functions described in Sections 6.5 and 10.6, the following general theorem (which cannot be proved here) will be used: *For every* $n = 1, 2, 3, \ldots$, *let* X_n *be a random variable with distribution function* F_n *and moment-generating function* M_n. *Also, let* X *be a random variable which has a distribution function* F *and a moment-generating function* M. *If* $M_n(\theta) \to M(\theta)$ *as* $n \to \infty$ *for every* θ *in* $-h \leq \theta \leq h$ *for some* $h > 0$, *then* $F_n(x) \to F(x)$ *as* $n \to \infty$ *for every value of* x *at which* F *is continuous.* This theorem asserts that a sequence of distribution functions converges to a distribution function F if the corresponding sequence of moment-generating functions converges to the moment-generating function of F. Convergence in the sense of this theorem is usually called *convergence in distribution;* thus we say, for example, that the sequence $\{X_n\}$ converges in distribution to X. (This theorem remains true if the moment-generating functions are replaced by discrete generating functions.)

The theorem stated above is essentially a special case of part of an extremely general and useful theorem usually called the *continuity theorem* of probability theory. This continuity theorem will merely be stated here, since some readers may wish to base a general proof of Theorem 12.1 on it. *For every* $n = 1, 2, 3, \ldots$, *let* X_n *be a random variable with distribution function* F_n *and characteristic function* φ_n *(as described in Section 6.6). In order that a distribution function* F *exists such that* $F_n(x) \to F(x)$ *as* $n \to \infty$ *for every value of* x *at which* F *is continuous, it is necessary and sufficient that there exists a function* φ *such that* $\varphi(u)$ *is continous at* $u = 0$ *and* $\varphi_n(u) \to \varphi(u)$ *as* $n \to \infty$ *for every real* u. *Under these conditions,* φ *is the characteristic function of* F.

Returning to the proof of Theorem 12.1, we will let F_n and M_n be the distribution function and the moment-generating function of the standardized sum $(S_n - n\mu)/\sigma\sqrt{n}$, so that

$$F_n(z) = P\left(\frac{S_n - n\mu}{\sigma\sqrt{n}} \leq z\right) \qquad (-\infty < z < \infty).$$

We will show that $M_n(\theta) \to \exp(\theta^2/2)$ as $n \to \infty$ for all θ near zero. Since $\exp(\theta^2/2)$ is the moment-generating function of the unit normal distribution function Φ, and $\Phi(z)$ is continuous at every real z, the conclusion of Theorem 12.1—that is, $F_n(z) \to \Phi(z)$ as $n \to \infty$ for every real z—will then follow directly from the theorem stated above.

A relatively detailed derivation will be given, so that the reader can see clearly every step of the argument. By assumption, the random variables X_k have a common moment-generating function M^*. To evaluate M_n, first note, as indicated in Section 6.5, that $M^*(\theta)$ can be written in the form

$$M^*(\theta) = E(e^{\theta X_k}) = \sum_{i=0}^{\infty} \frac{\theta^i}{i!} E(X_k^i), \qquad (12.20)$$

where the series converges absolutely for all θ near zero. Now let M be the common moment-generating functions of the standardized random variables $(X_k - \mu)/\sigma$, whose means and variances are 0 and 1; i.e., let

$$M(\theta) = E\left[\exp\frac{\theta}{\sigma}(X_k - \mu)\right] = e^{-\mu\theta/\sigma}M^*\left(\frac{\theta}{\sigma}\right). \qquad (12.21)$$

Of course, the series

$$e^{-\mu\theta/\sigma} = \sum_{i=0}^{\infty}\left(\frac{\mu\theta}{\sigma}\right)^i \frac{(-1)^i}{i!} \qquad (12.22)$$

converges absolutely for all θ near zero, since $\sigma > 0$. Since the product of two absolutely convergent series is an absolutely convergent series, Eqs. 12.20 through 12.22 show that $M(\theta)$ can be written as an absolutely convergent series for all θ near zero. This series can therefore be arranged in the form

$$
\begin{aligned}
M(\theta) &= E\left[\exp\frac{\theta}{\sigma}(X_k - \mu)\right] \\
&= E\left[1 + \theta\left(\frac{X_k - \mu}{\sigma}\right) + \frac{\theta^2}{2}\left(\frac{X_k - \mu}{\sigma}\right)^2 + \sum_{i=3}^{\infty}\frac{\theta^i}{i!}\left(\frac{X_k - \mu}{\sigma}\right)^i\right] \\
&= 1 + \frac{\theta^2}{2} + \sum_{i=3}^{\infty}\mu_i\frac{\theta^i}{i!}, \qquad (12.23)
\end{aligned}
$$

since the mean and variance of $(X_k - \mu)/\sigma$ are 0 and 1 and μ_i is the ith central moment of X_k.

Since $M(0) = 1$ and M is continuous for all θ near zero, we can now use the known formula

$$\log(1 + t) = t - \frac{t^2}{2} + \frac{t^3}{3} - \cdots \qquad (-1 < t < 1)$$

to find from Eq. 12.23 that

$$\log M(\theta) = \left(\frac{\theta^2}{2} + \mu_3 \frac{\theta^3}{3!} + \cdots\right) - \frac{1}{2}\left(\frac{\theta^2}{2} + \mu_3 \frac{\theta^3}{3!} + \cdots\right)^2 + \cdots$$

$$= \frac{\theta^2}{2} + \sum_{i=3}^{\infty} a_i \theta^i, \tag{12.24}$$

where the constants a_i depend on the μ_i's. Moreover, we can choose any one of many constants $h > 0$ for which the last series in Eq. 12.24 converges absolutely for all θ in $-h \le \theta \le h$; let us choose any such fixed h and note below that all statements made hold for all θ satisfying at least $-h \le \theta \le h$.

For $k = 1, 2, 3, \ldots, n$, the random variables $(X_k - \mu)/\sigma\sqrt{n}$ are independent, because the X_k's were assumed to be independent. Furthermore, Eq. 12.21 shows that these random variables have the common moment-generating function $M(\theta/\sqrt{n})$, with θ replaced by $\theta/\sqrt{n}$. Therefore, it follows from Eq. 10.19 and the relation

$$\frac{S_n - n\mu}{\sigma\sqrt{n}} = \frac{X_1 - \mu}{\sigma\sqrt{n}} + \frac{X_2 - \mu}{\sigma\sqrt{n}} + \cdots + \frac{X_n - \mu}{\sigma\sqrt{n}}$$

that

$$M_n(\theta) = [M(\theta/\sqrt{n})]^n. \tag{12.25}$$

Now, Eqs. 12.24 and 12.25 imply that

$$\log M_n(\theta) = n \log M(\theta/\sqrt{n})$$

$$= n\left(\frac{\theta^2}{2n} + \sum_{i=3}^{\infty} \frac{a_i}{n^{i/2}} \theta^i\right)$$

$$= \frac{\theta^2}{2} + \frac{1}{\sqrt{n}} \sum_{i=3}^{\infty} b_{ni}\theta^i,$$

where $b_{ni} = a_i/n^{(i-3)/2}$. Since the last series in Eq. 12.24 is absolutely convergent and $|b_{ni}| \le |a_i|$ for every $n = 1, 2, 3, \ldots$ and $i = 3, 4, 5, \ldots$, it follows from the comparison test for convergence of series that the series

$$h_n(\theta) = \sum_{i=3}^{\infty} b_{ni}\theta^i$$

is absolutely convergent and therefore has a finite value for every positive integer n. Hence,

$$\log M_n(\theta) = \frac{\theta^2}{2} + \frac{h_n(\theta)}{\sqrt{n}}$$

$$\rightarrow \frac{\theta^2}{2} \quad \text{as } n \rightarrow \infty,$$

and therefore $M_n(\theta) \rightarrow \exp(\theta^2/2)$ as $n \rightarrow \infty$, which concludes the derivation.

12.4 Exercises

12.1 Suppose that an airplane contains 36 people, from a population in which the weights of people have a normal distribution with mean 160 pounds and standard deviation 20 pounds. What is the probability that their total weight is larger than 6000 pounds? Between 5600 and 5900 pounds? State any assumptions made; in particular state whether your result would apply if these 36 people happen to be a professional football team on its way to a game.

12.2 A computer adds 1200 real numbers, each of which is rounded off to the nearest integer. Suppose that all of the rounding-off errors are independent, and that each such error has a rectangular distribution between -0.5 and 0.5. (a) Find approximately the probability that the magnitude of the error in the sum will exceed 10. (b) Find the number y_0 such that the probability is approximately 0.99 that the magnitude of the error will be less than y_0.

12.3 Use the answers to Exercise 11.11 in estimating the likelihood that the sum of 25 independent observations of X will exceed 160, and that it will lie between 100 and 160.

12.4 (a) Use Eq. 12.8 to estimate the likelihood that the average found in Exercise 11.11 differs from the (unknown) true mean μ by at least 1, and by at least .5. (b) Repeat part (a) for the data of Exercise 11.8.

12.5 Let $\bar{X}_{50}$ be the average of the 50 numbers obtained when 50 independent trials of Experiment 1.1 are made. Compute approximately the probability that $\bar{X}_{50}$ will differ from its mean by no more than 1.

12.6 Refer to Example 12.2, and show that

$$P(|\bar{X}_n - \mu| \leq \epsilon) \geq \alpha$$

for given ϵ and α, if $n \geq (z\sigma/\epsilon)^2$ where z satisfies $\Phi(z) = (1 + \alpha)/2$.

12.7   Use the central limit theorem to make the estimates described in (a) Exercise 11.4, (b) Exercise 11.5, and (c) Exercise 11.9. Compare these values with those provided by Chebyshev's inequality.

12.8   A truck is loaded with three types of cartons. It contains 10, 40, and 80 cartons whose weights are random variables with respective means and standard deviations of 100, 10; 50, 5; and 25, $\sqrt{20}$. Estimate the probability that the load on the truck is more than 5100 pounds.

12.9   Let S_n have the binomial distribution with parameters n and $p = q = \frac{1}{2}$, and let

$$S_n^* = (S_n - np)/\sqrt{npq}.$$

Use appropriate tables to sketch, on ordinary (x, y) coordinates, the graphs of $y = P(S_n^* \leq x)$ for a few values of n (e.g., 2, 4, 7, 10), and the graph of the unit normal distribution function $y = \Phi(x)$.

12.10   When a certain coin is tossed independently 10,000 times, 5100 heads occur. If the coin were unbiased, what would be the probability of 5100 or more heads? Is it reasonable to say that this coin is unbiased?

12.11   For 100 independent tosses of an unbiased die, write an exact expression for the probability that the outcome "2, 4, or 6 spots appear" will occur at least 40 times but not more than 55 times. Use the normal approximation with, and also without, the continuity correction to approximate this probability.

12.12   For successive independent tosses of an unbiased die, estimate the minimum number of tosses required for the probability to be at least 0.95 that the relative frequency of one spot showing will lie between $\frac{9}{60}$ and $\frac{11}{60}$.

12.13   Four percent of the screws made by a certain factory are defective. Evaluate exactly the likelihood that a box of 100 screws chosen at random from the output of this factory will contain at most two defective screws. Also, use normal and Poisson approximations to find approximate values, and note which of these is closer to the exact value.

12.14   (a) When $n = 100$, $k = 8$, $p = .08$, and $q = .92$, evaluate by any means and compare the right sides of Eqs. 12.16 through 12.19. (b) Repeat part (a), for $n = 100$, $k = 2$, $p = 0.04$, and $q = 0.96$ (as in Exercise 12.13). Also, evaluate

$$\binom{n}{k} p^k q^{n-k}.$$

12.15   If X has a Poisson distribution with parameter 100, use Eq. 12.19 and a continuity correction to approximate $P(X \geq 115)$.

THEORETICAL EXERCISES

*12.16   If $\sigma_{12} \neq 0$ or $a_n \to a \neq 0$ as $n \to \infty$, show that the sequence $\{X_k\}$ of dependent random variables described in Exercise 11.14 obeys the central limit theorem but does not obey the law of large numbers.

12.17   Use Stirling's formula,

$$n! \sim \sqrt{2\pi n}\, n^n e^{-n},$$

to derive Eq. 12.17. *Hint:* Let $h = k - np$, and let $k \to \infty$ and $n \to \infty$ in such a way that $h^3/n^2 \to 0$, and therefore $h/n \to 0$. Use Stirling's formula to show that

$$\binom{n}{k} p^k q^{n-k} \sim \left(\frac{n}{2\pi k(n-k)}\right)^{1/2} \left(\frac{np}{k}\right)^k \left(\frac{nq}{n-k}\right)^{n-k}$$

$$= \left[\frac{n}{2\pi(np+h)(nq-h)}\right]^{1/2} \left(\frac{1}{A_n}\right),$$

where $A_n = (1 + h/np)^{np+h}(1 - h/nq)^{nq-h}$. Then use the power series for $\log(1 + x)$ to see that

$$\log A_n = \frac{h^2}{2npq}\left[1 + \frac{p-q}{3pq}\left(\frac{h}{n}\right) + \cdots\right] \sim \frac{h^2}{2npq},$$

where the quantity in square brackets is a power series in the variable h/n. Finally, note that $np + h \sim np$ and $nq - h \sim nq$. (Recall that $a_n \sim b_n$ denotes that $a_n/b_n \to 1$ as $n \to \infty$.)

12.18   Use Theorem 12.1, parts (2) and (3) of Exercise 10.24, and parts (2) and (3) of Exercise 10.25 to show that the (a) Pascal, (b) gamma, (c) negative binomial, and (d) Poisson distributions can be approximated by the normal distribution. In each case, express Eq. 12.7 in terms of the usual parameters of each distribution, and state general conditions on the parameters required for a good approximation.

12.19   Use moment-generating functions to show directly that the standardized version (mean 0 and variance 1) of the (a) gamma, (b) negative binomial, (c) Poisson distribution approaches the unit normal distribution as $\alpha \to \infty$, $r \to \infty$, $\lambda \to \infty$, respectively.

APPLICATIONS IN ENGINEERING

12.20   Use Exercise 10.29 and Theorem 12.1 to show that the density function of Exercise 5.28(b) can be written for large n (e.g., $n > 25$) as

$$f(t) \doteq \frac{\sqrt{n}}{\tau\sqrt{2\pi}} \exp\left[-n(t-\tau)^2/2\tau^2\right].$$

*12.21   A single reactor (particularly a section of packed pipe) can often be modeled approximately by a finite series of well-stirred reactors connected as described in Exercise 7.19. For this purpose, suppose that τ_1 is small so that λ is large enough. (a) Use the central limit theorem to show that $p(k, t)$ of Exercise 7.19 can be written approximately as

$$p(k, t) \doteq \frac{1}{\sqrt{2\pi\lambda t}} \exp\left[-(k - \lambda t)^2/2\lambda t\right].$$

(b) Let h be a relatively small but positive number, and let $x \doteq kh$, $u \doteq \lambda h$, and $2D \doteq \lambda h^2$. Show that
$$p(k, t) \doteq g(x, t)h,$$
where

$$g(x, t) = \frac{1}{\sqrt{4\pi Dt}} \exp\left[-(x - ut)^2/4Dt\right].$$

(Here, h is the "diameter" of each well-stirred reactor, $x \geq 0$ is the distance from the reactor entrance, u is the average fluid velocity, D is a diffusion coefficient, and $g(x, t)h$ is approximately the probability that a molecule which enters the reactor at time zero is between x and $x + h$ at time t.) (c) Show that g satisfies the partial differential equation

$$\frac{\partial g}{\partial t} = D\frac{\partial^2 g}{\partial x^2} - u\frac{\partial g}{\partial x}.$$

(d) Compare this situation with Brownian motion of Exercise 10.10.

APPENDIXES

BIBLIOGRAPHY

The books by Feller [4], Parzen [9], and Wadsworth and Bryan [12] are excellent introductory texts, which also contain a wealth of problems and applications. Feller's book is simultaneously an introductory textbook and a treatise on certain aspects of mathematical and applied probability theory, but it is restricted to discrete sample spaces. Parzen's book is a comprehensive introduction to modern probability theory and its applications. The book by Wadsworth and Bryan is especially appropriate for those readers interested primarily in applications.

In 1933, Kolmogorov [7] presented the first systematic development of probability theory on an axiomatic basis. The treatises by Cramér [2], Doob [3], Gnedenko and Kolmogorov [5], Loève [8], and Wilks [13] contain advanced developments of the modern mathematical theory and some of its applications. We remark that Cramér's book contains a very readable introduction to measure theory and that the first seven chapters of Wilks' book contains a concise, more advanced development of substantially the same material as is covered here. There is a unique book by Kac [6] for mathematically advanced readers interested in applications of probability theory in physical sciences, particularly in statistical mechanics. Some idea of the innumerable other applications of the advanced theory, as well as many references to other works, can be obtained from the recent books by Bharucha-Reid [1], Parzen [10], and Rosenblatt [11].

1. Bharucha-Reid, A. T., *Elements of the Theory of Markov Processes and Their Applications*. New York: McGraw-Hill Book Company, Inc., 1960.
2. Cramér, H., *Mathematical Methods of Statistics*. Princeton, N.J.: Princeton University Press, 1946.
3. Doob, J. L., *Stochastic Processes*. New York: John Wiley & Sons, Inc., 1953.
4. Feller, W., *An Introduction to Probability Theory and Its Applications*, 2nd ed. New York: John Wiley & Sons, Inc., 1957.
5. Gnedenko, B. V., and A. N. Kolmogorov, *Limit Distributions for Sums of Independent Random Variables*. Reading, Mass.: Addison-Wesley Publishing Company, 1954 (translated by K. L. Chung from the Russian book of 1949).
6. Kac, M., *Probability and Related Topics in Physical Sciences*. New York: Interscience Publishers, Inc., 1959.
7. Kolmogorov, A. N., *Foundations of the Theory of Probability*. New York: Chelsea Publishing Company, 1950 (translation of *Grundbegriffe der Wahrscheinlichkeitsrechnung*, 1933).
8. Loève, M., *Probability Theory*, 2nd ed. Princeton, N.J.: D. Van Nostrand Company, Inc., 1960.

9. Parzen, E., *Modern Probability Theory and Its Applications*. New York: John Wiley & Sons, Inc., 1960.

10. ———, *Stochastic Processes*. San Francisco: Holden-Day, 1962.

11. Rosenblatt, M., *Random Processes*. New York: Oxford University Press, 1962.

12. Wadsworth, G. P., and J. G. Bryan, *Introduction to Probability and Random Variables*. New York: McGraw-Hill Book Company, Inc., 1960.

13. Wilks, S. S., *Mathematical Statistics*. New York: John Wiley & Sons, Inc., 1962.

The following references are to works discussed between Exercises 5.26 and 5.27:

14. Danckwerts, P. V., "The effect of incomplete mixing on homogeneous reactions," *Chemical Reaction Engineering*, 12th Meeting European Federation of Chemical Engineering, Amsterdam, 1957, pp. 93–102.

15. Gilliland, E. R., E. A. Mason, and R. C. Oliver, "Gas-flow patterns in beds of fluidized solids," *Industrial and Engineering Chemistry*, vol. 45, 1953, pp. 1177–1185.

16. Levenspiel, O., *Chemical Reaction Engineering*. New York: John Wiley & Sons, Inc., 1962.

17. Zwietering, Th. N., "The degree of mixing in continuous flow systems," *Chemical Engineering Science*, vol. 11, 1959, pp. 1–15.

TABLE OF THE NORMAL DISTRIBUTION

x	$\dfrac{1}{\sqrt{2\pi}}\, e^{-x^2/2}$	$\dfrac{1}{\sqrt{2\pi}} \displaystyle\int_{-\infty}^{x} e^{-t^2/2}\, dt$
0.0	0.39894	0.50000
0.1	.39695	.53983
0.2	.39104	.57926
0.3	.38139	.61791
0.4	.36827	.65542
0.5	.35207	.69146
0.6	.33322	.72575
0.7	.31225	.75804
0.8	.28969	.78814
0.9	.26609	.81594
1.0	.24197	.84134
1.1	.21785	.86433
1.2	.19419	.88493
1.3	.17137	.90320
1.4	.14973	.91924
1.5	.12952	.93319
1.6	.11092	.94520
1.7	.09405	.95543
1.8	.07895	.96407
1.9	.06562	.97128

TABLE OF THE NORMAL DISTRIBUTION

x	$\dfrac{1}{\sqrt{2\pi}}\, e^{-x^2/2}$	$\dfrac{1}{\sqrt{2\pi}} \displaystyle\int_{-\infty}^{x} e^{-t^2/2}\, dt$
2.0	0.05399	0.97725
2.1	.04398	.98214
2.2	.03547	.98610
2.3	.02833	.98928
2.4	.02239	.99180
2.5	.01753	.99379
2.6	.01358	.99534
2.7	.01042	.99653
2.8	.00792	.99744
2.9	.00595	.99813
3.0	.00443	.99865
3.1	.00327	.99903
3.2	.00238	.99931
3.3	.00172	.99952
3.4	.00123	.99966
3.5	.00087	.99977
3.6	.00061	.99984
3.7	.00042	.99989
3.8	.00029	.99993
3.9	.00020	.99995

ANSWERS TO EXERCISES

Chapter 1

1.1 (a) The two letters H, T.

(b) The integers 1, 2, 3, 4, 5, 6.

(c) The integers 1, 2, 3, 4, 5, 6, 7.

(d) The integers 1, 2, . . . , 20.

1.2 Assuming equal likelihood in all cases, (a) $\frac{1}{2}$, (b) $\frac{1}{6}$, (c) $\frac{1}{7}$, (d) $\frac{1}{20}$.

1.3 (a) $\frac{1}{36}$, $\frac{2}{36}$, $\frac{3}{36}$, $\frac{4}{36}$, $\frac{5}{36}$, $\frac{6}{36}$, $\frac{5}{36}$, $\frac{4}{36}$, $\frac{3}{36}$, $\frac{2}{36}$, $\frac{1}{36}$.

(b) $\frac{30}{36}$.

1.4 $\frac{9}{24}$, $\frac{8}{24}$, $\frac{6}{24}$, 0, $\frac{1}{24}$.

1.5 (b) $\frac{1}{4}$, $\frac{1}{8}$.

1.7 $\frac{1}{36}$, $\frac{1}{8}$.

1.8 $\frac{1}{3}$, 0.

1.9 $\frac{1}{4}$.

1.10 $\frac{2}{3}$.

1.11 $2 \int_{1/\sqrt{2}}^{1} \sqrt{x^2 - \frac{1}{2}}\, dx = \frac{1}{2}\left[\sqrt{2} + \log\left(\frac{1}{1 + \sqrt{2}}\right) \right].$

1.12 $1{,}111{,}111/3{,}000{,}000$.

1.13 $\frac{365}{3}$.

1.14 50.

1.15 (a) $\frac{3}{10}$, $\frac{2}{10}$, $\frac{5}{10}$.

Chapter 2

2.1 *aem, cfm, adm* plus *bfm, abfmcd*.

2.3 $\{1, 2, 3, 4, 5, 6, 7, 8, 9, 10\}$,

$\varnothing$,

$\{7, 9\}$,

$\{1, 3, 5, 6, 7, 8, 9, 10\}$,

$\{1, 2, 3, 4, 5, 7, 9\}$,

$\{1, 2, 3, 4, 5, 6, 7, 8, 9, 10\}$.

2.6 $\frac{26}{27}$.

2.15 (a) At least 10 percent.

Chapter 3

3.2 $\frac{3}{5}$, $\frac{3}{5}$, $\frac{3}{10}$.

3.3 64×14.

3.4 $\frac{1}{4}$, $\frac{5}{12}$, $\frac{1}{12}$.

3.6 0 if $r \geq \dfrac{n}{2}$, $\dfrac{(2n)(2n-2)(2n-4)\,\cdots\,(2n-4r)}{(2n)(2n-1)(2n-2)\,\cdots\,(2n-2r)}$ if $r < \dfrac{n}{2}$.

3.7 25^3, $(25)(24)(23)$, $\dbinom{25}{3}$, $25^3 - (25)(24)(2) - 25$, $25^3 - (2)(23)$.

3.8   For each m the possibilities are $(13 - m - j, j)$ for $j = 0, 1, \ldots ,$ $\left[\dfrac{13 - m}{2}\right]$, with $[u]$ denoting the largest integer not exceeding u. The corresponding probabilities are

$$\frac{2*\dbinom{13 + m}{13 - j}\dbinom{13 - m}{j}}{\dbinom{26}{13}}$$

where the asterisk indicates that the 2 is absent if $j = (13 - m)/2$.

3.9 $\dfrac{611}{1150}$.

3.10 $\dbinom{4}{1}\dbinom{13}{5}$, $\dbinom{10}{1}\dbinom{4}{1}^5$, $\dbinom{10}{1}\dbinom{4}{1}\dbinom{4}{1}$, $\dbinom{13}{1}\dbinom{12}{1}\dbinom{4}{1}$,

$\dbinom{13}{1}\dbinom{4}{3}\dbinom{49}{2}$, $2\dbinom{13}{2}\dbinom{4}{3}\dbinom{4}{2}$, $\dbinom{13}{2}\dbinom{4}{2}\dbinom{4}{2}$ 49 all over $\dbinom{52}{5}$.

3.11 $\dbinom{4}{1}\left[\dbinom{13}{5} - \dbinom{10}{1}\right]$, $\dbinom{10}{1}\left[\dbinom{4}{1}^5 - \dbinom{4}{1}\right]$, $\dbinom{9}{1}\dbinom{4}{1}$,

$\dbinom{13}{1}\dbinom{12}{2}\dbinom{4}{3}\dbinom{4}{1}\dbinom{4}{1}$, $\dbinom{13}{2}\dbinom{4}{2}\dbinom{4}{2}$ 49 all over $\dbinom{52}{5}$.

3.13 $m = 7$: $(4, 2)$ @ $\frac{390}{805}$
                 $(3, 3)$ @ $\frac{286}{805}$
       $m = 8$: $(3, 2)$ @ $\frac{156}{230}$
                 $(4, 1)$ @ $\frac{65}{230}$
       $m = 9$: $(3, 1)$ @ $\frac{286}{575}$
                 $(2, 2)$ @ $\frac{234}{575}$.

3.15 $1/2^{k+1}$.

3.16 $e^{-1}\displaystyle\sum_{n=5}^{\infty}\frac{1}{n!}$.

3.17 0.

3.18 $\frac{1}{6}(1 + \log 6)$, $\frac{1}{6}(6 - 2\sqrt{3})$, $\frac{1}{6}(\frac{1}{3} + \log 2)$, $\frac{1}{6}(\frac{20}{3} + \log 3 - 2\sqrt{3})$, $\frac{1}{6}(\frac{2}{3} + \log 3)$.

3.19 $1 - \dfrac{\sinh\frac{1}{2}}{\sinh 1}$.

3.20 $1/2^k$.

Chapter 4

4.1 $\frac{1}{3}$, $\frac{1}{2}$.

4.2 $\frac{1}{2}$.

4.3 $\frac{1}{6}, \frac{1}{6}, \frac{1}{36}, \frac{1}{6}, \frac{1}{6}$, yes.

4.4 $\frac{7}{32}$.

4.5 $\frac{1}{8}$.

4.6 $\frac{12}{23}$.

4.7 $\frac{1}{11}, \frac{1}{9}$.

4.8 $\frac{9}{48}, \frac{4}{48}$.

4.9 One in 4: $[1 - (\frac{5}{6})^4] > [1 - (\frac{35}{36})^{24}]$.

4.10 $1 - (1 - p)^n$.

4.11 $\frac{1}{2}(\sin 50° - \sin 40°)$.

4.12 $$8 \int_{\sqrt{3}/2}^{1} \left(\sqrt{x^2 - \frac{1}{2}} - \sqrt{1 - x^2} \right) dx$$
$$= \frac{2}{4 - \pi} \left[\sqrt{2} - \frac{\pi}{3} + \log \left(\frac{\sqrt{3} + 1}{\sqrt{2} + 2} \right) \right].$$

4.13 $\frac{25}{69}, \frac{28}{69}, \frac{16}{69}$.

4.14 0.72, 0.94, 0.77, 0.27.

4.15 $\frac{6}{11}$.

Chapter 5

5.1 $\{E_i \colon i = 1, 2, \ldots, 20\}$, $X(E_i) = i$, $g(i) = \frac{1}{20}$ $(i = 1, 2, \ldots, 20)$.

5.2 $\{E_{ij} \colon i, j = 1, 2, \ldots, 6\}$, $X(E_{ij}) = i + j$,
$g(k) = \begin{cases} (k - 1)/36 & (k = 2, 3, \ldots, 7) \\ (13 - k)/36 & (k = 8, 9, \ldots, 12). \end{cases}$

5.3 $\{0, 1\}$, $X(k) = k$, $g(0) = \frac{1}{3}$, $g(1) = \frac{2}{3}$.

5.4 $\{0, 1, \ldots, 5\}$, $X(k) = k$, $\binom{5}{k} \left(\frac{1}{5} \right)^k \left(\frac{4}{5} \right)^{5-k}$ $(k = 0, 1, \ldots, 5)$.

5.5 $\{1, 2, 3, \ldots \}$, $X(k) = k$, $(\frac{1}{2})^k$ $(k = 1, 2, 3, \ldots)$.

5.6 (a) $\{1, 2, \ldots, 9\}$, $X(k) = k$, $g(k) = \frac{1}{9}$ $(k = 1, 2, \ldots, 9)$.
(b) $\{1, 2, 3, \ldots\}$, $X(k) = k$, $(\frac{1}{9})(\frac{8}{9})^{k-1}$ $(k = 1, 2, 3, \ldots)$.
(c) $\frac{1}{9}, \frac{1}{3} \doteq 0.33, 1$; $\frac{1}{9}, \frac{217}{729} \doteq 0.30, 1 - (\frac{8}{9})^9 \doteq 0.65$.

5.7 $\{E_{xy} \colon 0 \leq x \leq 1/\sqrt{\pi}, 0 \leq y < 2\pi\}$, $X(E_{xy}) = x$, πx^2 $(0 \leq x \leq 1/\sqrt{\pi})$.

5.8 $\{x \colon 0 \leq x \leq L\}$, $X(x) = x$, x/L $(0 \leq x \leq L)$.

5.9 (a) $\{(x, y) \colon 0 \leq x \leq \sqrt{3}, |y| \leq 1 - x/\sqrt{3}\}$, $X(x, y) = x$, $(x/3)(2\sqrt{3} - x)$ $(0 \leq x \leq \sqrt{3})$. (b) $F(\frac{1}{2}) \doteq 0.49$.

5.10 (a) $\{(L, R) \colon \pi \leq L \leq 4\pi, 1 \leq R \leq 2\}$, $X(L, R) = \pi L R^2$, $F(x) = (\sqrt{x} - \pi)^2/3\pi^2$ for $\pi^2 \leq x \leq 4\pi^2$, $= (8\pi\sqrt{x} - x - 10\pi^2)/6\pi^2$ for $4\pi^2 < x \leq 16\pi^2$. (b) $\frac{1}{2}$.

5.11 (a) $g(0) = \frac{1}{6}$, $g(1) = \frac{1}{3}$; $\frac{1}{3}, \frac{2}{3}, 1, \frac{1}{6}, \frac{1}{2}, 1$. (b) $g(0) = \frac{1}{4}$; $0, \frac{1}{2}, \frac{1}{2}, \frac{1}{4}$, $0, \frac{1}{2} - \frac{1}{4}e^{-1} \doteq 0.408$.

5.13 (a) $\frac{1}{2}$, (b) $\frac{1}{2}$, (c) $\frac{1}{4}$.

5.14 (a) $\frac{1}{21}$, $k(k + 1)/42$ for $k \leq x < k + 1$ and $k = 1, 2, \ldots, 5$.

(b) e^{-2}, $e^{-2} \sum\limits_{i=0}^{k} 2^i/i!$ for $k \leq x < k+1$ and $k = 0, 1, 2, \ldots$.

(c) 2, $(\frac{1}{3})^n$ for $1/(n+1) \leq x \leq 1/n$ and $n = 0, 1, 2, \ldots$.

5.15   (a) $2\pi x$ $(0 \leq x \leq 1/\sqrt{\pi})$, (b) $1/L$ $(0 \leq x \leq L)$,
(c) $(\frac{2}{3})(\sqrt{3} - x)$ $(0 \leq x \leq \sqrt{3})$, (d) $(1 - \pi x^{-1/2})/3\pi^2$ $(\pi^2 \leq x \leq 4\pi^2)$
and $(4\pi x^{-1/2} - 1)/6\pi^2$ $(4\pi^2 < x \leq 16\pi^2)$.

5.16   (a) $\frac{1}{36}$, $(\frac{1}{144})(24x^2 - x^4)$ $(0 < x < \sqrt{12})$.

(b) $\pi/2$, $1 - \exp(-\pi x^2/4)$ $(0 \leq x < \infty)$.

(c) $1/\pi$, $\frac{1}{2} + (1/\pi)$ arc tan $(x - 1)$ $(-\infty < x < \infty)$.

5.17   (a) $g(k) = \frac{1}{10}$ $(k = 1, 2, \ldots, 10)$, (b) $(1 - p)p^n$ $(n = 0, 1, 2, \ldots)$,
(c) ax^{a-1} $(0 < x \leq 1)$, (d) $ae^{-a(x-5)}$ $(5 \leq x < \infty)$,
(e) $(\pi/2)$ sin πx $(0 \leq x < 1)$.

5.18   (a) $\frac{7}{8}$, $\frac{3}{32}$, $\frac{31}{32}$, 0, 0, 0; yes, no. (b) $\frac{2}{3}$, $\frac{3}{10}$, $\frac{4}{5}$, $\frac{1}{6}$, $\frac{5}{9}$, $\frac{1}{4}$; no, no.

5.20   (a) $a = b = \frac{1}{2}$, $F_d(x) = \frac{1}{3}$ and $F_{ac}(x) = x$ for $0 \leq x < 1$. (b) $a = \frac{1}{4}$,
$b = \frac{3}{4}$; $F_d(x) = 0$ for $x < 0$, $= 1$ for $x > 0$; $F_{ac}(x) = (\frac{1}{3})e^x$ for $x < 0$, $= \frac{1}{3}$
for $0 \leq x < 1$, $= 1 - (\frac{2}{3})e^{-(x-1)}$ for $x \geq 1$.

5.21 $S = 10 + X$, $\binom{5}{n-10}\left(\frac{1}{5}\right)^{n-10}\left(\frac{4}{5}\right)^{15-n}$ $(n = 10, 11, \ldots, 15)$.

5.22 $(\frac{6}{125})(\theta - 20)(25 - \theta)$ $(20 < \theta < 25)$.

5.23   (a) $1/2a\sqrt{y}$ $(0 < y < a^2)$, (b) $1/a$ $(0 < y < a)$,
(c) $(1/a)e^{-y/a}$ $(0 < y < \infty)$, (d) $1/\pi(a^2 - y^2)^{1/2}$ $(|y| < a)$.

5.24 $h(y) = \log(1 + y)$.

5.25   (a) $(2x/a)(x^2 - 3a^2/4)^{-1/2}$, $(2/a)(x^2 - 3a^2/4)^{1/2}$ for
$\sqrt{3}\,a/2 < x < a$. (b) $(3\sqrt{3}\,a/\pi x)(x^2 - 3a^2/4)^{-1/2}$,
$(6/\pi)$ arc sec $(2x/\sqrt{3}\,a)$ for $\sqrt{3}\,a/2 < x < a$.

5.26   (a) $4\pi(m/2\pi kT)^{3/2}$. (b) $2\pi(k\pi T)^{-3/2}\sqrt{w}\,e^{-w/kT}$ $(0 < w < \infty)$.

5.28   (a) $1/(\tau - a)$, (b) $(n/\tau)^n/(n - 1)!$.

5.29   (a) $\dfrac{1}{1 - b}\exp\left(-\dfrac{s - b}{1 - b}\right)$ $(a/\tau = b \leq s < \infty)$,

(b) $n(ns)^{n-1}\exp[-ns]/(n - 1)!$ $(0 \leq s < \infty)$.

Chapter 6

6.4   (1) 10.5, (2) 7, (3) $\frac{2}{3}$, (4) 1, (5) 2, (6) 5, 9, (7) $2/3\sqrt{\pi}$, (8) $L/2$,
(9) $\sqrt{3}/3$, (10) $35\pi^2/6$.

6.7   (a) $16\sqrt{3}/15$, $(12 - 6\sqrt{2})^{1/2}$, 2.

(b) 1, $[(4/\pi)\log 2]^{1/2}$, $2/\pi$.

(c) No mean, 1, 1.

6.8   0.5 cents.

6.10   (a) $a^2/3$, (b) $a/2$, (c) a, (d) 0.

6.11   \$2.20.

6.12   (a) $F(y) = \alpha/(\alpha + \beta)$, (b) $100(\log 1.5)^{1/2}$.

6.13   (1) 33.25, (2) $\frac{35}{6}$, (3) $\frac{2}{9}$, (4) 0.8, (5) 2, (6) $\frac{20}{3}$, 72, (7) $\pi/18$, (8) $L^2/12$, (9) $\frac{1}{6}$, (10) $1687\pi^4/180$.

6.14   (a) $(2kT/m)^{1/2}$, $(8kT/\pi m)^{1/2}$, $[(3 - 8/\pi)(kT/m)]^{1/2}$.
  (b) $(4.17)10^4$, $(4.71)10^4$, $(1.99)10^4$.

6.15   (a) $(\frac{3}{2})kT$, (b) $(\frac{3}{2})(kT)^2$.

6.16   (a) $\mu = (4 + 3 \log 3)(a/8) \doteq 0.9120a$, $\sigma = [(\frac{5}{6})a^2 - \mu^2]^{1/2} \doteq$ $0.0399a$. (b) $\mu = (3 \sqrt{3} \, a/2\pi) \log 3 \doteq 0.9085a$, $\sigma = (3 \sqrt{3} \, a^2/2\pi - \mu^2)^{1/2} \doteq$ $0.0394a$. (c) $r = (3 \sqrt{3}/2\pi)^{1/2}a \doteq 0.9094a$.

6.19 $(\frac{1}{8})(e^\theta + 1)^3$, $\frac{3}{2}$, $\frac{3}{4}$.

6.20   (a) $(\frac{1}{20})(e^\theta - e^{21\theta})(1 - e^\theta)^{-1}$ for $|\theta| < \infty$, 10.5, 33.25.
  (b) $(1 + 2e^\theta)/3$ for $|\theta| < \infty$, $\frac{2}{3}$, $\frac{2}{9}$.
  (c) $e^\theta(2 - e^\theta)^{-1}$ for $\theta < \log 2$, 2, 2.
  (d) $(e^{\theta L} - 1)/\theta L$ for $|\theta| < \infty$, $L/2$, $L^2/12$.
  (e) $(\frac{2}{3}\theta^{-2})(e^{\theta\sqrt{3}} - \theta \sqrt{3} - 1)$ for $|\theta| < \infty$, $\sqrt{3}/3$, $\frac{1}{6}$.

6.21   (a) $(\frac{1}{6})[1 + 2e^\theta + 3\theta^{-1}(e^\theta - 1)]$ for $|\theta| < \infty$, $\frac{7}{12}$, $\sqrt{23}/12$.
(b) $(\frac{1}{4})[1 + (1 + \theta)^{-1} + 2e^\theta(1 - \theta)^{-1}]$ for $|\theta| < 1$, $\frac{3}{4}$, $\sqrt{37}/4$.

6.22 $(1 - \mu\theta)^{-1}$ for $\theta < \mu^{-1}$, μ, μ, $n! \, \mu^n$ $(n = 0, 1, 2, \ldots)$.

6.23   (a) Exponential, parameter 5. (b) Exponential, parameter μ.

6.24 μ, μ, $e^{-\mu}\mu^n/n!$ $(n = 0, 1, 2, \ldots)$.

6.26   (a) np, npq, $\binom{n}{k} p^k q^{n-k}$ $(k = 0, 1, \ldots, n)$.
  (b) p/q, p/q^2, qp^k $(k = 0, 1, 2, \ldots)$.

6.30   (a) $e^{a\theta}[1 - (\tau - a)\theta]^{-1}$ for $\theta < (\tau - a)^{-1}$, τ, $\tau - a$.
  (b) $(1 - \tau\theta/n)^{-n}$ for $\theta < n/\tau$, τ, $\tau/\sqrt{n}$.
  (c) $\dfrac{a}{1 - \tau\theta/2a} + \dfrac{1 - a}{1 - \tau\theta/2(1 - a)}$ for $\theta < 2a/\tau$, τ, $\tau[1 + (1 - 2a)^2/2a(1 - a)]^{1/2}$.

6.33   (a) $E(T^2)/2\tau = \tau/2 + \text{Var}(T)/2\tau$, $E(T^3)/3\tau - E^2(T^2)/4\tau^2$, $(1/\tau\theta)[M_T(\theta) - 1]$.
  (b) $(\tau/2)(1 + 1/n)$, $\tau^2(n + 1)(n + 5)/12n^2$.

6.35 $t_0 = \tau$, 0.

6.36   (b) $c_0 e^{-ak}[1 + (\tau - a)k]^{-1}$, $c_0(1 + \tau k/n)^{-n}$.

6.38 $c_e' = c_0 \displaystyle\int_0^\infty \frac{e^{-x}}{1 + kc_0\tau x} \, dx$, $c_e'' = \dfrac{c_0}{2kc_0\tau} (\sqrt{1 + 4kc_0\tau} - 1)$.

Chapter 7

7.1 $\frac{5}{16}$, $1 - 2(\frac{5}{6})^5$, $1 - (\frac{29}{19})(\frac{19}{20})^{10}$.

7.2 $g(k) = \dbinom{10}{k} \left(\dfrac{1}{3}\right)^k \left(\dfrac{2}{3}\right)^{10-k}$ $(k = 0, 1, \ldots, 10)$, 0.0034.

7.3   (a) $(0.999)^{36}$, $(0.036)(0.999)^{35}$, $1 - 1.035(0.999)^{35}$.
  (b) $1 - (0.999)^{36\times10^6} \doteq 1$.

7.5 μ, μ, $e^{\mu(e^\theta - 1)}$.

7.6 $\frac{17}{2}e^{-3} \doteq 0.42.$

7.7 $1.3e^{-.3} \doteq 0.35.$

7.8 $\binom{90}{10} / \binom{100}{10}.$

7.9 $\binom{50}{30} / \binom{100}{30}.$

7.10 $2^{-300}.$

7.11 $(0.9)^{10}.$

7.12 $1 - e^{-50/52}(1 + \frac{50}{52}) \doteq 0.25.$

7.13 $e^{-25/20} \dfrac{(\frac{25}{20})^2}{2} \doteq 0.22.$

7.14   (a) $1 - 2e^{-1} \doteq 0.26,$

   (b) $\left(\dfrac{326e^{-1}}{120}\right)^{300} \doteq 0.838.$

Chapter 8

8.1   5 minutes.

8.2 $\dfrac{b + a}{2}, \dfrac{(b - a)^2}{12}, \dfrac{e^{b\theta} - e^{a\theta}}{(b - a)\theta}.$

8.3   0.003, 0.046, 0.317.

8.4   0.67, $c = 0.67\sigma.$

8.5   0.343, 0.317.

8.6   (a) B, (b) A, (c) Very, very small.

8.7   (a) $f_D(d) = \dfrac{1}{\sqrt{2\pi}\,\sigma_x d} \exp\left[-\dfrac{1}{2\sigma_x^2}(\log d - \mu_x)^2\right]$ $(0 < d < \infty).$

   (b) $\mu_x = \log \mu_D - \sigma_x^2/2; \sigma_x^2 = \log[1 + (\sigma_D/\mu_D)^2].$

8.8 $e^{-10/3} \doteq 0.036.$

8.9   3 hours.

8.10   (b) $\beta(\alpha + 1), \beta^2(\alpha + 1).$

8.11   0.05.

8.12   (b) $\alpha, \lambda > 0, \dfrac{\alpha}{\alpha + \lambda}.$

8.15 $-\frac{14}{15}, -\frac{11}{15}.$

8.16   2, 1.

8.18 $c_0 \exp(-k\tau + k^2\sigma_T^2/2), c_0(1 + k\sigma_T^2/\tau)^{-(\tau/\sigma_T)^2}.$

Chapter 9

9.1   (a) $\Omega = \{E_{xy}: x = 0, 1, 2; y = 1, 2, \ldots, 6\}$, etc.,
$X(E_{xy}) = x, Y(E_{xy}) = y.$

(b) $g(x, y) = \frac{1}{24}\begin{pmatrix}2\\x\end{pmatrix}$ $(x = 0, 1, 2,; y = 1, 2, \ldots, 6)$,

$\quad g_X(x) = \frac{1}{4}\begin{pmatrix}2\\x\end{pmatrix}$ $(x = 0, 1, 2)$,

$\quad g_Y(y) = \frac{1}{6}$ $(y = 1, 2, \ldots, 6)$.

(d) $\frac{1}{4}, \frac{1}{2}$.

9.2 $\Omega = \{E_{xy}: x = 0, 1; y = 0, 1, 2\}$, $X(E_{xy}) = x$, $Y(E_{xy}) = y$.
$g(0, 0) = g(0, 2) = 0.1$, $g(0, 1) = 0.4$, $g(1, 0) = g(1, 1) = 0.2$, $g(1, 2) = 0$.
$g_X(0) = 0.6$, $g_X(1) = 0.4$. $g_Y(0) = 0.3$, $g_Y(1) = 0.6$, $g_Y(2) = 0.1$.

9.3 $g_X(x) = \exp[-\lambda]\lambda^x/x!$ $(x = 0, 1, 2, \ldots)$.
$\quad g_Y(y) = \exp[-\lambda p](\lambda p)^y/y!$ $(y = 0, 1, 2, \ldots)$.

9.4 (a) $F(x, y) = (1 - e^{-x^2/2})(1 - e^{-y})$ $(0 < x < \infty, 0 < y < \infty)$.
$\quad f_X(x) = xe^{-x^2/2}$ $(0 < x < \infty)$.
$\quad f_Y(y) = e^{-y}$ $(0 < y < \infty)$.
(b) $e^{-3} \doteq 0.050$, $1 - 2e^{-1} + e^{-2} \doteq 0.40$.

9.5 $c = \frac{1}{8}$, $f_1(x_1) = x_1^3/4$ $(0 < x_1 < 2)$,
$$f_2(x_2) = \begin{cases} \frac{1}{48}(16 - 12x_2 + x_2^3) & (0 \le x_2 < 2) \\ \frac{1}{48}(16 - 12x_2 + 5x_2^3) & (-2 < x_2 < 0). \end{cases}$$

9.6 (a) $F_X(x) = x/3$ $(0 < x < 3)$.
$\quad F_Y(y) = (y/6)[1 + \log(6/y)]$ $(0 < y < 6)$.
$$F(x, y) = \begin{cases} x/3 & (0 < x < y/2, 0 < y < 6) \\ (y/6)[1 + \log(2x/y)] & (y/2 < x < 3, 0 < y < 6). \end{cases}$$
(b) $f_X(x) = \frac{1}{3}$ $(0 < x < 3)$.
$\quad f_Y(y) = (\frac{1}{6})\log(6/y)$ $(0 < y < 6)$.
$\quad f(x, y) = 1/6x$ $(y/2 < x < 3, 0 < y < 6)$.
(c) $(1 - \log 2)/3 \doteq 0.102$.

9.7 Normal distributions with parameters (μ_1, σ_1) and (μ_2, σ_2).

9.8 $\frac{1}{54}$.

9.10 Yes, no, no, yes, no, no.

9.12 (a) $G(t) = \exp[-30b(a - t)^c]$ $(-\infty < t \le a)$.

$\quad g(t) = 30bc(a - t)^{c-1}\exp[-30b(a - t)^c]$ $(-\infty < t \le a)$.

9.13 $a_2/(a_1 + a_2)$.

9.14 $\frac{1}{21}$.

9.15 $\dfrac{ab}{a - b}(e^{-by} - e^{-ay})$ if $a \ne b$, a^2ye^{-ay} if $a = b$, for $0 < y < \infty$.

9.16 $1/\pi(1 + y^2)$ $(-\infty < y < \infty)$.

9.17 (a) $z, g_Z(z) = -1, 0.2; 0, 0.3; 1, 0.4; 2, 0.1$.
(b) $z, g_Z(z) = 0, 0.8; 1, 0.2$.

9.18 (a) $ue^{-u}(1 + v)^{-2}$, ue^{-u}, $(1 + v)^{-2}$ $(0 < u < \infty, 0 < v < \infty)$.
(c) Yes.

9.19 (a) $(4 - y)/8$ $(0 < y < 4)$. (b) $\frac{4}{3}$. (c) $\frac{8}{5}, \frac{4}{5}$.

9.20 $a^{-1}, b^{-1}, a^{-1} + b^{-1}$.

9.21 (a) 0.4. (b) 0.2. (c) No, $E(X) = 0.4$, $E(Y) = 0.8$, dependent.

9.22 $E(Y) = E(X) = 1.5$, $E(Z) = 1$, yes, independent.

9.23 $np,\ p^n$.

9.24 $\exp\left(\mu_1\theta_1 + \sigma_1^2\theta_1^2/2 + \mu_2\theta_2 + \sigma_2^2\theta_2^2/2 + \rho\sigma_1\sigma_2\theta_1\theta_2\right)$.

9.25   (a) $\frac{4}{225} \doteq 0.018$, $(\frac{4}{3})\sqrt{\frac{3}{22}} \doteq 0.49$. (b) $0,\ 0$. (c) -0.12, $-\sqrt{6}/6 \doteq -0.408$. (d) $-\frac{8}{225} \doteq -0.036$, $-\sqrt{14}/42 \doteq -0.089$. (e) 0.75, $\sqrt{21}/7 \doteq 0.655$.

9.26 ρ.

9.28   (a) $[y,\ g_{Y|X}(y|0),\ g_{Y|X}(y|1)] = [0,\ \frac{1}{6},\ \frac{1}{2}],\ [1,\ \frac{4}{6},\ \frac{1}{2}],\ [2,\ \frac{1}{6},\ 0]$.

(b) $g_{Y|X}(y|x) = \dbinom{x}{y} p^y q^{x-y}$ $(y = 0, 1, \ldots, x;\ x = 0, 1, 2, \ldots)$.

(c) $f_{Y|X}(y|x) = 1/2x$ $(0 < y < 2x, 0 < x < 3)$.

9.29   Normal distribution with mean $\mu_2 + (\rho\sigma_2/\sigma_1)(x - \mu_1)$ and variance $\sigma_2^2(1 - \rho^2)$.

9.30   (a) $m_Y(0) = 1,\ \sigma_Y^2(0) = \frac{1}{3}$,

$\qquad m_Y(1) = \frac{1}{2},\ \sigma_Y^2(1) = \frac{1}{4}$.

(b) $m_Y(x) = xp,\ \sigma_Y^2(x) = xpq$ $(x = 0, 1, 2, \ldots)$.

(c) $m_Y(x) = x,\ \sigma_Y^2(x) = x^2/3$ $(0 < x < 3)$.

9.35 $ab,\ a^{-1/b}\Gamma(1 + 1/b),\ \tau^{-1}ab(x + y)^{b-1}\exp\left[-a(x + y)^b\right]$, $\tau^{-1}\exp(-ax^b),\ \tau^{-1}\exp(-ay^b)$.

9.36   Yes, $g(x, y) = g_X(x)\ g_Y(y)$.

9.37   (a) $g_X(x) = \tau^{-1}$ $(0 \leq x < \tau)$, $g_Y(y) = \tau^{-1}$ $(0 \leq y < \tau)$.

(b) No, $g(x, y) \neq g_X(x)\ g_Y(y)$.

9.38 $\tau^{-1}z\ f(z)$.

9.40   (a) 0, (b) -1, (c) $P(X + Y = \tau) = 1$.

9.41 $1 - 2[2 + (\tau/\sigma_T)^2]/[5 + (\tau/\sigma_T)^2]$.

9.42   (b) $-[(\tau/\sigma_T)^2 - 1]/[(\tau/\sigma_T)^2 + 1]$.

(c) $(a/b)[1 - (x + y)/b]^{a-1}[1 - y/b]^{-a}$

$(x \geq 0, y \geq 0, 0 < x + y < b)$.

(d) $\tau(1 - y/b),\ [a\tau^2/(a + 2)](1 - y/b)^2$.

9.43   (a) $[(\tau/\sigma_T)^2 - 1]^2/[(\tau/\sigma_T)^2 + 1]^2$.

Chapter 10

10.2 $\dbinom{n}{k}\left(\dfrac{1}{5}\right)^k\left(\dfrac{4}{5}\right)^{n-k}$ $(k = 0, 1, \ldots, n)$.

10.3   (a) $mp_1q_1(p_1^{m-2} + q_1^{m-2})$, (b) $\frac{5}{16}$.

10.4   (b) $p^r(1 - qe^\theta)^{-1}$ for $qe^\theta < 1$.

10.6   (a) $(\frac{11}{16})^2 \doteq 0.47,\ 2.2$.

(b) $\dbinom{r + x - 1}{x}\left(\dfrac{5}{16}\right)^r\left(\dfrac{11}{16}\right)^x$ $(x = 0, 1, 2, \ldots)$.

(c) Note that $P(X_k = x) = pq^x$ $(x = 0, 1, 2, \ldots)$.

10.7 $n!\ 6^{-n}/n_1!n_2!\ \ldots\ n_6!$

$(n_1 \geq 0,\ n_2 \geq 0,\ \ldots,\ n_6 \geq 0;\ n_1 + n_2 + \cdots + n_6 = n)$, $5/6^4 \doteq 0.0039$.

10.8 $105/2^{10} \doteq 0.102$.

10.11 $2, 0.4 \sqrt{10} \doteq 1.26$.

10.12 $-10, 11$.

10.13 $200, 0.3$.

10.14 $rq/p, rq/p^2$.

10.15   Yes, if $n \geq 25$.

10.16 $144, \frac{48}{65} \doteq 0.738$.

10.19   Normal, with $(\mu, \sigma) = (-7, 6); 0.159$.

10.20 0.95.

10.22   (a) $E[X(t)] = (1 - t)^{-2}$ for $t < 1$, $x(t) = e^{2t}$ for $-\infty < t < \infty$.
   (b) $E[X(t)] = e^{-t+t^2/2}$ and $x(t) = e^{-t}$ for $-\infty < t < \infty$.

10.27   (a) $\mu_U = a_0 + a_1\mu_1 + a_2\mu_2$,
   $\sigma_U^2 = a_1^2\sigma_1^2 + a_2^2\sigma_2^2 + a_1a_2\rho\sigma_1\sigma_2$,
   $\mu_V = b_0 + b_1\mu_1 + b_2\mu_2$,
   $\sigma_V^2 = b_1^2\sigma_1^2 + b_2^2\sigma_2^2 + b_1b_2\rho\sigma_1\sigma_2$,
   Cov $(U, V) = a_1b_1\sigma_1^2 + a_2b_2\sigma_2^2 + (a_1b_2 + a_2b_1)\rho\sigma_1\sigma_2$.

10.28 $\alpha = (\mu_2 - \mu_1)^2/(\sigma_2^2 - \sigma_1^2) - 1$,
   $\beta = (\sigma_2^2 - \sigma_1^2)/(\mu_2 - \mu_1)$.

10.30   Gamma distribution with parameters β and

$$\alpha = \alpha_1 + \alpha_2 + \cdots + \alpha_n + n - 1.$$

Chapter 11

11.3   (a) $0.317, 0.134, 0.0455, 0.0027$.
   (b) $1.000, 0.444, 0.250, 0.111$.

11.4 500.

11.5 $5000, 3200$.

11.6   No, no mean.

11.7   (a) $0, 1/\sqrt{2}, 0, 0, \sqrt{n/2}$, no, yes. (b) Yes, $s_n/n \to 0$.

11.8 $11, 2$.

11.9 $320, 2000, 8000$.

11.11 $5, 5$.

Chapter 12

12.1 $0.023, 0.787$.

12.2 $0.317, 25.8$.

12.3 $0.081, 0.760$.

12.4   (a) $0.046, 0.317$; (b) $0.083, 0.387$.

12.5 0.780.

12.7   (a) 97, (b) $541, 346$, (c) $62, 385, 1537$.

12.8 0.048.

12.10   0.023, no.

12.11 $\displaystyle\sum_{k=40}^{55} \binom{100}{k}\left(\frac{1}{2}\right)^{100}$, 0.846, 0.818.

12.12   1921.

12.13   0.232, 0.223, 0.238, Poisson.

12.14   (a) 0.1462, 0.1470, 0.1396, 0.1410.

        (b) 0.1220, 0.1209, 0.1465, 0.1210, 0.1450.

12.15   0.074.

12.18   (a) $P(X \leq x) \doteq \Phi\left(\dfrac{x - rp/q}{\sqrt{rp/q}}\right)$ (large r).

        (b) $P(X \leq x) \doteq \Phi\left(\dfrac{x - (\alpha + 1)\beta}{\beta \sqrt{\alpha + 1}}\right)$ (large α).

        (c) $P(X \leq x) \doteq \Phi\left(\dfrac{x - rp/q}{\sqrt{rp/q}}\right)$ (large r).

        (d) $P(X \leq x) \doteq \Phi\left(\dfrac{x - \lambda}{\sqrt{\lambda}}\right)$ (large λ). .

INDEX

INDEX